American Water & Game Birds

American Water &

AUSTIN L

Chief Curat

A CHANTICLEER PRESS EDITION

Prepared in cooperation with the Chicago Natural History Museum

Game Birds

RAND

of Zoology, Chicago Natural History Museum

Silhouettes by

UGO MOCHI

Photographs by

ALLAN D. CRUICKSHANK

ELIOT PORTER

HELEN CRUICKSHANK

CY LA TOUR

ERIC HOSKING

and others

E. P. DUTTON & COMPANY, Inc.

NEW YORK 1956

CONTENTS

INTRODUCTION

IT HAS often seemed to me that of the simpler pleasures of life the enjoyment of nature and especially wildlife was among the most easily available. In this respect we in America are doubly blessed. We have not only a marvelous abundance of wildlife (although perhaps not as much as we once had), but by virtue of technological progress and a high standard of living we now have the leisure to enjoy these riches to the full.

Among the most familiar and most popular of our wildlife are birds, and of these our water and game birds form a great and beautiful part. Birds may be the special concern of the bird watcher, the sportsman and the scientist, but they belong to all of us and no one needs any special excuse to enjoy them. How many of us have been delighted by the sound and sight of a cock pheasant crowing in a field, the majesty of a large brown pelican slowly flapping its way near a southern wharf, the passage of a flock of geese or the soaring of a flight of cranes. The flashing wings of a flock of teal low over a marsh in late summer, as the birds twist and turn among the reeds and willows, may appeal in different ways to each of us. The bird lover who has seen these teal mating, and has followed the fortunes of their broods, pauses to watch them out of sight, wondering whether they have gone for the season. The sportsman, marking their flight, recalls memorable days spent in the marshes and relives exciting moments when the birds came within range. The artist sees the patterns of their wings, hoping some day to catch them forever on canvas.

To still others they may recall other scenes enlivened by the wings of other birds. Each part of America has its own bird scenery, as characteristic of the locality as is its water, its land contours or its vegetation. The great swarms of gulls and terns about our shores, the migratory flocks of geese or cranes winging high over the autumnal countryside, the white herons still as sentinels in their rookeries in cypress swamps, the myriads of ducks in their nesting marshes, and the clouds of sea birds swirling above their rocky island homes, are spectacular and distinctive elements of the scenery of the United States. Naturally the species you will see will depend on where you are, for each variety has its own special requirements which determine its choice of habitat.

But wherever you live you can see birds. The dweller in a northern city on the edge of the sea or on the shore of a great lake will see gulls along the waterfront, perched on wharves and pilings and roosting in masses on breakwaters, and old-squaws, scoters, and mergansers swimming and diving offshore. On southern city beaches, picnickers and sunbathers see sandpipers swarming, egrets stalking about, frigate birds sailing up and down, and terns, pelicans or cormorants feeding offshore. Where there are lagoons in city parks, pond ducks come to rest and black terns to feed, ignoring the tall buildings nearby. I have seen pheasants gathered to feed about a city dump in winter; many a farmer feeds quail and pheasants within sight of his windows; and I once saw a covey of sage grouse coming to drink at the overflow from the home watertank of a ranch. Wherever I have lived, I have found I need not go far to see birds, and in many places, waking in the night, I have heard the calling of wild geese flying over in migration.

The bird scenery changes not only from place to place, but also from season to season. It is only on their migratory flights that the cranes stop to wade along the shallows of the Platte River in Nebraska, and the shearwaters' wings skim over the green rollers off the Pacific coast; only in winter are the blue geese on the Louisiana marshes. The prairie slough that was alive with nesting ducks and gulls throughout the long days of summer is a bare, desolate expanse of wind-whipped snow in the stubborn nights of winter, while the birds themselves have long since flown to the milder weather of the southern states. The Arctic terns that summered on the New England coast may be spending the winter in the Antarctic; others among the hordes of migrating shore birds that stream back and forth across our familiar countrysides each spring and fall are en route between their summer homes in the Arctic and their winter homes in the Argentine.

Let us glance at some of the most notable congregating places of these birds in America, starting with Florida, well known for its "pond scroggins," the local name for the long-legged wading birds, the ibis, herons, and egrets. It would be a very unobservant person who could travel any distance over the grassy pastures or through the Everglades without seeing the flocks of these tall, white birds feeding in the half-flooded fields, those watery expanses of grass or mud, or perched like decorations in the cypress trees. But really to see these birds one must go where they are nesting.

On one occasion near Eagle Hammock, across a wide stretch of flooded grass from the Big Cypress, I watched the evening flight of egrets and wood ibis. As the setting sun cast pink and purple lights on the high-massed cumulus the great white birds came winging their way toward their roosts. It was late in the season and the water was high, so the birds were scattered and the flocks small. In the stand of tall cypress trees the ibis nests are fifty to eighty feet up, and the colony is so dense at the height of the breeding season that there may be as many as twenty-five nests in the crown of one of the larger trees. When the young are in the nests, the grunting, squealing and bleating of the birds makes a volume of sound audible from quite a distance.

Such colonies, some large, some small, may be found almost anywhere in the state, but especially along the headwaters of rivers and where trees are standing in water. Probably the most impressive are the congregations at the extreme southern tip of Florida. There the shallow sea and the adjacent waterways and lagoons that sprawl inland yield abundant food; the mangrove trees growing on the partly submerged land provide a large number of nesting places, and the colonies of birds include the spoonbills, a half-dozen or more species of herons, the white ibis, the cormorants and the anhingas. These birds nest by the thousands in such rookeries.

Other notable bird spectacles in Florida include the dancing of the cranes on the Kissimmee prairie; the ducks wintering on Okeechobee, where a flock rising from the lake makes a noise like a freight train; and the brown pelicans beating with slow, powerful flight along the ocean just off the beach or nesting in huge colonies on islands along the coast, in mangrove trees or on the sand.

The lowlands of the Texas coast are unrivaled for bird scenery. In the low shrubs of the offshore islands ibis, egrets, herons and spoonbills nest in abundance, and sometimes in the protective isolation of these islands herons nest close to or even on the ground. The rookeries are usually mixed, and to add to the bewildering variety of bird life in the trees, shrubs and cactus, where perhaps a dozen species of long-legged wading birds are nesting, pelicans, laughing gulls, Cabot's and royal terns occupy the adjacent sand and shell beaches. Some of these gull and tern colonies have been described as "fields of eggs," and one island was estimated as having about thirty thousand nests of laughing gulls and nine thousand of Cabot's terns. The confusion and tumult may be imagined. In the live oak mottes and in clumps of bushes in the coastal marshes or on the prairies, herons also nest, while in wooded marshes the white ibis and the wood ibis build their homes in the trees. It is on one of the coastal prairies of Texas that the last of the whooping cranes make their winter home.

The Carolina coast has herons and ibis in abundance, some nesting in the cypress swamps while others of the same species place their colonies in low bushes on the tiny banks of oyster-shell islands miles out in salt water. The narrow barrier islands along this coast are particularly rich in terns and the air is filled with gyrating clouds of screaming birds. The least tern is the most abundant and characteristic bird of these sea islands, though it nests in relatively small colonies made up of dozens, scores and hundreds of birds rather than thousands, and some of these nesting places may be only a few yards from main highways. The royal tern's rookeries are more concentrated than those of the least tern, and Alexander Sprunt, an authority on the birds of this area, estimated that one colony contained eleven thousand nests. The black skimmer has its home on more remote islands. The willet, making up in vociferous, scolding calls what it lacks in massed numbers, is there too, and the greater part of the oyster-catcher population of the Atlantic coast winters here in the Cape Romain area.

The coast from Pamlico Sound north to Chesapeake Bay and Delaware Bay is a country of long, shallow inlets where inflowing rivers bring fresh water to the upper parts of the bays, the waters of which change to brackish and then to salt as they near the sea. This coast is well known as the home of great numbers of waterfowl; whistling swans winter here, as do all the greater snow geese in the world, Canada geese, brant, and hosts of ducks. Chesapeake Bay is also associated, at least in my mind, with great wintering flocks of canvasback ducks and redheads.

In spring and fall great numbers of shore birds migrate up and down the east coast, the migrations along the New England and eastern Canadian seaboard being particularly heavy. Especially in the autumn, when the hordes of sandpipers and plovers have quit their summer homes on the tundra and in the muskeg country of the north and are on their way to winter homes in the southern United States or in South America, countless shore birds swarm on the beaches and in the salt marshes of the New England coast. As the vast flocks wheel and turn in the distance they look like swirling smoke. Some of them return north in the spring by way of the Mississippi Valley, others along the east coast, so that there are great numbers of them in Massachusetts in April. Thousands upon thousands of small sandpipers or knots in a flock will swing and turn as a single bird, or alight and feed on the mud flats or beaches, covering them as with live carpets.

Besides the shore birds there are also sea-bird colonies of considerable size along the New England coast. One of the largest laughing gull colonies, with perhaps forty thousand nesting birds—along with perhaps thirty thousand herring gulls and several thousand terns—is located on an island off Massachusetts. There are tern colonies of ten to fifteen thousand birds, most of them common terns, but some of them Arctic terns, that migrate across the Atlantic and down the African coast on their way to the Antarctic for the winter. On Cape Cod there is a rookery of black-crowned night herons estimated to contain several thousand birds; here, instead of nesting over the water like many of this species, the birds make their homes in tall trees on dry land.

Southern New England is not rich in nesting ducks, the black duck being the only species that nests there commonly, but many pond ducks pass through in migration. Even more interesting are the northern sea birds that winter off the New England coast: the vast flocks of eiders; three species of scoters; and a great concentration of loons, horned grebes, black-backed gulls, auks and puffins.

Some northern water birds nest on the little, rocky, offshore islands of the northern Maine coast. Eiders, black-backed gulls, guillemots and puffins make their homes here, attracting many visitors to these outpost colonies. To see the nesting colonies of these birds best, however, one must go north to the Gulf of St. Lawrence where the bird cities are among the most populous on the Atlantic seaboard. On certain of the islands there, nesting murres are massed on some ledges, gannets on others, while many puffins sit about the entrances of their burrows among the rocks. Eider ducks are also common. To see the dovekie at home, however, one must journey still farther north, to Greenland, where those tiny auks swarm like mosquitoes about the rocky talus slopes in which they nest, and where the waters are darkened by them.

Though the Arctic tundra of Canada is far beyond our borders, it sends so many birds south to us each year that we must mention it in any survey of our game and water birds. Here in summer the old-squaws nest; the whistling swans and the snow and blue geese dot the tundra, and such shore birds as sandpipers, knots, turnstones, and black-bellied and golden plovers use the Arctic prairies for their nurseries. Fortunate are they that their nesting habitat is still not threatened by human use. Although at one time they suffered because of heavy shooting, they have been able to replenish their numbers in part through breeding on the undisturbed tundra of the far north.

The chief nurseries of our waterfowl, however, are lakes and marshes on the prairies of the Midwest and in the plains and the intermountain country of the West. Much of this area is dry, and when heavily grazed, the prairie becomes sere and brown and the extent of bird life then is limited to an occasional savanna sparrow or horned lark. But how different this country is where a shallow depression in the prairie holds a lake or slough, making an oasis of green reeds and grasses, the shallow water filled with aquatic vegetation and swarming everywhere with water birds.

As many as fifteen species of ducks may nest on a single slough, and often, as you walk about, a duck flushes from its nest at every few steps and flocks of birds swirl overhead. If you venture onto an island in the lake, you may have to walk with care to avoid stepping on nests. To tell how many ducks are in a marsh is difficult, for the number of visible birds varies with the season. Early in the year, when they are mating, they are conspicuous as they chase each other over the surface of the water and make their courtship flights over the marshes. Later, while the ducks are occupied with family matters, the drakes may be moulting in the seclusion of the reeds or may have left the marshes entirely to congregate on favored lakes. In the autumn they may again become conspicuous.

[9

There are, of course, many other kinds of bird life besides ducks in these areas. On some lakes colonies of white pelicans and cormorants nest on suitable islands. Black-crowned night herons and, in the far West, the glossy ibis make their homes on the tules. Here Franklin's gulls nest in the reeds in congregations of tens of thousands, while ring-billed and California gulls also form large colonies on some of the lakes. The flights of Franklin's gulls over the prairies from their breeding marshes to their feeding grounds are one of the great bird spectacles of the continent.

Two, three, or even four different species of grebes make their floating nests among the reeds here, and the nests of the eared grebe are sometimes so close together that it is impossible to force a canoe through the colony without upsetting some of them. Black terns are widespread, but other species, such as the common, Forster's and Caspian terns, are more conspicuous since their colonies are usually in the open. In addition to the great concentrations of water birds on the surface, in the marshes, or circling overhead, there are always noisy, scolding shore birds, such as willets, avocets, and godwits, that flock around an intruder on the margins of a slough.

One of the outstanding bird concentrations in this part of the United States occurs in the Souris River region of North Dakota. Once one of the important duck-shooting areas in America, it lost much of its bird population when it went through a cycle of drainage, agriculture, drought and reclamation. Now dams and dykes have returned thousands of acres to bird-rich water and marsh, and more than 100,000 waterfowl are said to be produced here in good years.

Another great concentration occurs in Utah where the Bear River flows into Great Salt Lake and breaks up into a series of channels which enclose a great delta marsh. This marsh is easily accessible from highways and makes available to any traveler the spectacle of a "million" birds in one place. In addition to ducks, avocets, and stilts there are colonies of Franklin's gulls, snowy egrets, glossy ibis and grebes. On islands out in the lake nest many white pelicans and tens of thousands of California gulls. In migration time great numbers of whistling swans may stop here, some even to spend the winter, and thousands of lesser snow geese break their flights to rest.

It is said that the Malheur region in eastern Oregon used to be the greatest waterfowl breeding ground in the West, and that the "magnitude of its bird populations stunned the observer." Pelicans, cormorants, grebes, herons, ibis, ducks, geese, gulls and terns made it their home. Bird students have written that the din of their cries was deafening at times and that observers were at a loss to estimate the numbers of the birds. Klamath Lake, lying across the California–Oregon line, was once another such paradise for birds. Drainage, use of the water for irrigation, and drought have all played their part in changing much of this marshland to dry flats, but today the United States Government has made them into bird refuges and is restoring the water, and thousands of Canada geese are being raised here every year.

In the delta of the Mississippi occurs one of the main concentrations of wintering waterfowl in the United States. There are vast numbers of geese, and three or four ducks to every goose, including dabbling ducks like the mallards and pintails in the shallow marshes, and diving ducks like the canvasback and scaup in deeper water. Farther west, in Louisiana, around the Sabine River, is another wintering ground for geese. I have seen this immense flat stretch of grass and water only from the air, but other ornithologists tell of packed flocks of waterfowl a mile long and three hundred yards wide, and flying strands of ducks and geese that seem to reach from horizon to horizon. Blue, snow, white-fronted, and Canada geese bulk large in these great flocks.

In the flooded bottom lands of the White River in Arkansas, the mallards congregate. There are other ducks here, too, but it is the mallards that must be counted in the hundreds of thousands, with a total winter population that probably passes the million mark. Since this area is one of flooded forests, with a bountiful supply of small acorns, the mallard, which is usually a pond duck, here becomes a forest bird for the winter.

In California the wintering areas are now more circumscribed than the extensive coastal marshes of the Atlantic and the Gulf of Mexico, and many of the waterfowl go on to the marshes of western Mexico. The Salton Sea and the Colorado River impoundments, however, hold myriads of migrating waterfowl as well as migrating grebes, herons and gulls, and accommodate the nests of many white pelicans. In the Sacramento Valley marshes the wintering geese, including Canada, white-fronted and snow geese, total in the hundreds of thousands, and the white, mallard-sized Ross's goose makes its only winter home there. Of the ducks the most common is the pintail. Since these marshes lie in part along the main highways, tens of thousands of feeding geese and ducks are in full view of passing motorists.

Perhaps the best known and certainly one of the most populous of West Coast "bird cities" is located on the Three Arch Rocks off the coast of Oregon. On these cliffs live a tremendous number of birds. The murres are by far the most numerous here and literally line the cliffs. Normally they stand with their dark-colored backs to the sea, but when disturbed they turn and face the water, their white fronts then becoming conspicuous. When alarmed, they pour off the ledges like a waterfall. The murres commonly nest on these rocks in very great numbers, and usually the gulls, cormorants and puffins are numerous also. At nesting time during the day these birds circle around the rocks like swarms of bees, and during the nights still other species, the petrels and auklets, become active.

The Farallon Islands off San Francisco Bay hold another well-known sea-bird colony, and because of its proximity to San Francisco this one has been studied by many ornithologists. Murres, horned puffins, cormorants and gulls are to be seen there in the daytime and petrels and Cassin's auklets during the "night shift." The birds here at times have numbered in the hundreds of thousands, though the colony has undergone considerable fluctuations in its bird population over the years.

We have mentioned large concentrations of birds in many places, but experienced observers agree that nowhere else in North America are such concentrations as in the Alaskan area. On the swampy tundra of the mainland there are tremendous nesting populations of gulls, terns, ducks, geese and shore birds, but these pale into insignificance compared to the number of birds that live on the rocky islands in the Bering Sea. Of these it has been said that they are simply innumerable. On these islands with names like Amchitka, Kasatochi, Amukta, Bogoslof, Walrus and Nunivak, sheer walls of rock rising several hundred feet from the water may be white with breeding kittiwakes and murres, and the calling kittiwakes make such an uproar that ordinary human speech cannot be heard above the din. The glaucous-winged gull takes the place of the western gull as a hanger-on about the bird colonies in these northern latitudes, and in some places they are so numerous that they literally cover the tops of the rocks.

There are enormous fulmar colonies on some of these cliffs and cormorants are conspicuous, too, but it is for the auks and their relatives, the auklets,

murres and murrelets, puffins and guillemots, that the Bering Sea area is especially noted. Most species of these birds nest here, many of them here only, and even the rare, whiskered auklet is found in hundreds on such islands as Kagamil. The least auklet, smallest of this family, is perhaps the most abundant of all. It nests among the heaped-up rocks that form the beaches and in the crevices of the talus slopes and rock faces, where the sitting birds are hidden from view. When they leave their nests they fly about in great swarms, often twisting and turning in unison.

These bird cities, of course, are occupied only seasonally. When nesting is over the auks and their kin go out to sea for the winter, keeping together in big flocks. Many of them do not travel much farther south but remain in the icy waters, even among the ice floes. It is different with the cormorants, whose plumage is not very water-resistant. For this reason the cormorants go ashore daily to dry their feathers, and presumably they also sleep on land. The gulls spread out along the coast and their winter flocks mingle with those of other species as they scavenge along the beaches.

Such are some of the notable concentrations of bird life in North America. Every state can point to impressive aggregations of birds that I have not mentioned, such as the cranes that stop on the Jasper-Pulaski game preserve in Indiana in the spring and fall and draw Sunday visitors from as far as Chicago and Indianapolis; the geese of Horseshoe Lake in Illinois; the egrets of Reelfoot Lake in Tennessee; the scaups and coots of the flooded fields of the Carolinas; the prairie chickens on their booming grounds in Wisconsin; the avocets in Colorado ponds; or the white-winged dove colonies on the mesquite flats in Arizona.

The quantity of food required by these vast congregations of birds is enormous and is drawn from a variety of sources. There are fish-eaters such as the herons; insect-eaters such as some nesting gulls; grass- and root-eaters such as the geese and some ducks; shellfish-eaters like some flocks of scoters and eiders which winter on the sea; and the eaters of a variety of invertebrates in the sand and mud at the water's edge, the shore birds. It is surprising how little any of these birds conflict with man's interests. Sometimes charges are made that cormorants or pelicans destroy enough fish to injure commercial or game fishing, but investigation usually shows the charges to be ill founded. In some areas the feeding of ducks and geese on crop lands does present local problems.

We have a sense of familiarity when we look at any of the land birds described in this volume, for we know their tame relatives of the barnyard and even the city streets. But the rest of the birds in this book live at least a part of the year on the water or by its edge. The ways in which evolution has adapted these birds for such a life are many, though, strangely, some get along without the special equipment that seems so important to others. A waterproof plumage would seem essential to a water bird, and most of them are thus equipped. But the cormorants, as was noted, do not have waterproofing, nor do the anhingas, though both these species feed by swimming and diving. They must therefore come ashore periodically to dry their feathers and to sleep. The noddy terns and the frigate birds do not have waterproof plumage either, but they avoid getting their feathers wet by feeding on the wing, flying low over the water and snatching food from the surface. Of course they, too, sleep ashore.

Most of the birds that swim have webbed feet: for example, loons, auks, ducks and pelicans. But grebes, which are as much at home in the water as loons, have each toe broadened into a flat paddle instead of having the toes webbed, and a few other birds, such as phalaropes and the rails known as coots, have lobed toes for swimming. However, other rails, the gallinules, swim a great deal but have neither webs nor lobes on their slender toes, and certain "water birds" with webbed feet, such as the noddy terns and the frigate birds, do not light on the water if they can help it.

While some of the web-footed sea birds feed by swimming and diving, others seek their food by flying far and wide over the water. These have long wings and an easy, sustained, often gliding flight— as is best seen in albatrosses, shearwaters, gulls, and frigate birds. Some of these long-winged skimmers may snatch the food from the surface without alighting; others, such as gulls and albatrosses, may alight and feed; and still others, such as gannets, brown pelicans, and many terns, may plunge into the water from flight.

Where the water is shallow, some ducks—such as the mallard, which rarely dives—swim about and reach to the bottom with their long necks. But another type of adaptation for feeding in the shallows is common: that of wading. Among the larger birds, herons and ibis, with their long legs, illustrate this to perfection. Along the beaches and mud flats there are other groups of long-legged birds, the sandpipers and plovers, which are restricted by their small size to wading in very shallow water. Where aquatic vegetation is dense some of the rails move about on floating plants, their long toes supporting them as snowshoes support a man. This type of adaptation reaches its extreme form in the jacana, in which not only the toes but even the toenails are greatly elongated.

A bird's bill must assume the function of hands in grasping food, which ranges from fish or invertebrates to leaves, stems, roots or seeds. Thus to seize animals in water, some birds such as loons, herons, anhingas and terns have a nearly straight, pointed, spearlike bill, and others such as gulls, albatrosses and cormorants have a hook at the end of an elongated bill. Sandpipers and plovers have slender, tweezer-like bills, adapted for picking up such small prey as insects.

The rather long but blunt bill of cranes and many rails is used for a diet of small animals and such plant material as seeds and greenstuff. The flattened bills of ducks, with a sievelike fringe around the edge, are obviously adapted for straining small animals and plant material from water and mud, but are also used in other ways; for example, the canvasback feeds sometimes on succulent parts of wild celery, and scoters detach certain shellfish from rocks and swallow them whole.

A few birds have special adaptations: the black skimmer, with a long, knifelike lower mandible and a short upper one, sometimes feeds by "plowing" the surface of the water. The oyster-catcher has a stout chisel-like bill which it uses to open oysters. The flamingo, on the other hand, has a very unusual combination: like a heron it has long legs for wading, but it also has webbed feet; and like a duck its bill has a sievelike fringe for straining small food items from the water but is so sharply bent in the middle that its top rests on the surface of the mud when the bird feeds.

From these samples it is plain that nature has many ways of solving the problems of birds that live in or by the water. What seems like a special characteristic may be used in a number of ways, and sometimes the same requirement is met by different adaptations. The variety of animate nature is very great.

Though a vast amount of food is needed daily by nesting colonies, it is not all gathered locally. Some sea birds go long distances for their food, and this is especially true of certain auklets and petrels that feed at sea during the day and return to the nesting colonies only at night. The white pelicans and the great blue herons nesting on the islands in Great Salt Lake are said to feed as far as one hundred miles from the colony, for the lake itself has no fish.

Apparently a satisfactory nesting place is more important to most birds than a supply of food close at hand. The birds nest in colonies because they are gregarious, apparently liking company, but the sites they choose must have certain definite characteristics.

Large colonies of nesting birds can exist only if they are protected from large carnivores, such as foxes and coyotes, which would like to prey upon the eggs and young. This protection the birds get by nesting in inaccessible places. Islands off the coast have been the answer for many sea birds both in the far north and in more temperate climates. In the interior the white pelicans and cormorants nest on islands in lakes, whereas ducks concentrate their nests on grassy islets in prairie sloughs. In western lakes where there are great floating masses of dead tules, the pelicans, cormorants and terns nest on these rafts of reeds as though they were islands, and the grebes go even further and build their own islands, floating or stationary, of dead vegetation. Other water birds of the inland marshes, for example the Franklin's gull, build their nests among the reeds out over the water, getting, in effect, island protection.

Not satisfied with the isolation provided by an island site, some of the auk tribe, as well as fulmars and kittiwakes, go further and nest only on the cliffs on islands. Sometimes these birds will also nest on isolated cliffs on the mainland. Another form of double protection is sought by the birds, including some of the smallest auks, such as auklets and dovekies, and the tiny petrels, which nest in burrows or in rock crevices on islands. These birds are so small that some of the larger gulls could rob them of their eggs if they were out in the open, and even the adult birds might be eaten. To guard even more completely against this last danger, the petrels and some of the auklets visit their burrows only during the night. It must, however, be noted that the puffin, which is as big as the murre and has a bill capable of inflicting a severe bite, also nests in burrows although it would seem to be able to defend its eggs from the gulls.

Isolation achieved by building in trees growing on dry ground was effective for the passenger pigeon in original or undisturbed conditions, and it seems also to be effective for the black-crowned night herons in their colony on Cape Cod. Herons in our southeastern states, however, prefer to nest in trees on islands or growing in water, and a heron rookery is therefore usually found in the trees of a wooded swamp. On small, isolated islands or in the larger swamps, however, the nests are frequently in low bushes and sometimes practically on the ground, while in remote regions of the West, herons nest in the reeds of marshes or on the ground on islands in lakes. The double-crested cormorant is even more adaptable and nests in some places on sea cliffs and islands, in others in trees in wooded swamps, and in still others on the floating tule or low islands of the larger lakes. That such preferences are not very deep-seated is indicated by a colony of brown pelicans in Florida that nested in mangrove trees on a small island until continued use and a freezing winter destroyed the trees, after which they nested on the ground on the same island.

Foxes and coyotes are the obvious predators that are thus foiled. In our southeastern states, however, the raccoon is another predator of birds' eggs, and one hard to avoid, for it can both swim and climb. It has been suggested that the alligator may be important in keeping raccoons from swimming out to the heron colonies.

Over the ages, by trial and error, our colonial birds learned to nest where they were fairly safe from predation. An occasional Arctic fox no doubt got across the ice to an Arctic island and caused havoc among the nesting birds, or the lowering of the water level sometimes enabled a coyote to make its way onto an island in a prairie slough and wipe out a large number of duck nests, but such occasions were unusual. Around the rookeries of the South, crows and vultures waited for an opportunity to seize an unattended egg, and around many coastal rookeries gulls did the same, but natural predation was held in check by natural means. With the arrival of civilized man at the colonies of birds, however, a new era opened for our wildlife.

We can be sure that the size of the bird concentrations has always varied from year to year. Such factors as disease, unfavorable weather at nesting time, either drought or heavy rains, changes in the food supply, unusual activity on the part of predators, or inexplicable disasters such as that periodically affecting the dovekie, have probably always been at work. When the first settlers came to America, however, a new predator was introduced. He worked in two ways: first by destroying the habitat in which the bird lived and nested, thus changing the country so that it was unsuitable for the bird; and secondly by killing the birds themselves. At first his felling of the forests and his killing of birds for his own use had no more than local effects, but as the population in the New World became more dense and transportation improved, the effects on the birds increased. Catastrophe resulted when it became possible to convert birds into money. The shooting of birds for the big food markets in the cities, and plume-hunting for the millinery trade, threatened to wipe out some species. Certain ones, such as the passenger pigeon, the Labrador duck, and possibly the Eskimo curlew, have actually disappeared forever. These birds went down before the market gunners, and other shore birds and the ducks and geese suffered severely. None of our birds was actually exterminated by the plume-hunters but many, like the egrets, the terns and some grebes, were much reduced in numbers, and the snowy egret and the spoonbill were practically wiped out.

It became clear, therefore, that market hunting had to stop if the birds were to be saved. Once public opinion was aroused on the birds' behalf and laws were passed to protect them, it was relatively easy to control this type of shooting.

The problem of plume-hunting was in some ways more difficult to handle. The silky breasts of grebes, the feathers of gulls and terns and the plumes of egrets were very valuable, and a hunter could collect and store them easily. The killing was done in the nesting colonies, partly because of the ease of killing the birds when nesting and partly because certain species were in their best plumage at that time. The tern colonies on our coasts, the grebe colonies, and especially the egret rookeries in the South therefore suffered badly. Public opinion was extremely important in meeting the problem of plume-hunting, and effective protection became possible only when it ceased to be fashionable for ladies to decorate their hats with the feathers.

Both these phases of bird protection now belong to history, for the tide turned against both market and plume-hunting early in the twentieth century. But we are only now emerging from a period of abuse of the marshlands. The decline in waterfowl brought about by overshooting, drainage and drought continued in the United States through the 1920's and the number of these birds reached a low in the 1930's. The breeding places of the water-

fowl were disappearing. Some of the land was being converted into productive wheatfields, but certain famous duck-breeding areas became only dusty alkali flats. The history of the drainage of the Malheur and Klamath Lakes in Oregon and of the Souris River marshes in North Dakota tells us that the drainage was followed by droughts, and that the eventual starting of reclamation projects not only brought back the water, the marshes and the birds, but in some cases also helped agriculture.

At the same time a change in the attitude of the sportsman took place. Each sportsman's kill was now only a fraction of that of the market gunner of a few decades earlier, but there were many more hunters. Roads and motorcars enabled them to get quickly to remote places. If there were to be enough ducks to go around at all, short open seasons and small bag limits had to be adopted and enforced. When this had been done, the size of the sportsman's bag soon ceased to be regarded as the mark of his skill. A goose or two and a brace or so of ducks became generally accepted as a successful day's tally.

It is useless to sigh over the vanished wilderness and its teeming wildlife in early America. We can look back regretfully at the period of overshooting of game birds, of plume-hunting, and of the destruction of breeding places and wintering grounds, but we can also regard with pride a people who have become bird-conscious and conservation-minded. We are learning to manage our wildlife resources well. Refuges and sanctuaries for birds now exist from Alaska and Washington to Florida, and from Maine to California. We have enacted protective laws and established wildfowl management practices of which we can be proud. But we must not become complacent. Much remains to be done, and we must guard the gains we have made. Especially is this true of our reserves and sanctuaries. Private interests are continually attempting to gain concessions for exploiting them, and various government agencies advocate changes in their use that would defeat the purpose for which they were set aside. We must be alert to keep the best of what we have and add to it. But already we have accomplished much, and we do have wildlife in abundance once more.

American Water & Game Birds

CHAPTER 1

Loons

THERE are only four species of loons in the world, all breeding in North America and three of them across Eurasia also. The most southern species in America, the common loon, nests on the lakes south through the belt of spruce forests that barely extends into the northern United States, except in the West where the bird follows the Rockies south to Northern California. The other three species of loons are found farther north, on the lakes and ponds of the barren grounds that fringe the Arctic seas. In winter, with the freezing of the waters, the loons move south, mostly onto salt water, and some pass the winter as far south as Lower California, Florida, the Mediterranean Sea and China.

The four species of loons are all much alike—large, stout-bodied water birds with long necks, strong, pointed bills, and big feet, the three front toes fully webbed. Their plumage, varying with each species, is predominantly contrasting—blackish above, white below. By a complete moult it is changed twice a year from a brighter, breeding plumage to a duller, winter one. The flight feathers are all moulted at one time, once a year, and during this period the birds are flightless.

Underwater, loons are in their element. They can reduce their buoyancy by compressing their feathers and their bodies. Because of this ability, and because when submerged their blood stream can use loosely combined oxygen in the muscles to augment the oxygen in the lungs, they are unexcelled as swimmers and divers. They pursue their prey, chiefly fish, underwater, propelling themselves with their feet and using their wings only in turning. When they return to the surface the smaller species can rise from the water easily. The larger ones need a take-off run, but once awing, the loon's flight, on narrow wings, is strong and direct, and has been timed at sixty miles an hour. In landing, it slides in on its breast with a splash like a flying boat, rather than feet first like a duck. But on land it cuts an awkward figure. Its feet, set far back on the body, are ill adapted for locomotion. Consequently the bird seldom comes ashore except to nest, and it places its nest at the water's edge so that unless receding water has left it high and dry, the bird has only to shuffle or hobble a few steps on land.

The nest, placed on an island in a lake or on a lake shore, is merely a flattened spot or a heap of vegetation. Two drab-colored eggs spotted with black form the usual clutch. Both sexes incubate and after approximately twenty-nine days the eggs hatch. The young at hatching are covered with down, dusky above, white on the belly, and are able to follow the parents almost at once. Both parents help to feed them.

In summer plumage the four species of loons are easily told apart. The two large species, about thirty-three inches long, have black heads, but they differ in that the common loon has a black bill whereas the yellow-billed loon has a whitish, up-turned bill. The two smaller species, each about twenty-six inches long, have grayish heads, the red-throated loon being distinguished by a chestnut patch on its throat and the black-throated loon by a black patch.

Common Loon

The common loon is *the* loon to Americans who take their vacations on lakes in the north woods from Maine to Alaska. Its voice is probably better known than its appearance, and with good reason. The wails, yodels and tremolos that are its ordinary calls have been likened to wild, uncontrollable laughter and have been mistaken for wolf howls or the shrieks of persons in pain. Depending on the state of mind of the hearer, these calls are beautiful and thrilling, or maniacal and bloodcurdling. Calling occurs at least as frequently during the night as during the day, and it is then, with other sounds stilled, that the loons' chorus is most impressive. One loon calls, other loons, even on neighboring lakes, join in, and the chorus swells until it echoes for miles around.

Though the call of the common loon is chiefly associated with the bird's breeding grounds, it can sometimes be heard in its winter quarters; one of my most vivid memories of a little palmetto-fringed Florida lake in mid-winter is the laugh of a loon that echoed clearly across it.

As soon as the ice goes out of the lakes in the north, pairs of loons arrive and take up territories, one pair of loons to a small lake, more to a large one, and these bailiwicks they defend against other loons. This is the time when calling and displaying are most vigorous. The displays include such performances as one or two birds running over the surface of the water, striking it powerful blows with their wings and executing erratic dives and surfacings. Later, when the chicks are hatched these loons become very bold and will call and display in frantic protest in the face of an intruding boat. Though fish is an important loon food, the fact that there are loons on a lake is not a guarantee of the presence of fish. In British Columbia some lakes without fish support summer populations of loons that seem to thrive on a diet of such things as mollusks, insect nymphs, and some aquatic vegetation.

When alarmed, the common loon usually dives rather than flies, and to such good effect that it can easily outdistance anyone pursuing it by canoe. This raises the question of how long loons can stay under water and how far down they can go. Usually they stay down less than a minute though submergences lasting as long as fifteen minutes have been recorded. In the Great Lakes, where loons have been caught in fish nets and on set lines, the records seem to show clearly that common loons do go as far down as two hundred feet.

It has been claimed that loons kill young ducks and thus deplete the duck population. But the evidence for this is very scanty and there is a body of very good evidence to the contrary. A study of this question was made in British Columbia, where many ducks of several species nest. Counts were recorded showing the sizes of the duck broods raised on lakes where there were no loons, and of those raised on lakes where loons were present. There was no difference. A study in Minnesota, where only black ducks and wood ducks nest, again exonerated the loon from the charge of having an adverse effect on the supply of young ducks.

While immature common loons are small they like to keep close to a lakeshore where they can hide, especially when they are left by their parents. As they grow up they become birds of the open water. At times they ride on their parents' backs, the old birds often helping them mount by partly submerging. By the age of ten to eleven weeks they can fly. At this time they still weigh somewhat less than the adults, who may reach nine pounds or more.

The number of loons in an area is never large, though they are conspicuous, but the number of young that grow up each fall still seems disproportionately small. Some pairs fail to nest, or eggs disappear from the nests, or young loons vanish while still small. In one study area in Minnesota, 110 adults (including 42 breeding pairs) produced only 21 young. In a similar study in British Columbia 150 adults, including non-breeders, produced only 21 young.

As the lakes freeze, the loons, already mostly in winter plumage, move to the sea, where the year-olds, who have another year to wait before they will get their adult plumage and breed, have been spending the summer.

Yellow-billed Loon

The yellow-billed loon takes the place of the common loon on the tundra of western Arctic Canada, northern Alaska, and eastern Siberia. These two species are so much alike in appearance, except for the pale, uptilted bill of the yellow-bill and minor details of gloss and pattern of plumage, that they could almost be called subspecies. Their ways of life, too, are much alike. Their ranges meet but do not overlap, nor do the two birds hybridize. They seem to be two geologically young species, their origins influenced by the last ice age, during which glaciers in the Bering Sea area separated them and gave them time to evolve differently.

The yellow-bill is credited with many supernatural powers in the legends of the Eskimos of the western Arctic. It is also claimed that when a kayak approaches one of their nests on the shores of a tundra lake, these birds dive and puncture it from below. The Eskimos prize the yellow-bill's head and neck as a decoration for dancers.

In winter the yellow-bill lives off Norway and in the Bering Sea area.

Black-throated or Arctic Loon

The black-throated loon (Plate 1) is one of the two small species, being only twenty-four to twenty-seven inches long. It nests on the tundra and adjacent forested lakes from Scotland and Norway to Siberia, Alaska and Baffin Land. It tends to favor larger lakes and even Arctic rivers in summer. Not only are the nests built on shore, but are sometimes made of heaps of aquatic vegetation in shallow water.

More than the other loons, this species seems to favor social gatherings during the summer, when displays and much chasing, diving and noisy calling take place. Their clamor is sometimes described as being gooselike, and some of their calls have been likened to the yapping of dogs. Of course they also give mournful wails. They commonly leave their nesting lakes and fly to others to fish. When bringing back fish, they carry it in the bill, not in the throat as do such other water birds as cormorants.

Red-throated Loon

The red-throated loon (Plate 2) is the other small species. Though it is largely tundra-nesting, it is very widespread in the Arctic, and also winters on both Atlantic coasts. Its way of life is not quite like that of the other loons. On the north shore of the Gulf of St. Lawrence these loons show a curious departure from the common loon's preference for inland lakes, often nesting on lakes on islands in the Gulf. Unlike the other loons, they are sometimes loosely colonial in nesting, and often choose ponds as small as a few yards across. Because it lives on such small ponds, the red-throated loon often flies off when alarmed, instead of diving. As is obvious from this, it can rise from the water without the long take-off run of the common loon. It is customary for it to go to other lakes or the sea for food, and to bring back fish which it feeds whole to the young. The young bird does not ride on a parent's back, but while it is small the parent will come ashore many times a day to take it under its wings and warm it. Reproduction is low. In one area in Quebec ten pairs raised only three young. This may have been an exceptional year, however, for when a pair loses its eggs it will sometimes re-nest. Since the red-throated loon has a twenty-nine day incubation period and an eight-week fledgling period, those individuals that nest late are handicapped, for the ponds will be frozen by October, that is, before the young are on the wing.

CHAPTER 2

Grebes

GREBES are swimming and diving birds. In summer their favorite haunts are fresh-water lakes or ponds with adjacent marsh; in winter most of the grebes from the more northern areas go to the seacoasts. These birds need a long, pattering run in taking off from water and then, their wings beating rapidly, their flight is swift and direct. In landing on water, where they are really at home, they skid in on their breasts. Floating placidly, they ride as high as ducks, or, preening, roll over on their sides so that their white bellies flash in the sunshine.

When alarmed they may quietly sink without perceptible motion until only their heads are out of water, and then disappear, or they may dive with a forward leap like a cormorant. When underwater they often chase and catch small fish, but they also get some of their food, such as crayfish and insect larvae, by diving under the water and poking around the edges of stones and among submerged vegetation.

Though the grebe resembles a duck in appearance, its bill is quite different, being either thin and pointed like that of the loon, or short and stout. It has some unique features, notably soft, silky plumage; a tail that is made up of short, soft feathers much like the rest of the plumage; and toes that are flattened and edged with broad lobes instead of being joined by a complete web.

Many species have bright colors and crests on their heads during the breeding season; these are changed by moult in the fall for the duller black-and-white winter plumage, and regained by moult again in the spring. These nuptial adornments are used in the elaborate displays that are customary between a mated male and female. Like loons, grebes have their legs far back on their bodies, an excellent arrangement for swimming but one that is poorly adapted for walking. Grebes rarely go about on land even at nesting time, but construct nests that are in effect small islands of aquatic vegetation built up as mounds in shallow water or as floating rafts anchored among reeds or rushes.

The eggs, usually three to eight, are whitish when they are first laid but are soon stained brownish. Generally both sexes take turns at incubating the eggs. When the eggs are left untended they are covered with vegetation from the edge of the nest, apparently as protection from such predators as crows.

Young grebes are down-covered and are usually striped. They are able to swim and dive shortly after hatching, but they are easily exhausted and are not nearly so strong and self-reliant as young ducks of the same age. The immature bird is often carried on the parent's back or is snuggled under its wings, and may stay there while the parent dives and swims away underwater. However, if it gets left behind when the old bird is trying to take it away from danger, it is usually abandoned. This placid desertion of the fledgling contrasts with the frenzied behavior of either loons or ducks under similar conditions. On some grebes' nesting grounds, young ones are sometimes found dead, as though pecked to death. One authority, J. A. Munro, suggests that as the young grow up they continue to try to ride on the backs of the parents, who, resentful of this continued close attention by the young, may actually kill them in an attempt to drive them away.

Another unique characteristic of grebes is that their stomachs usually contain large quantities of their own feathers. One writer, Dr. Alexander Wetmore, believes that this mass of feathers acts as a strainer to keep fish bones from passing into the intestines until they have been sufficiently sof-tened by digestive processes so that they will not injure the intestinal wall. It seems strange, however, that evidence of such a habit is found in no other fish-eating bird.

In the days when bird plumes were sought for millinery purposes, the silky plumage of the grebe was much in demand and great havoc was wrought among the birds in their nesting colonies.

The Americas have the greatest number and variety of grebes, some twelve species, six of them living north of Mexico. Eurasia has only five species, but representatives of some of these range to New Zealand and South Africa. Some species are widely distributed, as for instance the eared grebe, which is found in North America, Eurasia and Africa, but others have only a very limited range. One of these is restricted to a single lake in Central America; another to Lake Titicaca in the Andes.

Of our six species of grebes, the Western grebe is the largest, about twenty-eight inches long. In summer plumage this species is black above and white below; the red-necked grebe has a white chin and cheeks and red neck; the horned grebe in summer has a red neck, black ruff, and yellowish ear tufts; the eared grebe has a black neck and crest with yellowish plumes on the cheeks; the pied-billed is a dull species with a black chin and a black bar across the thick bill; and the tiny Mexican grebe has a slate-colored head and neck with a black throat patch.

Red-necked Grebe

The red-necked or Holboell's grebe (Plate 5) is a rather shy bird when it is nesting. It is found on the reed-fringed lakes and larger ponds among the spruce forests of Canada and Eurasia as far north as timber line. It also nests on the sloughs and lakes of the Canadian prairies and those of the adjacent United States. It is perhaps most common on certain Manitoba marshes where it builds its "island" or "raft" nests in small, loose colonies. When alarmed the birds dive and seek safety in distant, open water, or in the shelter of reeds.

Though silent in winter, the red-neck is, like most grebes, noisy on its breeding grounds and its common calls are reminiscent of those of loons. The birds are most vociferous in the morning and evening but on moonlight nights are noisy all night long. One ornithologist, Dr. Joseph Grinnell, found that they sing what amounts to duets. He reports one starting with a long wail, another chiming in and both then singing a series of quavering calls together.

Like the loon, this large grebe has been accused of attacking other water birds, but studies at nesting lakes have yielded no evidence of this.

In winter plumage this grebe is plain gray and black and white. It may spend the winter on large lakes but more typically winters off both coasts where, singly or in flocks, it dives for its food just offshore, generally in the company of loons, horned grebes, golden-eyes and scoters.

Horned Grebe

The horned grebe is one of the less shy and secretive of our grebes, whether in its ornamental breeding plumage on the small ponds of its summer home or in its black-and-white dress on coasts during the winter. It is equally at home on the prairie ponds and little lakes of the forests from the northern United States north to timber line, as well as in Eurasia. Nesting pairs seldom build their nests close together. Although they often place them where concealing vegetation is scanty, I still remember my surprise on the little muskeg lakes of the Yukon at seeing how inconspicuous were their raft-nests anchored in the thin fringe of reeds near the edge of the water.

To observe such birds as these when they are diving for food is not easy. We have to assume that they catch fish and probe for insects while they are under water, but this species has actually been watched diving and poking about under the edges of boulders while apparently in search of crayfish.

Eared Grebe

In the United States the eared grebe is a western bird summering from the great plains to the Pacific. From the northern part of its range, where the winter is severe, it withdraws to more southerly lakes or to the California coast. It also lives in Europe, Asia and Africa in slightly different forms and is there called the black-necked grebe.

It is abundant in our western sloughs and lakes, nesting in large, dense colonies, often where concealing cover is scanty. On an Alberta lake where an estimated two thousand pairs of these grebes were nesting, the nests were so numerous that as seen from across the lake the birds on them seemed to form a solid line. These nests are small flimsy rafts which rock and tilt as the parents climb aboard. Often grebe colonies merge with those of the Franklin's gulls, the two birds seeming to get along without friction. The eared grebe is not shy and, when disturbed, often does not dive or swim

away but floats about nearby as though to watch what is going on.

Least Grebe

The Mexican or least grebe is a tropical American species whose most northerly nesting area is in the Rio Grande region of southern Texas. It is our smallest grebe, being only about nine inches long, is shy and retiring in habits, and lives the year round on marshy lakes, both large and small.

Western Grebe

Its long, slender neck, which adds to its stately, swanlike carriage, and the contrasting black-and-white plumage, which remains much the same winter and summer, make the Western grebe a very distinctive bird. It is our largest grebe, being about twenty-eight inches long, and is our most gregarious species. On the Pacific coast, where it winters, and on inland lakes during migration, flocks number in the thousands. On its breeding grounds, which are the reed- and tule-margined sloughs and lakes of the western states, it forms crowded colonies with the nests sometimes only a few yards apart. East of the plains states the Western grebe is only a straggler.

The courtship of the grebe is especially spectacular. The two birds, swimming side by side, rise up vertically and with upstretched heads run pattering over the surface of the water, at first glance giving the impression of going arm in arm. Finally they fall forward onto their breasts with a splash and then dive. In another display two birds dive, come to the surface with water weeds in their mouths, and by treading water rise high and upright, their breasts almost touching.

When alarmed, this grebe frequently swims far out into open water rather than seek the shelter of the reeds. Its food, which it gets by dives that average only about half a minute each, is largely small fish augmented in summer by some insects. The young of the Western grebe are unusual in that they do not have the striped pattern that characterizes many grebes, but are simply plain gray, darker above and paler below.

Pied-billed Grebe

Watery marshes and reed-grown ponds where it can skulk and hide are the favorite haunts of the pied-billed grebe, one of the most secretive of the family. It nests from southern Canada to South America. So secretive is it that its loud, almost cuckoo-like "cow-cow" call in the spring is often the first intimation one gets that the grebes are back. The facility with which it can disappear, even from open water, by sinking quietly, without a ripple, and swimming underwater to the shelter of marsh vegetation, or, with its bill exposed, outwait the watcher, has earned it a variety of names. "Hell-diver" is a common one, referring to the apparent depth of its dive, but I personally prefer the names "dabchick" and "di-dapper," which are used for it in Florida.

Its nesting is solitary but otherwise is typically grebelike; the nest is a mass of aquatic vegetation built up in shallow water, or floating attached to reeds, and has a shallow depression in the top for the five to seven whitish eggs. Both parents take turns at incubation for about twenty-three days until the striped, downy young hatch. Many grebes move to salt water for the winter, but the pied-billed grebe still prefers fresh-water marshes as advancing winter sends the northern birds southward. All during the year the pied-billed grebe is a dull-colored species; in winter it is very inconspicuously marked, being more of a brownish hue and lacking the black markings on its head that are part of its nuptial plumage.

CHAPTER 3

Albatrosses

ALBATROSSES are long-winged sea birds with large, webbed feet, and are famous for their flying ability. Among sailormen they are commonly spoken of as "goneys," and "mollymawk" is a term often used in the forecastle for the smaller ones. There are thirteen species of albatrosses, three of which live in the North Pacific and are visitors to our American waters. Another species inhabits the tropical parts of the Pacific, and nine of the species live in the southern oceans with which the albatross is most closely associated in tradition. It is probable that some of the southern species, flying in the stormy latitudes south of Cape Horn and of the Cape of Good Hope, circle round and round the globe in the zone of the prevailing westerly winds. Two of them, the wandering and the royal albatross, have a wingspread of about eleven and a half feet, the largest of any flying bird.

Except for nesting, the albatross spends its life at sea. Stormy weather suits its flying better than calm. Its sailing, gliding flight, now skimming close to the surface of the water, now shooting up over the crest of a wave, or following and circling a ship in a breeze or a gale, is one of the grand sights of nature.

For food albatrosses scour the seas. Squid seem to be a staple item in their diet and since these, like many other small ocean creatures, come closer to the surface at night, albatrosses may do much of their feeding then. But no animal food is scorned. Fish are taken, as well as fat and flesh from whaling operations, and scraps from ships' galleys. When food is located, they alight on the water to eat it and if it is sinking may duck under or even dive to reach it. The long bill is strongly hooked at the tip and the nostrils open externally in a pair of tubes near the base of the bill. This last is a characteristic the albatrosses share with their near relatives, the petrels, and is the most obvious external structural characteristic that distinguishes albatrosses from the superficially similar, though mostly smaller gulls.

When nesting time comes, the birds gather on islands to breed; with the exception of the sooty albatross, they breed in colonies. Certain species carry on elaborate courtship ceremonies in which both sexes take part. The nest, which some species place on the ground and a few others on cliffs, is a simple hollow or a collection of available material, and is used and added to year after year. A single egg is laid. This is either plain white or spotted lightly with brown. The chick, on hatching, is covered with a dense coat of dusky-colored down and stays in the nest until nearly ready to fly. Both parents share in such nest duties as the incubating of the eggs and the feeding of the young.

The reproductive rhythm of albatrosses is slow. Some large species breed only every other year; the incubation period may be as long as eighty days, and the chick may not fly until it is about eight months old. The parents relieve each other of incubation duties at such long intervals as every few days, and during the latter part of the fledgling period the young may be fed only twice a week. It has been said that when the young albatrosses have grown very fat they are deserted by their parents, and, in the manner of some petrels, depend on the stored fat to complete their growth, but this has recently been questioned.

Six species of albatrosses have been recorded in American waters, but three of these have been accidental stragglers from far southern seas. The three mid-Pacific species are the only ones that are properly part of our bird life. These three species are relatively small: only twenty-eight to thirty-seven inches long, in contrast to the wandering albatross, which is sometimes as long as fifty-three inches.

In adult plumage the black-footed albatross is for the most part sooty brown, the short-tailed albatross mostly white, and the Laysan Island albatross white, with blackish wings and back.

Black-footed Albatross

The black-footed albatross (Plate 12) is the only one among the three North Pacific albatrosses that commonly approaches the American coast. It nests on subtropical islands in the western Pacific Ocean in the winter season (from November to April) and for the rest of the year ranges eastward and northward over the ocean to the Bering Sea area and off the coast of Lower California.

One incidental result of the wartime activities of our younger naturalists was that they were able to carry on natural history studies in otherwise inaccessible areas. One such study was that of the black-footed albatross made by Charles Yokom from February to September, 1945, in the eastern Pacific as far as a thousand miles from our coasts, the cruising limit of his ship. The nearest to shore Yokom saw an albatross was twelve miles. But from there to a thousand miles offshore they were his vessel's constant companions, seemingly being distributed evenly over the ocean. Usually there were from two to six birds following the ship. Identifying individual birds by variations in their color patterns, Yokom found that the same one followed the vessel for distances only up to about sixty miles. But when the ship was lying to, as it was for long periods, numbers of the birds gathered about it. They fed on scraps and garbage thrown from the galley, and rested in loose flocks on the water. Between 50 and 125 of them were often to be seen at one time.

Black-footed albatrosses have been characterized as "pigs" of the sea, and Yokom found they ate meat, bread, and pastry—indeed, everything from the ship's galley except raw fruit. The only time they quarreled and screamed was when galley scraps were thrown from the ship. At these opportunities distant birds came flying, but those in the water nearer the ship would swim as far as 200 to 300 yards rather than fly.

Like other albatrosses, they need a long, pattering take-off run to become airborne in calm weather, but in rough weather they rise into the gale from the crest of a wave. The black-footed albatross is a comparatively small species, having a wingspread of only about seven feet. This species seems to move its wings once or twice a minute—more often than do the larger albatrosses. Nevertheless, its soaring, scaling flight through the troughs and over the crests of the waves shows graceful mastery of the air. The actual speed of its flight has been estimated at about thirty miles an hour; that of the larger, wandering albatross has been estimated at twice that.

Because of its dark plumage this bird was never much prized or sought after by the plume-hunters and so escaped much of the havoc which they wrought on its white-plumaged kin.

Short-tailed Albatross

The short-tailed albatross, another of the North Pacific species, is a smaller replica of the wandering albatross of the southern hemisphere. It is nearly extinct, the result in part of volcanic action on one of its restricted island nesting sites, and in part owing to the activities of the plume-hunters in the late nineteenth and early twentieth centuries.

This species used to nest on a number of islands west of Hawaii in the winter season, and range over the Pacific to the Bering Sea and Lower California. It was at one time the most common albatross on our inshore Pacific waters and, judging by bones found in the shell mounds of California and Oregon, was taken by Indians for food. In the latter part of the nineteenth century, observers in Alaska reported having seen as many as eight to fifteen birds at a time. There have been very few records of this albatross in recent years, but several breeding pairs on Torishima Island, south of Japan, seen in 1954, indicate that the species has not completely disappeared.

Laysan Albatross

The Laysan Island albatross (Plates 6, 10, 13), like the other North Pacific species, nests in winter on islets west of Hawaii and then spreads out to the Bering Sea and toward the American coast. It keeps well offshore so that there are very few records of it in American waters, and it is a shy bird, seldom following ships.

Three species of albatross have straggled to our coasts from southern waters: the yellow-nosed albatross and the black-browed albatross to our Atlantic coast, and the white-capped albatross to our Pacific coast.

CHAPTER 4

Shearwaters, Petrels and Fulmars

SHEARWATERS get their name from their manner of flying. They glide on long, narrow, rigid wings in rapid flight close over the waves, tilting now to one side, now to the other. The tip of the lower wing seems to shear or cut through the water, and perhaps it does part of the time. Along with their relatives the petrels, fulmars and whale birds, the shearwaters form a family of about fifty species of sea birds, the largest as big as some albatrosses and the smallest no larger than some of the tiny storm petrels.

Southern waters are the headquarters of this extensive group, but several species live in the eastern Atlantic and one, the fulmar, is an Arctic nester. They are pelagic birds, and their food is the animal life of the sea: fish, squid, crustaceans and other small, floating creatures. One member of this family, the broad-billed whale bird of the southern oceans, has fringes on the sides of its mandibles. Like a right whale it gulps a mouthful of water and tiny floating animals, and closing its bill forces the water out through this sievelike fringe and keeps the food in its mouth to be swallowed. But any flesh or fat is acceptable fare, and the scraps and fat from the whaling stations and from fishing boats that clean fish at sea provide abundant food for these birds. The giant petrel of the Antarctic has become a predator that kills and eats smaller birds.

Only at nesting time do the birds of this family come to the land. Then many species nest in crannies in rocks, or in burrows, while a few make their homes on cliffs or in the open. Most of them seek the seclusion of an island for a nesting site. The birds' colonies often contain immense numbers of nests. A single, white egg is laid and both sexes take turns sitting on it until it hatches. The young bird is covered with a dense coat of down and food is brought to it by both parents. In at least some of the hole-nesting species, the birds are active about the nesting colony only at night, spending the day either at sea or hidden in their nests. Some of these birds abandon the young when it is well grown and very fat but still unable to fly. The parents may even set out on migration, leaving the fledgling to finish its feather growth, make its way to the sea and begin life there by itself.

This family is closely related to both albatrosses and storm petrels, which they somewhat resemble in certain of their habits and in their rather long, hooked bills in which the nostrils open in a pair of tubes on the upper surface. The legs are rather short and the toes are united by a web. Gray, brown and white are common colors in their plumages and many species are very similar in appearance.

Another peculiarity of the "tube-noses," which they share with albatrosses and storm petrels, is that most of them manufacture a stomach "oil," a musky-smelling fluid which they vomit up, especially when disturbed. It is this fluid, no doubt, that gives their plumage and nesting grounds their characteristic musky odor. Speculation is still rife as to its use; one theory is that it is an actual excretion of excess fat and vitamin A; another that it is a substance for preening the feathers; and a third that it is spat out at an enemy when the birds are nesting.

North America is poor in nesting species of this group of birds. We have only the fulmar of the Arctic and three species that nest or have nested in Bermuda, yet we have eighteen species recorded as occurring here. Some are regular migrants from more southern waters, some wander from the eastern Atlantic, and a few are strays from their normal range in far southern oceans.

Some of the nine species that occur more or less regularly in our waters present difficulties in identification. The greater shearwater is about twenty-one inches long, with brown upperparts, white underparts, and a dark cap which is sharply contrasted with the white of its cheeks and the sides of its neck. The Cory's shearwater is slightly larger and is similar in color, but the dark of its crown shades gradually into the white of its throat. The pink-footed shearwater of the Pacific is very similar to the Cory's shearwater of the Atlantic. The cahow is similar to the greater shearwater but smaller, being only sixteen inches long, and has a whitish nape and upper tail coverts. The Manx shearwater is a small species, about fifteen inches long, with its upperparts blackish and its underparts white, with or without black in the undertail coverts and flanks, and the dark of its head shading into the white of the throat. Audubon's shearwater resembles the Manx shearwater in color but is still smaller, about twelve inches long. The sooty shearwater, about eighteen inches long, is generally blackish-brown with its underwing coverts whitish. The slender-billed shearwater is similar but smaller, about fourteen inches long, and with darker underwings. The fulmar is twenty inches long and in one color phase has a gull-like color pattern, being white with a gray back, the upper sides of the wings gray, and no black tips to the wings; in the other color phase the fulmar is entirely ashy brown.

Greater Shearwater

It seems almost incredible that the greater shearwater, so common in the North Atlantic, nests only on the tiny islands of the Tristan da Cunha group in the central South Atlantic. Not only that, but most of them nest only on Nightingale Island, which has an area of about one square mile. Here, at the start of the breeding season, clouds of shearwaters darken the sky in the afternoon and it is impossible to walk about in the evening without stumbling over the birds. The soil is so honeycombed with their burrows that the surface of the earth collapses underfoot as one walks along. The breeding population on Nightingale Island is estimated at about four million, or one burrow and pair to approximately each square yard. The birds on nearby islets may number an additional million, and the non-breeding birds at sea may increase the total population to considerably more than five million.

Though this species was first described in 1818, its nesting place was long unknown and was discovered only in the present century. The first adequate account of it was published as recently as 1952 by M. K. Rowan, who was stationed on Tristan da Cunha. This report clarifies so many points in the little-known biology of shearwaters that it is worth seeing how it correlates with the behavior of the birds when they are in the waters off our Atlantic coast.

In September, the austral spring season, the birds arrive at Tristan. Their days are spent at sea but the nights are passed ashore in courtship, in display, and in vocalization in which hundreds of birds join—a genuinely communal affair. Burrows are occupied or dug. Sometimes two birds are to be found in an unfinished burrow, one digging, the other near the entrance scratching out the loose soil. Only scant nest material is carried into the burrows, but where crowded conditions have forced some of the birds to nest in rock crevices, they add considerable material to their nests. Egg-laying takes place in early November and every female lays her single egg in the same week. During incubation, one bird spends the day in the burrow, while the other flies out to sea, returning at dusk to spend the night with its mate, bickering and croaking. Most of the young hatch in early January after an incubation period of about seven to eight weeks. Again the pattern of life changes; the adults come and go day and night, bringing food to the nestlings. In April, while the young birds are still heavily clad in down, and very fat, the adults abandon them. Huge rafts of adults assemble on the water in the evening and are gone by dawn, evidently leaving on migration en masse.

The nestlings, drawing on their store of fat, complete their growth alone. The earth and grass found in their stomachs at this time indicate attempts to assuage their hunger with such substitutes for food. In late May or in June, when they are perhaps five months old, the young leave the island gradually, rather than all at once like the adults. Some earlier observers were puzzled at finding greater shearwaters in their burrows in May and thought they were breeding then, but the answer seems plain: these were young birds whose parents were already off the American coast some thousands of miles away.

The greater shearwaters move north across the tropical waters quickly, and up through the western Atlantic. In about the latitude of Maine they spread out, and most of them spend the summer (their winter) farther north. With the approach of autumn the birds disappear from the middle Atlantic. Presumably these are the birds that arrive in September at Tristan to breed. But many birds remain much later, into October and November, in the eastern and western Atlantic. Presumably these are the young birds, and perhaps also some non-breeding adults.

The ocean is the home of shearwaters. Though they gather in flocks at migration time they are much less social during most of their stay in the north and are more or less spread out over the ocean. They do not follow steamers, but among the men who go to the fishing banks these birds are known for their greed for fish gurry and for their fearlessness. Where fish are being cleaned, the hagdons, as the fishermen call them, gather in a struggling, screaming mass, paying little attention to the men in the boats. Once satiated, they light on the water to bathe and rest.

Their natural food is squid and small fish. These they hunt with typical shearwater flight, scaling low over the waves, gliding with rarely a wing beat if the day is windy. One observer watched one traveling parallel to his steamer and reported that it glided for a mile and a half without a wing beat. To feed, they land on the water, and then may even dive for food, swimming underwater with the aid of their wings. To get into the air again they need a pattering run for a take-off, but if the day is calm they may have difficulty in getting off at all.

At an earlier period fishermen caught shearwaters on hook and line to use for fish bait and it was no uncommon sight to see a Grand Banks schooner with hundreds of these birds hanging in the rigging.

Manx Shearwater

The Manx shearwater is a common species from the European side of the North Atlantic which has nested as far west as Bermuda. In its home waters it is more an offshore than a pelagic species, and this perhaps is why there are only a few records of it on our Atlantic coast. A subspecies of this bird, often known as the black-vented shearwater, breeds off the Pacific coast of Mexico. When the breeding season is over, some of these birds migrate northward, like the egrets that visit our northern states in late summer. Then these shearwaters appear on our Pacific waters, where they are most common in the Santa Barbara and San Pedro Channels, off California, in July, August and September.

A Manx shearwater holds the long-distance record for homing. One was removed from its nest and flown by airplane from Britain to Boston, where it was released. Twelve and a half days later it was back on its nest, having flown the 3,200 land miles across the trackless Atlantic from a point outside the normal range of the species. This and other experiments on the homing ability of the Manx shearwater carried out by G. V. T. Mathews in Britain have shown that the birds home better in fine than in dull weather, suggesting that they actually use the sun as an aid in navigation.

While the general habits of the Manx shearwater are like those of its near relatives, there are differences. The birds are active at sea by day and nocturnal at their breeding grounds. They do not come in directly to their nests after dark, like many petrels, but toward dusk, huge flocks gather on the water offshore, resting and milling about, and then come to their nests about two hours after dark. They are sociable birds and besides nesting in colonies, they go back and forth to their feeding grounds in flocks. Some are said to seek food as much as six hundred miles from their nests. As the birds take turns incubating the eggs, the periods they spend on and off the nest are long. The usual interval is about five days, but periods as long as ten days have been recorded, and experimentally this has been extended to sixteen days; during this time the incubating bird is without food and water. Shearwaters catch their food of small fish and cephalopods chiefly at the surface, often paddling with their feet and slowly flapping their wings like the smaller petrels. This is one of the species in which the parents abandon the nestlings ten to fifteen days before the immature birds are ready to quit the nest burrow, leaving them to find their own way to sea.

Cory's Shearwater

Off our Atlantic coast, especially that part from New York to New England, the Cory's or North Atlantic shearwater arrives in August and leaves by November. The birds come west from their breeding grounds in the Azores and the Canaries and pause with us for a while before going to more southerly waters for the winter. To be sure of seeing them one must go out on a fishing boat, for they are offshore and pelagic birds, though they sometimes come within sight of our coast and even into our harbors. Their habits are much like those of the greater shearwater and despite the latter's name, the Cory's is the largest shearwater to visit our Atlantic coast. They not only eat plankton, fish, gurry, and any refuse that comes their way, but are said to join the jaegers in harrying the terns and in robbing them of their food.

Sooty Shearwater

A visitor from its breeding grounds in the subantarctic waters of New Zealand and Cape Horn, the sooty shearwater, called the "mutton bird" by the New Zealanders, is the commonest of the shearwaters on our Pacific coast. A few non-breeding birds stay all the year, but great numbers are present here during the northern migration in May and June, and again on the southern migration in September. One hundred thousand of these birds have been seen off the Pacific coast in a day; they fly low over the water, dipping into the troughs and reappearing over the crests of the waves, and the great flocks may take hours to pass a given point.

Ordinarily one must go from three to five miles offshore to see sooty shearwaters, and most of them remain still farther out to sea. Perhaps when they are on the open ocean they depend mainly on squid for food, but they do follow schools of fish at times and then may come close inshore. One such flock, feeding on the water in a Washington bay, looked like an island about three-quarters of a mile long, and the thousands of birds in the air obscured the view of the opposite shore of the bay. Much of the time the sooty shearwaters are silent, but a flock feeding on a school of anchovies is a great, screaming mass of birds. Off the Washington coast a daily routine has been observed: the flocks sleep on the water until daybreak, feed until midmorning, rest until midafternoon, and then feed again before settling on the water for the night.

The sooty shearwater is much less common on our Atlantic coast, where the greater shearwater outnumbers it one hundred to one. Here it is greedy for fish offal, like other shearwaters, and follows fishermen's dories, even diving for the baited hooks as they sink.

Slender-billed Shearwater

The slender-billed shearwater migrates north in the western Pacific to the Bering Sea area, and it is only on its southward migration that it occurs off our Pacific coast. Then it is a smaller companion of the sooty shearwater, which it resembles in habits though it is not nearly as common. It breeds in the Australian area, where like the sooty shearwater in New Zealand it is known as the "mutton bird," and is exploited for its oil and flesh.

Pink-footed Shearwater

The pink-footed shearwater travels and feeds with the more numerous sooty shearwaters off our Pacific coast, but when it rests on the water it likes to gather in little groups of from two to ten birds of its own kind. It breeds only on certain islands off the coast of Chile, and although strays can be found off California throughout the year, spring, summer and autumn are the seasons when the species is common off our west coast.

Audubon's Shearwater

The Audubon's shearwater nests in the Bahamas and Bermuda, its breeding places closest to America, and is of casual occurrence off our Atlantic coast. Its flight is like that of other small shearwaters: it flaps its wings a few times, then sails over the water for a few seconds, and so on. In feeding it alights, swims and dives freely for fish, sometimes assembling in considerable flocks. In Bermuda, where the cahow nests in burrows, this species is its neighbor but makes its home in crevices in the rocks. Besides living in the warmer waters of the Atlantic it also occurs in tropical Pacific and Indian Ocean waters.

Shearwaters—Casual Species

There are three shearwater species of the southern hemisphere that reach our Pacific coast casually or as strays: the pale-footed shearwater, which nests in the Australian area and wanders north and east, though rarely as far as California waters; the New Zealand shearwater, which nests in the New Zealand area and migrates over the Pacific, rarely to California; and the black-tailed shearwater of southern oceans, which has been recorded once in California as a stray. The allied shearwater is a bird of the warm waters of the eastern Atlantic, the Pacific and the Indian Oceans. It nests among rocks and crevices on islands and seems not to range far from its breeding colonies; there are a very few records of it on our Atlantic coast.

Cahow or Bermuda Petrel

In the first part of the seventeenth century the early settlers in Bermuda found a sea fowl they called the "cahow" because of its voice. It was fabulously abundant and helped to save the colonists from starvation in lean times, such as the famine of 1614 to 1615. Even earlier the Spanish explorers had devoured thousands of these birds and had salted and dried their carcasses for food on long voyages. Through exploitation by man, compounded probably by destruction by introduced rats and pigs, the cahow disappeared from human ken and for nearly three hundred years there was no record of it; not a specimen had been preserved and ornithological texts that mentioned it contained only a mixture of fact and legend. Then in 1906 a specimen was collected at Bermuda. Ten years later it was officially described and given a scientific name. The cahow was next heard of alive in 1935 when the famous naturalist William Beebe secured a fledgling that had struck a lighthouse. Another ten years passed and an American Army officer stationed on Bermuda found recent remains of this bird. Apparently it really had survived. This led Robert Cushman Murphy of the American Museum of Natural History and L. S. Mowbray of Bermuda to institute a search for it in 1951. In the two weeks' study Murphy and Mowbray made in late January and early February of that year they found the cahow had indeed survived, though it was woefully reduced in numbers from its once "fabulous abundance." There were at most one hundred birds and these were breeding on isolated islets off Bermuda. Apparently the cahow cannot survive—or can only barely survive—either where rats exist, suggesting one conservation measure, or on rocky islets, since it must have soil in which to burrow.

A brief study of their habits and a comparison with those of their relatives suggested the following cahow timetable: mid-June to mid-October—presumably wandering somewhere at sea, since no one has ever seen a bird during this period; mid-October to December—courtship on their breeding grounds and digging burrows; January and February—incubation; March to May—fledgling period under parental care, and finally departure of adults; early June—departure of young.

This basic picture was one of typical petrel behavior. During the study, the cahows were incubating, and all day some of the birds were away at sea while the rest were in their burrows with the eggs. The vociferous calling from which the cahow got its name is apparently a characteristic of the courtship period, for while incubating the birds were almost silent. After dark they returned from the sea to their burrows; in one case mutual display continued thereafter for about three hours before the relieved bird departed, presumably to take its turn at sea. Unlike the behavior of some petrels, the cahow makes a bulky nest of twigs and green leaves in the chamber at the end of its burrow, and does not eject stomach oil when handled.

Petrels—Casual Visitors

Strays in America are the scaled petrel, which comes from the southern oceans and has been found in such widely separated localities as Maine and Alaska; the South Trinidad petrel, with a record of a single waif found at Ithaca, New York; and the Pintado petrel or Cape pigeon, recorded in Maine and California. The Cook's petrel is a Pacific bird that has been recorded in the Aleutians.

Though the black-capped petrel, still another species, is of only accidental occurrence in the eastern United States, many of our records of it concern birds found at inland localities from Florida to Ohio and Ontario—strays that had been blown far out of their normal range in the West Indies area. This species used to nest very commonly in burrows on the mountains of Guadeloupe and Dominica in the Lesser Antilles, and most of what we know about it comes from picturesque accounts of hunts for fledglings, which were used there for food. Extinction has for some time threatened the species, but a few still survive. Where they now nest, in what mountain area, free from man and introduced mongoose, we do not know. Our recent records are of only an occasional bird seen at sea.

Fulmar

Gull-like in color and size, but with the sturdy, graceful flight of the shearwater, the fulmar has been likened to a miniature albatross. It is a bird of colder, northern waters, in winter ranging southward in the Pacific to California and Japan, while in the Atlantic the southern edge of its normal range runs from New England waters to the Bay of Biscay. The wide oceans are its home, and in the Atlantic an estimated two million fulmars range over five million square miles of water. For nesting, the fulmar retires northward to the Bering Sea area; to the Arctic from Baffin Land, Greenland and Iceland to Nova Zembla; and in the northeastern Atlantic, to Britain.

Its favorite breeding places are ledges on cliffs facing the sea, such protection providing the seclusion that many of this family seek on the islands. Also, unlike many shearwaters, it lays its single egg in the open, not in a burrow, and the birds fly about their colonies by day. The rookeries are sometimes very large, one at Cape Searle, Baffin Land, being estimated at approximately 100,000 nests and another on Bear Island, north of Norway, at approximately 200,000 nests.

There has been a spectacular increase in the fulmar population of the northeastern Atlantic, in Iceland, the Faroes and Britain, in the last two hundred years. Up to 1877 there was only one colony—at St. Kilda off the Outer Hebrides, but by 1949 cliffs were occupied from the Shetland Islands to Land's End by a population of approximately 130,000 nesting birds. This increase seems to be correlated with changes in man's activities and a corresponding alteration in the fulmar's food habits. The fulmar normally ate the small, pelagic animals that live floating near the surface of the sea, the creatures also eaten by right whales and called "brit" or "krill" by the whalers. But the fulmar was also a scavenger and did not neglect any animal matter it found afloat. The rise of the whaling industry provided these birds with a new abundance of food—whale flesh and scraps of fat—for feeding their young. When whaling declined, steam trawlers carrying ice to preserve their catches began to make longer offshore trips. These vessels, gutting their catches at sea, poured a flood of offal into the water. The increase of fulmars, correlated with this rich new food supply, continued. But is the future bright for the fulmar? Man is changing his ways again. Fishermen are now experimenting with turning fish offal into some commercial product, such as cattle food, and so there soon may be no more waste for the fulmar. Perhaps then the birds again will decline in numbers.

The effectiveness of the oil "spitting" or "vomiting" of the shearwater, petrel and fulmar family has been studied, especially among the fulmars. These birds can forcibly eject a gobbet of oil a distance of four or five feet. Even newly hatched fulmars have this oil-spitting ability and it appears to be an effective defense against marauding gulls that might eat the eggs or the young.

The fulmars are variable in color: some are white and blue-gray; others are a smoky blue-gray all over, and some are intermediates. In the Atlantic the more southern birds are all white and gray, the northern birds mostly dark; in the Bering Sea area the reverse is true.

1. *Black-throated or Arctic Loon*

[ERIC HOSKING]

2. *Red-throated Loon*

[DAVID G. ALLEN]

3. *Brown Pelican*

[DON CASKEY: SHOSTAL]

4. *White Pelican with breeding-season knob on bill*

[CY LA TOUR]

5. *Red-necked Grebes and young*

[CLEVELAND P. GRANT]

6. *Laysan Albatross in dance*
[LEWIS WAYNE WALKER: NATIONAL AUDUBON]

7. *British Storm Petrel*
[ERIC HOSKING]

8. *Brown Pelican colony*
[ANDREW H. DUPRE: FISH AND WILDLIFE SERVICE]

9. *Magnificent Frigate Birds* (*male at right*)

[DONALD DICKEY: NATIONAL AUDUBON]

10. *Laysan Albatross at nest*

[RICHARD LOOMIS: NATIONAL AUDUBON]

11. *White-bellied Booby and young*

[ALEX WETMORE: FISH AND WILDLIFE SERVICE]

12. *Black-footed Albatross*

[ALFRED BAILEY: NATIONAL AUDUBON]

13. *Laysan Albatross*

[ALFRED BAILEY: NATIONAL AUDUBON]

14. *White-bellied Booby*

[LEWIS WAYNE WALKER]

15. *Gannet and young*

[JOHN MARKHAM]

16. *Gannet colony*

[DAVID TUCKER]

17. *Common Egret* (*young*)

[CY LA TOUR]

18. *Common Egret*

[ALLAN D. CRUICKSHANK : NATIONAL AUDUBON]

19. *Snowy Egret*

20. *Cattle Egret*

[SAMUEL A. GRIMES]

22. *Water-turkeys* (*male at right*)

[DAVID GOODNOW]

21. *Double-crested Cormorants*

23. *Reddish Egret*

24. *Green Heron*

[ALLAN D. CRUICKSHANK : NATIONAL AUDUBON]

25. *Louisiana Heron at nest*

[ALLAN D. CRUICKSHANK : NATIONAL AUDUBON]

26. *Least Bittern*

[ALLAN D. CRUICKSHANK: NATIONAL AUDUBON]

27. *Yellow-crowned White Heron*

[ALLAN D. CRUICKSHANK: NATIONAL AUDUBON]

28. *Least Bittern* (*young*)

[MASLOWSKI AND GOODPASTER]

29. *Snowy Egret*

[SAMUEL A. GRIMES: FISH AND
WILDLIFE SERVICE]

30. *Great Blue Heron* (young)

31. *Little Blue Heron*

[ALLAN D. CRUICKSHANK : NATIONAL AUDUBON]

32. *Black-crowned Night Heron*

[MASLOWSKI AND GOODPASTER]

33. Great White Heron

[ELIOT PORTER]

34. Great Blue Heron

[ELIOT PORTER]

35. *White-faced Glossy Ibis*

[ALLAN D. CRUICKSHANK : NATIONAL AUDUBON]

36. *White Ibis*

[HELEN CRUICKSHANK :
NATIONAL AUDUBON]

37. *Wood Ibis*

38. Roseate Spoonbill

[ALLAN D. CRUICKSHANK: NATIONAL AUDUBON]

Storm Petrels

STORM PETRELS are tiny sea birds ranging from the size of a sparrow to that of a robin. They flutter and dart over the ocean with bat- or swallow-like flight, pausing with outspread wings and lightly pattering over the water as if walking on it as they snatch their food of small pelagic animals. It is this habit, tradition has it, that gave them their name petrel, from St. Peter and his walking on the water. But another school says the name comes from one of the bird's calls.

Though small and fragile-looking birds, one or another of the twenty-four known species occurs on every ocean from the Antarctic to the Bering Sea and Greenland, and they come to land only to nest. They weather storms by keeping in the lee of waves, taking shelter in the troughs lest they be blown away. How they manage to sleep during storms that last weeks, if not months, in the far southern latitudes, is a mystery.

Typically the storm petrels nest on islands among rocks or dig burrows in the ground where the single egg is laid and the down-covered nestlings are raised. A musky smell like that of the oil they vomit up when disturbed often characterizes their burrows. The rhythm of reproduction is slow, despite their small size: incubation of the single egg may take six weeks and fledging of the young even longer. Both parents take turns at nest duties, including incubating and bringing food to the young. In some species at least, the fat, well-grown young bird is left by the parents to finish its growth alone in its burrow, using its fat for food, and to venture into the world by itself.

These storm petrels form a group related to the shearwaters and the albatrosses, all of them having nostrils that open into a pair of tubes on top of a slender, hooked bill. The storm petrels' legs are rather slender and long in proportion to the body and their toes are webbed. Besides the five species that appear only occasionally in American waters there are five that breed on our offshore islands or migrate off our coasts in numbers. These five species are all between six and nine inches long. The fork-tailed petrel is pearl gray; the ashy petrel is sooty black; the Leach's, Wilson's and British storm petrels are sooty black with whitish bands on the wings and with white rumps. The Wilson's petrel has a square tail, long legs, and yellow webs between the toes; the British storm petrel has a nearly square tail and shorter legs with black feet, and the Leach's petrel has a forked tail and black feet.

Leach's Petrel

Although thousands of Leach's petrels may be nesting on a tiny offshore island at one time, not one will be in sight during the day. Some of the birds will be away at sea; others will be in their underground burrows. Thus the petrels avoid their major enemies, the gulls. At sea the birds are active by day. They may circle about ships, springing and bounding through the air in a strange, erratic manner, but they do not habitually follow in a ship's wake, differing in this from some of their relatives. Hovering over the water, they snatch up the small, floating, animal life that is their food.

When the birds come on land they do not stand on their toes like most birds, but rest on the whole tarsus and scuttle about on their "heels." They can, however, rise on their toes and take off easily from the ground. The males come ashore by night and dig their nesting burrows, using their hooked bills to loosen the soil and their webbed, clawed feet to push it aside and pack it down. This burrowing may take three days. Then the male sits in his burrow nightly, uttering a staccato call of several notes, and in the darkness outside the females fly about calling. The birds are mutually attracted by this calling back and forth and the female finally enters a burrow. Then from underground come warm cooings, trills or purring calls indicating mating. Ordinarily the parents take four-day turns at incubating the single egg. After the downy chick is five days old it is left alone all day, the parents bringing

it food after nightfall and leaving before dawn.

Leach's petrel, a species breeding in the northern hemisphere, nests on islands from the Bering Sea to California, from New England to Greenland, and off the European coast. In winter many of these birds move southward over the oceans into tropical waters, while some remain as far north as the waters around Greenland.

Fork-tailed Petrel

Along the Pacific coast from Alaska to California nests the fork-tailed petrel. One ornithologist, Dr. Joseph Grinnell, spent a night on St. Lazaria Island near Sitka, Alaska, where this bird and Leach's petrel had their nesting burrows in the porous sod of the forest that crowned the island. They had as neighbors thousands of other sea birds: violet-green cormorants, guillemots, and murres on the steep, broken sides of the island, and glaucous-winged gulls and tufted puffins on the grassy banks. Not a petrel was seen by day, but at dusk the birds' calls began coming from the ground in every direction. As it grew darker the ground came alive with petrels struggling to get into the air, and as they flew about they collided with trees, branches and even the observer. Dr. Grinnell tried to start a fire, but his smouldering blaze was put out by petrels flying into it and after several attempts he gave up. By sunrise not a petrel was to be seen or a petrel voice heard.

Away from its breeding islands, the fork-tailed petrel spreads over the North Pacific as far as Japan. It flutters over the water from which it gathers the tiny sea animals on which it lives.

Ashy Petrel

The ashy petrel breeds off the California coast, on the Farallon and some of the Santa Barbara Islands, and on the Coronado Islands just to the south. It contrasts with such wide-ranging species as the Leach's petrel in being restricted at nesting time to these few islands, and also differs from such far-wandering and migrating species as the Wilson's petrel in spending its non-breeding season at sea only in the restricted area of the waters off California and Lower California.

As long ago as 1911 the ornithologist William L. Dawson wrote a summary of the breeding habits of this species that has been found to apply to other species as well. Dawson discovered that the ashy petrels have a lengthy period of courtship during which they spend their nights ashore, chiefly in their burrows, returning to sea during the day. Then comes a "honeymoon period" of perhaps a week in which they remain ashore, spending the daytime at least in their burrows. After the single egg is laid both parents share incubation.

British Storm Petrel

Nesting only on the islands on the eastern side of the Atlantic from Norway to the Mediterranean, the British storm petrel (Plate 7) wanders into northern Atlantic waters after nesting and then goes south in winter to the seas off the Cape of Good Hope and beyond.

It shares with the Wilson's petrel the habit of following ships, and is usually seen fluttering to and fro astern, sailing over the smooth, upswelling water of the wake. Its fluttering flight, interrupted only occasionally by short glides, recalls that of a large moth or a bat.

Wilson's Petrel

One of the petrels that nest in the Antarctic is Wilson's petrel, and this species migrates north during the southern winter. From April to September it is found off our Atlantic coast, but in the Indian and Pacific Oceans it rarely seems to cross equatorial waters and there are but two West Coast records, both from California.

This is a pelagic species. Along with the British storm petrel it follows ships, picking up from the ocean its natural food of small sea animals or bits of refuse from the vessels. It also gathers around fishing boats for gurry and, in the far southern waters, around whaling stations for scraps of fat. Its abundance off our Atlantic coast can be judged from the report that one thousand birds were estimated within sight of an observer equipped with binoculars on a Long Island beach during one June day.

Despite this record, the Wilson's petrel is not ordinarily a gregarious bird, and over wide stretches of ocean it is usually met with only singly or in twos or threes. As it feeds, it flaps its wings and sails low over the water in swallow-fashion, sometimes giving a thrust at the water with its feet or hovering with its feet in the water. When on the water it floats buoyantly, like a miniature gull.

Traditionally storms do not bother petrels, but this is not always so, for after one severe August storm thousands of dead or dying birds were washed up on a Carolina beach.

Storm Petrels—Casuals and Strays

The black petrel and the least petrel nest only on islands about the peninsula of Lower California, and wander north to the waters off the state of California, as well as south to South America. Three other species, mostly of more southern waters, are known as accidentals in America or off its coast: the white-bellied petrel, the white-faced petrel and the Madeira petrel.

CHAPTER 6

Tropic-birds

THERE ARE two different accounts of the way tropic-birds got their other name of boatswain (usually pronounced "bosun") birds: first, from their habit of giving a shrill, whistling cry as they circle a ship at sea as though inspecting the rigging; and second because of the marlinspike shape of the bird's central tail feathers. But the name tropic-bird suits them well, too, for tropical waters are the homes of the three species in the family. They nest on tropical islands and range far over tropical oceans, preferring, unlike most albatrosses and petrels, to inhabit calm seas. As one might expect,

their flight is quite different from that of the tube-noses: they do not sail, but fly with a quick, flapping wing beat that recalls that of a pigeon.

The three species are rather similar, all of them the size of a small gull, with white predominating in their plumage. The beak is stout and pointed, and the four toes on the disproportionately small feet are webbed. Like other sea birds they get their food from the ocean. Fish and squid are their chief diet, and these they locate from the air, hovering over them, and then plunge downward into the sea after them. Sometimes they go completely underwater. Surfacing, they float lightly like a gull but with long tail cocked up, and they rise easily. They go on land to nest. Like the shearwaters a single egg is the rule, and it is heavily marked with brown. The young bird, down-covered, stays in the nest until full feathered.

The two species of tropic-birds that visit our coasts are from thirty to forty inches long, but the elongated central tail feathers account for more than half this length. The adult yellow-billed tropic-bird is white, with black in the wings. Despite the accepted name of the species, the yellow bill is characteristic only of the immature bird; the adult has a red bill. Some authors prefer the more accurate name of white-tailed tropic-bird. The adult red-billed tropic-bird is similar but has a black-barred back.

Yellow-billed or White-tailed Tropic-bird

The yellow-billed tropic-bird lives where the tropical sun is brilliant and the shallow, warm seas are a vivid, pale green. White sea birds flying over the waters catch the reflection and appear pale green below. More than one naturalist in Bermuda, writing of the beauty and grace of these long-tailed birds, dazzling white against the blue sky or the cliff faces, speak of this reflected green on the underparts of the birds. The Bermudas are in the latitude of the Carolinas, about six hundred miles offshore, and are influenced by the warm Gulf Stream, which gives them a mild, subtropical climate. Here the yellow-billed tropic-bird reaches the most northerly of its breeding stations. Although these birds are not gregarious, many of them come together in a small compass on the numerous little cliffs of Bermuda, as many as seventy-five nests in a hundred yards of cliff having been reported. The birds do not actually construct a nest but lay the single whitish, brown-blotched egg on the bare rock. Both parents take turns at incubating the egg for

at least twenty-eight days. On the ledges they shuffle about, barely raising their bodies from the rock, and sometimes even using their wings to help them move about. At this time they are very tame, and a cautious observer can approach close and even stroke them. The newly hatched young, a grayish-white ball of down, stays on its ledge. There the parents attend it closely for about two weeks, then leave it alone most of the day, visiting it only in the early morning to feed it two or three times by regurgitation. The fledgling acquires its complete plumage on its nest ledge and grows fat and heavier than the adult. Finally, when about two months old it flutters down to the water and swims out to sea. Despite its well-grown wings and its frequent exercise of them on its nest ledge, it cannot yet fly. Presumably it lives on its stored fat, like some young petrels and shearwaters, until it reduces its weight and is able to fly and to catch its own food.

The range of this species is in the warm waters of the Atlantic, Pacific and Indian Oceans, approaching our coasts closest in the West Indies, Bahamas and Bermuda. Only as a stray does it occur occasionally within our borders from Florida to Nova Scotia.

Red-billed Tropic-bird

The red-billed tropic-bird is considered the most primitive of the three species, because the adult has the back barred with black, a characteristic that only the young of the other species have retained. It is another species widespread in tropical waters and ordinarily approaches the United States no closer than the Lesser Antilles and the Gulf of California. Like many sea birds, individuals occasionally stray far outside their normal range to unlikely places. Besides being of casual occurrence on the coast of California, the bird has been reported from Arizona and from the Banks of Newfoundland.

CHAPTER 7

Pelicans

PELICANS are very large water birds of which there are only six kinds in the world. All are very similar in form and general appearance, with a heavy body, a long neck and a long, wide bill with a capacious pouch. The pelican's wings are long and broad, its tail and legs are short, and its webbed feet are large. In color, some pelicans are mostly white, and others predominantly gray and brown.

The pelicans make their homes in the tropics and in the temperate regions of the globe; some of them live mostly on fresh water and others on salt water. All are fish-eaters, with a surprising diversity of fishing habits. Pelicans are sociable at rest, in flight and when nesting. Their nests, built on the ground or in trees, may be little more than hollows, or may be substantial structures made of sticks. The eggs are from two to four in number, bluish white and with a rough, chalky texture, and need incubating for from four to six weeks before they hatch. Both parents share in the nest duties and, later, in

the care of the young pelicans. When hatched, the young are naked and nearly helpless. In hot and arid nesting sites, where the thermometer may read 112° Fahrenheit, the parents are assiduous in shading the young with their own bodies—an important factor in the survival of the nestlings. When the nestlings are about two weeks old they acquire a coat of whitish down. As they develop and gain strength those in ground nests begin to wander about and show the adults' trait of gregariousness by gathering into bands, while those in tree nests stay in them until ready to fly. They are fed on fish brought in the parent's gullet. The young pelicans in a colony make it a noisy place, but the adults are practically voiceless at all times.

The two species of pelicans in America are quite different in color and size. The white pelican has white plumage, with black ends to its wings, and may be nearly six feet long, with a wingspread of as much as ten feet. The brown pelican, as his name implies, is mostly brown and may be as much as four and a half feet long, with a wingspread of up to seven feet.

White Pelican

Our western lakes are the summer home of the white pelican (Plate 4) along with a host of other marsh or waterfowl. To an observer the pelican's size is impressive as it floats buoyantly or swims among the lesser waterfowl, towering above them. A flock of pelicans resting on a sandbar or floating on the water's surface in the distance gleams white like a snowbank. The birds may be a little slow in getting into the air but once awing they have an air of majesty and dignity. The great black-tipped wings of each bird in a flock keep "step" in their measured flight and now and then the birds cease their wing beats and glide in unison. Aerial antics are also engaged in, the birds soaring high, plunging earthward in a steep dive, and then zigzagging away.

The nesting colonies, consisting of any number from a few score to a few thousand birds, are located on secluded islands. Some of the larger present-day colonies are in Great Salt Lake. Since this lake is without fish, the pelicans that nest there must go elsewhere for their food and for that of their offspring. Some of them go as far as Utah Lake, one hundred miles away. Others, probably most of them, go to the Bear River marshes only about thirty-five miles away, although this means flying over a 2,500-foot mountain ridge.

Whereas the brown pelican dives to catch its food, the white pelican swims along, locates a fish, large or small, and scoops it up in its gullet, dipping only its head and neck under water. Like cormorants, these birds co-operate in their fishing. They not only form a line and drive fish onto a beach, but they will also encircle a school of fish, gradually narrowing the circle and driving the fish to the center where the converging pelicans can capture them.

In winter the northern-nesting pelicans go to California and the Gulf of Mexico and southward. There they live on the shallow bays and lagoons along the coast, resting on the beaches and catching their food along the edge of the tide.

The white pelican has suffered heavily at the hands of man. A big, conspicuous, fish-eating, colonial-nesting bird, it was an obvious target for the fisherman's spleen and was often accused of ruining the fishing. There have been wholesale massacres at some colonies, but these were local and were soon over. What has weighed more heavily against these birds has been the lowering of water levels in lakes in irrigated areas, so that their nesting islands are no longer islands, as well as the draining of lakes and marshes, turning their feeding areas into hayfields. Once suitable environment no longer exists, the bird must disappear.

Brown Pelican

The fishing methods of the brown pelican (Plates 3, 8) are similar to those of the gannet. It flies over the water until it locates a fish, then plunges down on partly closed wings, hitting the water with a clumsy splash and sometimes disappearing completely into it. The dive is at an angle and there is a twist to it, as with the tropic-bird's dive, so that the pelican's back, rather than its breast, hits the water. Also, the dive is downwind, but when the bird comes to the surface it is headed upwind, the proper direction for a take-off. Evidently it executes some sort of underwater somersault.

The pouch of the brown pelican can hold eight and a half quarts of water, and the first thing the pelican does on coming to the surface is to point the tip of its bill down and let the water run out. Then it tips the bill up and swallows the fish it has caught. At this point part of its catch is often pilfered by a laughing gull which alights on the pelican's head and snatches a fish from the uplifted bill.

One wonders just how useful the pelican's pouch is in this type of fishing, for gannets as well as terns, tropic-birds and kingfishers, all without pouches, make similar dives for fish, and with good results. The pouch is not for food storage, since the parent birds carry food to their nestlings in their gullets rather than in their pouches. One authority, Dr. G. A. Bartholomew, has found that the pouch, with its great expanse of vascular surface, is an important cooling organ and that the birds when exposed to a hot sun open their mouths and flutter the pouch walls to facilitate cooling through evaporation.

The range of the brown pelicans is mostly on salt water and chiefly tropical, and extends northward only as far as the coasts of California and of the Carolinas. They like especially to patrol the edge of the surf, and as they fly in line, keep time with slow, ponderous wing beats and glide in unison. Perched singly on pilings or gathered in flocks on sandbars and mud flats, these birds are grotesque features of the landscape along our southern coasts.

Pelicans show an erratic response to the turn of the seasons in Florida. On Pelican Island in eastern Florida, where there have been as many as five thousand nests, the birds tend to breed in the autumn, with variable and prolonged dates of egg-laying, while on the west coast they breed in the spring. Their nests are built in colonies on islands and, depending on the terrain, are located in trees, on flat ground or on steep, rocky slopes.

The young ones that hatch in tree nests do not wander far, but those from ground nests do, and at feeding time numbers of them will mob a parent bird returning with food. But each adult seems to recognize its own young and vigorously drives away strange ones. The regurgitated food is dropped from the tip of the parent's bill into the mouth of the very small nestlings, but as the young birds gather strength they thrust their head and neck into the old bird's gullet for the food.

CHAPTER 8

Gannets and Boobies

THE gannets and boobies are fish-eating sea birds about the size of large ducks but with pointed wings, stout, tapered bills, long wedge-shaped tails, and all four toes united by webs. The birds are sociable, usually flying about in flocks when at sea, and nesting in colonies. Some species scrape

out a shallow cavity in the ground for a nest, while others make a substantial home on the ground, among rocks, or in a tree. They lay one to three eggs, which have a bluish shell overlaid with a white, chalky coating. The young bird is naked when hatched but soon grows a coat of down. It is fed partly digested fish which it gets by thrusting its head into the parent's throat.

Only one species, the gannet, occurs regularly in our waters. It is about thirty-six inches long, white except for a yellowish tinge on its head, and has black-tipped wings. During the first year the birds are brownish speckled with white.

Gannet

Off the East Coast of the United States, spring and fall, the gannets (Plates 15, 16) move between their nesting grounds in the Gulf of St. Lawrence and their wintering grounds off Florida and in the Gulf of Mexico. They sleep on the water and come ashore only to nest. Though they are sea birds they do not go far out over the oceans but live in the offshore waters.

When feeding, gannets present a spectacular sight. Alternating a steady, flapping flight with sailing, they prospect for fish. It is believed that the gannets fly low when the fish are close to the surface, and high when the fish are deep. When a fish is spotted, the gannet checks its flight and plunges down with half-closed wings, making a half twist as it goes. At the last moment it closes its wings and hits the water with a terrific splash that may send the spray fifteen feet into the air. The bird disappears for five to ten seconds and by the time it emerges will have swallowed the fish, unless it was especially large. Then, with a run, it takes off again. To take up the shock of hitting the water in its plunge, the gannet has a built-in air mattress consisting of a system of inflatable air sacs beneath its skin.

Small, offshore islands of the North Atlantic, from the Gulf of St. Lawrence to Iceland and Britain, are the breeding places of the gannet. It is one of the few species whose total numbers have been carefully estimated. Through correspondence and by personal survey, two English naturalists, James Fisher and H. G. Ververs, estimated in 1940 that the total world population of gannets was 167,000 breeding pairs. The three southernmost colonies on the American side of the Atlantic were in the Gulf of St. Lawrence and were as follows: Bird Rock in the Magdalene Islands, 1,000 pairs; Bonaventure Island, 7,200 pairs; and Anticosti Island, 5,000 pairs. The birds nest mostly on the broader, inaccessible ledges on the precipitous sides of the islands, where as neighbors on the smaller ledges they often have kittiwakes, razorbilled auks and two kinds of murres.

Among gannets courtship is carried on by both sexes, the members of a pair facing each other with spread wings and tail, bowing and moving their heads and sparring with their bills. During this time the colony is noisy with hoarse and strident cries; when they are at sea the birds are silent. The nests on the ledges may be so close together as almost to touch, and the ledges are white with setting birds. The nests are added to year after year and the older ones are thus substantial affairs of seaweed, grass and trash. A single white egg is laid and this the bird covers with the webs of its feet before it settles to brood. Both male and female share in brooding the egg, which takes from forty-two to forty-five days. The young are nearly naked at hatching, later getting a short coat of creamy down and, later still, a thick, white, woolly coat. The parents feed the nestlings on regurgitated fish for two months or more, and during this time the old birds may bring the food from as far as a hundred miles from the colony. Then the adults abandon the young birds, by this time well grown and feathered. The fledglings stay on the ledges for about ten days more, then flutter down to the water, where they swim and drift about for several weeks, living on their store of fat, before they begin to fly and to fish for themselves.

Boobies—Casual Visitors

The gannet has a number of close relatives that live in tropical waters and are called boobies. This name comes from the apparent stupidity of the birds in often failing to recognize a man as an enemy. Although some of these birds nest as close to the United States as the West Indies and the Gulf of California, they do not normally range within our waters. Four species have been recorded in our area. The blue-faced booby, which used to nest in the Bahamas, has occasionally been recorded in the Tortugas and has straggled to Florida, Louisiana and Texas. The white-bellied booby (Plates 11, 14) which Audubon reported breeding in the Tortugas, has since been found only casually in Florida waters, with stray birds reported farther north. The two other species are the red-footed booby, of which there is a Florida record; and the blue-footed booby of the western coast of Mexico, which has strayed to California.

CHAPTER 9

Cormorants

CORMORANTS are swimming and diving birds that pursue their fish prey underwater. Though they are water birds, their plumage is not waterproof, and unlike that of the ducks, loons and auks, it soon gets soaked. Because of this, cormorants sleep ashore and also come ashore during the day to dry their feathers. They perch on trees, buoys, spars and rocks, and also gather on sand beaches although they walk awkwardly on level ground. Whether feeding, resting or nesting, they are gregarious.

The size of these birds varies from that of a duck to that of a goose. They have long necks, well-developed wings and fairly long tails. Their legs are short, their feet large, and all four toes are joined by a web. Their bills are long, slender and armed with a sharp hook at the tip, and they have an extensible gular pouch which is often brightly colored. The North American species are mostly glossy black, but pied black-and-white cormorants occur in the southern hemisphere.

Cormorants' nests are substantial structures of sticks, grass, or seaweed built either on the ground, on rocks, islands, or ledges of cliffs, or in trees and bushes growing in or near the water. The eggs are bluish or greenish in color with a limy or chalky outer layer; the clutch is up to seven in number. The chicks are naked when hatched but later acquire a dense coat of down. They stay in the nest for several weeks and are cared for by the parents. In some species, the incubation period is about four weeks and the period in the nest approximately six weeks.

It has been fashionable to consider some water birds such as the cormorants as having little intelligence, but arguing against this view is the long history of cormorants that have been tamed and taught to catch fish for their masters. They are even said to recognize and show affection for such masters.

The six species of cormorants in America vary from twenty-six to forty inches long. Some species have special tufts of plumes or crests at breeding time but at a distance these are not evident. The birds appear generally black but the young are of a brownish color. Of the two species on the Atlantic coast, one is the large common cormorant, from thirty-five to forty inches long, with the bare skin of its face yellow, a whitish area surrounding the face and throat, and white flank patches when it is in full breeding plumage. The other is the double-crested cormorant, from twenty-nine to thirty-five inches long, with no white patches and with the bare skin of its face and throat orange. In the lower Mississippi Valley is found the Mexican cormorant, similar to the double-crested, but with the bare skin of its throat dull yellow. On the Pacific coast are three common species: the double-crested cormorant; the Brandt's cormorant, thirty-three inches long, with the naked skin of the throat blue and a fulvous patch below it; and the small, slender-billed pelagic cormorant, twenty-six inches long, which has brownish bare skin on its face, a red throat and, in the breeding season, a white patch on each flank. In the Bering Sea area is the sixth species, the red-faced cormorant, thirty inches long, with the bare skin of its face red, and that of its throat blue.

Double-crested Cormorant

The double-crested cormorant (Plate 21) gets its name from the tufts of feathers, one above and one back of each eye, worn by both sexes for a brief period in the spring when the birds are courting. This fully adult plumage may not be attained until the bird is four years old.

These cormorants thrive in a variety of living conditions: some of them feed in the cold salt waters of the Gulf of St. Lawrence, nest there on bare, rocky islands, and move to Florida waters for the winter; others feed in the warm seas of Florida the year round and nest there in mangrove and cypress trees; still others summer in fresh-water lakes from north of the Canadian prairies to the Salton Sea in California, or live on the Pacific coast. The double-crested cormorant is the only cormorant found in the interior of the country, except for the Mexican cormorant, which ranges into the lower Mississippi Valley.

The double-crested cormorants are seen inland or on the Atlantic coast migrating in lines or in "V" formations like geese. Unlike geese they are black and have long tails and occasionally interrupt their slow wing beats to sail. In feeding, these birds sometimes gather in flocks that may number as many as two thousand individuals. A certain amount of organization takes place among the birds in such flocks, investigators reporting that they line up across the mouths of shallow bays and estuaries and drive fish before them. The birds in these big flocks are also much more active than those that fish by themselves, and such flocks generally present a scene of almost frenzied activity. The splashing of the cormorants as they dive, leaping almost clear of the water, and the swishing noise they make as they fly to better positions, can be heard several hundred yards away. This flock organization seems very effective, judging by the large percentage of birds that come up with fish.

These cormorants spend only a small part of their day fishing. The rest of the time they perch on rocks, buoys, spars, piers and trees, sitting with outspread wings to dry their plumage, or simply resting. At night large numbers repair to favorite roosts. One roost that has been studied intensively is located in San Francisco Bay. There over two thousand cormorants may retire for the night, perching on a cable that extends from the mainland to an island nearly two miles offshore, lining up like blackbirds on a wire.

In many places these cormorants have incurred the enmity of fishermen by eating fish. Investigations have shown that their effect on fish populations, especially on those sought by man, is small, but that they do cause losses by taking fish from nets. Otherwise the birds themselves are of little economic importance, for neither their flesh nor their eggs are particularly palatable. In the Gulf of St. Lawrence area, however, the young birds are taken and salted for dog food and the eggs used for human consumption.

Cormorants tend to be silent away from their nesting colonies, but they do have a fairly extensive vocabulary and a colony can be noisy with the calls of the young and the croaks and cries of the adults. During their courtship, according to one authority, H. F. Lewis, they also sing a genuine song, which he recorded as "oak oak oak . . ." and which was loud enough to be heard for about two hundred yards through the hubbub of the colony.

The naked young when hatched are nearly help-less and are at first fed partly digested food re-gurgitated into their mouths by the parents. Later, however, the young insert their heads into the gul-lets of the parents. The young usually stay in the nest until well grown and if the nest is in a suitable place will wander about it on foot until they begin to fly at the age of from six to eight weeks.

Mexican Cormorant

The Mexican cormorant takes the place of the double-crested cormorant throughout Central and South America and enters the United States only in the lower Mississippi Valley. It, too, nests in colonies in treetops or on rocks, fishes in salt and fresh water, and perches on trees, buoys, piers, spars, rocks and on the bars in lagoons and river mouths. However, it seems to prefer sitting on mud banks rather than sandbars. In some places it rests by the sea and flies inland to feed in fresh water. Rapids seem favorite places for the feeding birds to gather, and like the double-crested cormorant they organize their flocks into lines for co-operative fish-ing.

Unlike the double-crested, which is usually silent away from its nesting grounds, the Mexican cor-morant is a noisy bird. The roosting birds con-tinually utter piglike grunts, which have earned them the name of "pig-duck" in some Latin-America countries.

Common or European Cormorant

On the Atlantic coast of the United States, the common cormorant, the larger of the two species of cormorants occurring there, is much less nu-merous than the double-crested cormorant. From its breeding grounds on cliffs along the eastern Canadian coast the common cormorant moves south in winter along the shore as far as New York, and individuals occasionally get as far as the Carolinas or turn up on the Great Lakes.

The common cormorant, much like the double-crested, feeds in the ocean within sight of land and comes ashore to dry its plumage by spreading its wings, or to sleep on rocks or bouys.

Though it has a restricted distribution in the New World, this species is widespread in the Old World. It is one of the birds the Japanese and Chinese have trained for fishing, and in England when falcons were in common use as hunting birds it was also used for fishing.

Brandt's Cormorant

Along our Pacific coast the Brandt's cormorant is abundant and conspicuous. It is a salt-water bird exclusively but it does not go far from land, often fishing in shallow water, sometimes within or just outside the surf. From a pier on the Oregon coast, Dr. I. N. Gabrielson, the well-known ornithologist, saw one of these birds dive deep, get below a school of fish, drive the school to the surface, and in the re-sulting confusion capture its prey.

The birds gather to rest on outlying rocks, or perch wherever there is standing room along the coast, so that every buoy, stranded spar and floating log may be decorated with a cormorant or two.

For their nesting they select rocky islands or promontories and the whitewash from their drop-pings on the rocks makes landmarks of their colo-nies. The nests are placed not on the cliffs but on the more level parts of the island tops or on the gen-tler slopes of the capes. The nests may be so close together that it is a problem to find foot space among them. The birds are tame and are tolerant of intrusion into their colonies. But it takes a true enthusiast to investigate such a colony closely, for they are noisome places, with excrement and rotting fish giving out a stench that attracts myriads of flies.

Gregarious birds such as these seem to have an urge for companionship that transcends species limits and this sometimes lands them in strange com-pany. Solitary cormorants have been seen flying in a line with murres, and a pelican has been seen flying in formation with cormorants.

Pelagic Cormorant

The smallest, glossiest, and most slender of our cormorants is the pelagic or Baird's cormorant of the Pacific coast. Like Brandt's cormorant, it is a salt-water species but has a wider range—from Mexico to the Bering Sea and in Asia as far south in winter as Japan.

Unlike our other West Coast cormorants it nests only on little ledges on the most inaccessible cliffs so that the colonies are of necessity small and often contain only eight to ten pairs of birds. It feeds on fish which like other cormorants it catches under-water.

Red-faced Cormorant

The red-faced cormorant, another member of this family, breeds in the Bering Sea and winters south to Japan, straying only occasionally to Alaska.

CHAPTER 10

Anhingas or Water-turkeys

THE anhingas form a small, easily recognized family of four species, with one in the Americas and one each in Africa, Asia and Australia. They are birds of tree-fringed fresh waters in tropical and temperate areas. They swim and dive well and also have good powers of flight. Like cormorants they have short legs and big webbed feet, but their tails are long and broad, necks and heads slender, and bills slender and sharp-pointed. The single American species (Plate 22) is about thirty-four inches long and the male is blackish with gray patches on the wing, while the female is similar but has a brownish breast.

The American water-turkey seeks its food under-water, swimming about and diving for it; often the bird flies up and circles high in the air, but much of its time is spent perched in the tops of willow bushes or on stubs or branches of trees at the edge of a lake or pond. Often after a swim it spreads its wings and tail to hasten drying of its plumage, for its feathers are not waterproof and prolonged immersion will soak them.

When alarmed on its perch it may fly away or dart straight down into the water and disappear; hence one of its local names—the darter. When it emerges it will probably show only its slender head and neck, which have the snakelike appearance that has earned it another name, the "snake bird." The name "water-turkey," which refers to its ample wings and tail, does not seem appropriate. It ranges in South and Central America and the southeastern United States; I for one associate it especially with the cypress-edged ponds of Florida.

Only moderately social, the water-turkey is usually found in pairs or small parties, and it nests in small colonies, though often in rookeries that contain many other marsh birds: ibis, herons of several species, and cormorants. The nest is placed in the fork of a bush or a tree, and is a rather solid structure of twigs, often containing Spanish moss and lined with green leaves. The eggs are usually four in number, pale bluish white, with more or less of a chalky coating and usually nest-stained some shade of brown. Both parents share in incubating the eggs and caring for the young. The young hatch quite naked and yellowish in color but soon acquire a thick coat of buff-colored down.

The food of the water-turkey is almost exclusively fish, some of which are surprisingly large considering the slender head and neck of the bird.

CHAPTER 11

Frigate or Man-o'-war Birds

THESE sea birds of tropical waters are relatives of the pelicans but are especially adapted for flying. A frigate bird's wings are very long, its tail long and deeply forked, its body small, and its feet small and only partly webbed. One of these birds, with a wing-spread of seven feet, may weigh only three and a half pounds. A large mallard of similar weight would have less than half that wingspread.

Though they are sea birds, the plumage of frigate birds becomes easily watersoaked and apparently they never voluntarily alight on the sea. Indeed it is doubtful that they could take off from the water;

they do so with difficulty even from level ground and usually must launch themselves from an elevation such as a treetop, bush, or cliff. Their day is spent on the wing, soaring, seemingly floating, and often at considerable height. When a frigate bird sights food, such as a fish, it swoops down at great speed, snatches it from the water with its long, slender bill, which has a hook at the tip, and turns quickly up again without wetting its plumage. Or it may hover on slowly beating wings close over the water and strike down with the bill. These birds are scavengers, too, and finally they are also pirates, robbing other sea birds, a practice that has given them the name of man-o'-war birds. Their favorite victims are boobies, the tropical relatives of the gannet, and the frigate birds pursue, harry and even strike these successful fishers until they disgorge recent meals, whereupon the frigate birds swoop down and snatch up the secondhand food before it reaches the water.

Though capable of sustained flight, frigate birds do not range far offshore and seem little given to pelagic wanderings. Each evening they repair to favorite trees on the coast to sleep, often in roosts filled with many birds. There the noisemaking is limited to the clattering of bills, for the birds are nearly voiceless, except for the gurgling and chuckling noises of courtship.

The five species in the family are much alike in general habits and appearance. The species called the magnificent frigate bird (Plate 9) is the only one occurring in the United States. It is from thirty-seven to forty-one inches long; the male is generally blackish with a red throat-patch of naked skin that can be inflated like a balloon during courtship; the female has a white throat and breast whereas the young bird's whole head and underparts are white. The species nests as far north as the Bahamas and the west coast of Mexico. The nests, built in colonies, are scanty platforms of sticks, usually placed in the tops of trees or shrubs. A single white egg is laid and both sexes share incubation, though the smaller male seems to do the greater share of the work. The young is hatched quite naked, later acquiring a coat of white down. From their nesting grounds the birds commonly wander north to our more southern coasts, with strays reported as far northward and inland as Wisconsin and Kansas.

CHAPTER 12

Herons and Bitterns

MEMBERS of this family are characterized by long legs, long necks, and sharp, spearlike bills, which fit them for wading and getting their food in marshes and shallow water, the favorite home of most of these species. Fish, frogs, tadpoles and aquatic insects are generally important foods for herons, but in some areas crabs, crayfish and aquatic salamanders bulk large in their diet. Though these are typically wading birds, some species often walk about in dry grassy fields and eat quantities of such insects as grasshoppers.

Herons have, among other things, unusual equipment for preening their feathers. On each side of both the breast and the lower back are special powder-down patches hidden in the feathers. From these patches the heron spreads down over its plumage with its bill as it dresses its feathers. It is possible that this powder-down also acts as a dry-cleaning agent, epecially when a bird has slime on its feathers from its fishing. This substance gives a beautiful, delicate, hoary bloom to the feathers of some dark-colored herons.

The marshes of the warmer parts of the globe are richest in animal life and it is here that herons are most common, though some of them live in the temperate zones too. Of the fifty-nine species in the world about thirteen are found in the United States, and they are most abundant in the southeastern states, especially from Florida to the Texas coast.

One tends to think of herons as birds that scorn concealment and often stand up bold and straight in shallow water, their necks outstretched or held in a graceful "S"-curve; this is true of most species, but a few are solitary and retiring. Some species like to feed in flocks and associate not only with members of their own kind but also with other marsh birds such as white ibis and wood ibis. The birds exhibit the same gregariousness whether they are perched in treetops during the day, roosting in favorite trees for the night, or nesting.

The nests of all of our herons are basically similar—a frail platform of twigs placed in a tree. But local conditions vary so much that the same species may make a stick nest high in a tree in one area, and a nest of grass on the ground in another. Usually, however, nests are placed in trees growing in water or on islands so that they are protected and isolated. Herons are usually gregarious and a colony may contain half-a-dozen species and perhaps some ibis, water-turkeys, cormorants and even pelicans, depending on the location. When the herons first come to the colony in the spring they indulge in elaborate courtship ceremonies in which males and females, who are alike in plumage, display their ornamental plumes to each other. Both sexes share in building the nest and in brooding duties, so that the eggs and the young are always guarded by one parent or the other. The chicks at hatching are down-covered and stay in the nest a few weeks, the parents bringing food to them and feeding them by regurgitation.

A rookery with young herons in it is a noisy place. Herons' calls are usually limited to squawks of alarm when startled or when quarreling, love songs when courting, and the vociferous calling of the fledglings in the nest. Equally noticeable in any rookery is the smell from the copious droppings of the birds and from the regurgitated scraps of fish that the offspring have missed.

The immature herons, even before they are able to fly, go scrambling about through the branches around the nest, using claws, wings and bills in climbing. When the young can fly and nesting is over, many birds of several species, especially the common egret and the little blue heron, wander northward for part of the summer and autumn, and then withdraw southward again for the winter. This is migration of a sort, but pronounced migrations are made only by those species that nest in the northern states and Canada, where the winters are severe. The flight of these herons is firm, buoyant and graceful. The neck is folded with the head back against the shoulders, the body is small and light for the size of the wings, and the wing beats, especially of the large herons, are slow and steady.

Adult herons are relatively unaffected by predators other than man, but their nests and eggs are more vulnerable. Crows and grackles take the eggs when they can; raccoons are said to climb to the nests; and alligators lie in the water below the nests waiting for young herons to fall out. It is even said that the predators sometimes interfere with each other, as when alligators in the water around the trees holding a heron's colony are said to discourage raccoons from swimming out to raid the nests.

The major predator against heron populations is man. Particularly was this true of the egrets in the period from 1880 to 1910, when fashion demanded plumes for the millinery trade and plume-hunters invaded the rookeries when the brooding birds were wearing their ornamental nuptial plumes and shot the birds at the nests. Common egrets, snowy egrets and reddish egrets were especially sought after and the populations of these birds were practically wiped out. Other species also suffered, but to a lesser extent. Fortunately fashions changed, public sentiment was aroused on behalf of the birds, protective measures were enacted and enforced through the agencies of the United States Government and the Audubon Society, and the herons increased and have become common again. Even the reddish egret is common locally now and is expanding its range. Man is no longer an active predator, though he can still affect the birds in a rookery adversely just by going there. The presence of a man taking pictures may keep the parent birds from their nests, giving crows and grackles, which are less shy, an opportunity to come and eat the unprotected eggs.

The thirteen species of this family that occur regularly in the United States vary in size from the least bittern, which is about twelve inches long, to the great blue heron, which stands about four feet high. Six of them are white or have a white color phase. The largest, the great white heron, is about four feet long and has a yellow bill and greenish-yellow legs. The American egret is about thirty-eight inches long and has a yellow bill and black legs. The snowy egret, about two feet long, has a black bill and black legs with yellow toes. In its rare white phase, the reddish egret is about twenty-nine inches long and has a flesh-colored, black-tipped bill. The little blue heron, in its first year, is also white with a bluish, black-tipped bill and greenish legs. The cattle egret, about the size of the snowy egret, has yellow legs and bill, and in some plumages has a buff tinge on head and body.

The largest of the dark-colored species in the family is the great blue heron. It is bluish gray with a paler head and neck. The reddish egret, about twenty-nine inches long, is in its normal dark phase a slate-colored bird with a reddish-brown head and neck. The Louisiana heron, about twenty-six inches long, is slaty with a white belly and rump. The adult little blue heron is all slate-colored, with black legs. The little green heron, about eighteen inches long, is dark with a reddish neck and yellowish or orange legs. The black-crowned night heron, about twenty-six inches long, has in its adult plumage a black back and crown, gray wings and white underparts, the juvenile plumage being grayish-brown streaked with white. The adult yellow-crowned night heron, about twenty-six inches long, is generally grayish with a black head on which the cheeks and crown are whitish, the young being slaty-brown, streaked and speckled with whitish. The American bittern, about twenty-eight inches long, is streaked and mottled with buff and warm brown. The least bittern, the smallest of the family, is only about a foot long and the adult is buff below, with a black back and crown, and buff wing patches.

Great Blue Heron

The great blue heron (Plates 30, 34) is the largest and most majestic of our herons. It is widely distributed, ranging from Canada to the West Indies and Central America. In winter it withdraws from the northern part of its range but can even then be found as far north as New York State.

Its favorite feeding places are the edges of rivers, lakes and the sea, and shallow marshes. In such places it commonly has two methods of fishing. It either stands as still as a statue, waiting for fish to swim within range of its spearlike bill, or it "still-hunts" by stalking with slow dignity through shallow water. On rare occasions it actually alights on the water, catches a fish there, and then rises into the air easily and flies away, a surprising achievement in a bird so well equipped for wading but so poorly adapted for swimming.

Though fish constitute a large part of its food, it eats a great many other small water animals such as frogs, salamanders, snakes and insects. Nor is the great blue heron's feeding restricted to the water. Sometimes it hunts in the fields, catching grasshoppers and field mice. In Florida this bird has been accused of catching and eating the young chickens of settlers in the Everglades.

The great blue heron likes to feed alone. It may even drive away other individuals that intrude on a favorite fishing spot. However, in migration these birds travel in small flocks, often high in the air, and in the spring numbers of them gather to perform a courtship dance in which many birds move about on the ground with outspread, flapping wings.

They also like company when they nest, and their nests are typically in colonies. The favorite site for the flat, stick nests is high in a grove of tall trees, but in those parts of their range where such sites are lacking, they use whatever sites are available. In Florida they nest in low mangroves; on the islands in Great Salt Lake they nest on the ground amid the rocks; and along the Colorado River they sometimes place their nests on the ledges of cliffs above the river.

Great White Heron

The great white heron (Plate 33) occurs from southern Florida to Yucatán, Jamaica and Cuba. It is like the great blue heron except that its plumage is white and the color of its bill and legs is paler. Individual birds, intermediate in color between the great white and the great blue heron are sometimes found and have been given the name of Wurdemann's heron. Birds of all three types of coloration are found in the same areas and have the same habits. Though some bird books list all three names, it is probable that the great white heron and Wurdemann's heron are not different species but simply white and partly white color phases of the great blue heron, and occur in only part of its range. Many similar cases of dimorphism, as the condition of having different color phases is called, are known.

European Heron

The European heron, a bird of Europe, Asia and Africa, which is rather similar to our great blue heron, has wandered to Greenland on a few occasions.

Common Egret

The common or American egret (Plates 17, 18) is widespread in the warmer parts of the world. In America it nests as far north as the central part of the United States. Strangely, after the breeding season is over, large numbers of these egrets, as well as a few other herons, fly northward, even as far as southern Canada, so that in late summer the birds are common north of their breeding range. Long before the weather becomes cold they retreat south again to the southern states and there they are fairly common throughout the year.

The egret is a gregarious bird. Not only is it usually found in small flocks of its own kind but it is often seen with flocks of snowy egrets, wood ibis, and other marsh birds that feed in grassy swamps, along lake margins or on muddy seashores. There it stalks about, catching fish, frogs, small snakes and insects, and probably any other small animals it comes across. When common egrets finish feeding, they may stand motionless, resting, or the flock may fly up and perch on top of nearby trees. As evening approaches the flocks fly to some favorite roosting trees where other water birds may also gather to roost.

As the breeding season approaches, the long, white, ornamental plumes of the back, worn by both sexes, are used in courtship, and later in a mutual ceremony when the birds change over to take turns at sitting on the three or four greenish eggs. The nests of the common egret are built in colonies, and these are sometimes a part of large, mixed rookeries of hundreds or even thousands of birds such as cormorants, pelicans, white ibis, snowy egrets and other herons. They place their frail stick-nests in trees, but where there are no trees, the nests may be in bushes, or, as in Oregon, on bent-over tule stems within a foot or so of the water.

Snowy Egret

The snowy egret (Plates 19, 29) feeds in flocks in grassy marshes, in ponds and in the margins of waterways and on the edge of the sea. The white plumage of these birds makes the flocks conspicuous features of the landscape. The snowy egret is a more agile and active bird than most herons. Instead of waiting quietly, or sedately stalking after its food, it often runs about through the shallow water, darting here and there, and sometimes spreading its wings to aid it in pursuit of its prey.

The varied food that it takes from the water includes fish, frogs, snakes, insects and crayfish, and from drier grasslands grasshoppers and cutworms. In Florida flocks of these egrets have been seen accompanying droves of pigs or cattle, catching the grasshoppers that the animals frighten into activity. The snowy egret even does some of its hunting from the air, and flocks fly low over ponds, apparently circling schools of small fish, the birds on the wing snatching fish from the water.

Like many wading birds of southern climates, when the day ends snowy egrets fly to a common roost for the night, one that is often shared with other species, especially the little blue and Louisiana herons.

The plumage decoration of the snowy egret is elaborate: the adult birds have an elongated crest on the head, an elongated tuft of feathers on the breast, and most important of all, elongated feathers on the back that are filmy in texture and recurved at the tip. When the birds are courting their mates in the spring, all of these ornamental plumes are raised and spread to enhance the elegant, lacy effect.

After their mates are selected, the nests are built in colonies, often in association with other herons or with ibis. Sometimes the herons construct shallow platforms of sticks in cypress or mangrove trees or in bushes in a marsh or a pond, as in Florida; in the more western part of the country their nests may be made of reed stems and built on bent-over reeds in sloughs and marshes. The nests contain four or five greenish eggs and the parents take turns at sitting on these. When one bird takes the place of the other, they display to each other. Later, when the young are hatched, a similar display is made to the young birds by the parents approaching with food.

The snowy egret is an American species, ranging from the central United States to South America. The plume-hunting that began about 1885 drastically reduced the numbers of these birds, which reached a low from about 1900 to 1910, and curtailed their range. Since then, protection has helped them increase in numbers and expand their range again. Like common egrets and little blue herons, individual snowy egrets move north in late summer after the breeding season, returning south later in the autumn.

Reddish Egret

The reddish egret (Plate 23) ranges from Central America to Texas and Florida. It used to be common before the plume-hunters of the 1880's depleted its numbers. Unlike other herons, this egret has failed to recover its numerical losses since it has been given protection. There now exist some sizable colonies, notably one on the Texas coast, containing thousands of birds, but these aggregations are few and scattered compared with those of an earlier period.

This bird is largely a coastal species that feeds in the shallows over mud flats and in lagoons, the small fish of such areas forming an important part of its diet. Frequently the bird is an active fisherman, walking rapidly or even running through the water after its prey, and occasionally spreading its wings as though to startle or confuse the fish it is trying to catch.

This species is dimorphic, having two quite different types of plumage, one bluish and one white. The little blue herons also have this characteristic, but in their case the white plumage is a sign of immaturity. In the reddish egret pairs of bluish adults may have some blue and some white young, and each of the offspring will retain this color throughout life. Blue and white birds may also mate together. The white-plumaged adult is similar to the snowy egret but can always be distinguished by the black tip and pale, flesh-colored base of the bill.

For display purposes the reddish egret has not only an elongated, filmy tuft of plumes on its back that it can erect, but also elongated feathers on the head and neck that can be raised in a bristly ruff.

In Florida the bird nests in the mangroves along the edge of the sea, but on the Texas coast it prefers low, dry islands, placing its platform nest on bushes and even on the ground, and using grass rather than sticks as building material.

Cattle Egret

A newcomer to the New World is the cattle egret (Plate 20). It is common in Africa and southern Asia, but not until 1930 was there a record of it in the Americas, when the naturalist E. R. Blake discovered it in British Guiana. In subsequent years it increased and spread in northern South America. Suddenly, in 1952, birds were seen from Florida to Newfoundland and Chicago. The next year at least three pairs nested at Lake Okeechobee, Florida; there was an autumn record from as far north as Maine; and more than one hundred of the birds wintered in Florida. It now seems likely that the cattle egret will increase and spread and become an important member of the bird population of our southeastern states. Perhaps it will also wander northward after the breeding season and appear with the common egret and the little blue heron in the central states in the summer.

How this bird first arrived in the western hemisphere we do not know. Possibilities of human aid in transportation, of deliberate importation and release, or of escape from some zoo, have all been suggested, but there is no corroboration of these speculations. It seems more probable that a flock of the birds became lost while flying along the northwest coast of Africa and, aided by the prevailing easterly winds of these latitudes, actually flew across to South America. If so, it is the first such arrival of any bird in the Americas within historical times.

The cattle egret characteristically feeds in flocks in grassy fields and walks about catching grasshoppers and other insects. In Africa they accompany big game animals, even elephants, for the sake of the insects that the beasts stir up, and attach themselves to cattle for the same reason; hence their name. In Florida they associate with cows on the prairies around Lake Okeechobee. It has been said that they also perform the service of eating ticks from the bodies of cattle, but there is little evidence for this.

At nesting time in the Old World, thousands of these egrets may congregate in rookeries along with other herons, build frail platform nests of sticks in trees or bushes, and lay their greenish-blue eggs and raise their young. The few nests found in North America so far have been in huge rookeries on Lake Okeechobee, where their neighbors included little blue and Louisiana herons, common and snowy egrets, and white and glossy ibis.

Louisiana Heron

The Louisiana heron (Plate 25) is one of the common small herons of open marshes and mud flats from South America to Mexico and the southeastern United States. It is partly migratory but remains common in winter as far north as South Carolina. Fortunately for the species, its small, dark plumes were not in demand when the feather trade flourished and it escaped the great reduction in numbers suffered by herons with more ornamental plumage.

Especially when going only a short distance, the Louisiana heron often flies with its neck more extended than is usual in other herons, a habit that adds to the appearance of slenderness of this graceful bird. In feeding, it is as active as the snowy egret, running or walking with quick steps through the shallow water in pursuit of its prey. Frequently one or both wings are flicked open as it runs, and it has been suggested that this is not to help maintain its balance but to frighten its prey out of hiding. According to one expert, E. A. McIlhenny, when the weather is cold in the winter, and small water creatures such as fish, tadpoles and aquatic insects on which this heron feeds are sluggish, it shares with the snowy egret the following method of stirring its prey out of cover: as it walks along in shallow water, it stretches one foot far out in advance of the other and as it slides it along the bottom vibrates it rapidly. Using this technique it makes more catches than do little blue herons feeding nearby.

The Louisiana heron is often the most common of the several species of herons nesting together in a colony. The nests are located in mangrove trees, in bushes, in reeds practically on the ground, or in the lush herbaceous vegetation of a swamp. The bird's neighbors vary with the location of the large colony, and include not only the snowy egret and the little blue heron, with which it commonly nests, but water-turkeys, reddish egrets, great blue herons and night herons, ibis, grackles and vultures, as well as terns, black skimmers and gulls.

Little Blue Heron

One of the outstanding characteristics of the little blue heron (Plate 31) is that the adult is slaty blue but the young bird is white. Not until the young have passed through their first winter and the breeding season is approaching do the young birds moult from their immature feathers to the adult dress.

The little blue heron is found from South America to Mexico and the southeastern United States. Like the common and snowy egrets some little blue herons move north after the breeding season. Most of the birds appearing in the northern states for a time in the summer and early autumn are in the white plumage of young birds. In this dress they are remarkably like the young snowy egrets, and many a beginning bird student has been confused by their similarity. The best way to tell them apart is to remember that the snowy egret has black legs and yellow toes, while the young little blue heron has dull, greenish-yellow legs and toes.

The little blue heron is one of the commonest species in open marshes and in ponds filled with vegetation. The feeding flocks may consist either of adult, blue birds or of immature, white ones, or may contain birds of both types. This species is less active than the Louisiana heron and often prefers to wait quietly for its fish, frog or insect prey to come within striking range of its bill. Sometimes it eats mostly crayfish and sometimes it goes into dry fields for grasshoppers and other insects. It shares with the snowy egret the habit of accompanying droves of pigs for the insects the animals scare up. Flocks of these herons have also been reported circling low over ponds and snatching fish from the surface of the water. Toward evening flocks that have been feeding or resting in the marshes fly to favorite roosts and spend the night with others of their kind.

At nesting time the little blue heron is gregarious, and its colonies may contain anywhere from a dozen nests to as many as a thousand. The Louisiana heron and the snowy egrets are often found in the same rookeries; all three of these species like to place their frail platform nests in bushes and trees.

Green Heron

Unlike other herons, this species (Plate 24) ordinarily feeds singly and is not very conspicuous. Though it occasionally comes into the open, it usually stays under the protection of trees or grass fringing a creek or pond, or in a marsh, or at least near some vegetation that affords cover. When alarmed it flushes with a startled "skeow" and flies with rapid wing beats to perch within a tree or bush, but not, like other herons, on the top in plain sight. In pose, too, it is peculiar, since its legs are rather short for a heron and it sometimes stretches out its long neck as it walks, twitching its tail and raising and lowering its crest. Often, however, the bird is hunched up, with the head drawn down to its shoulders so that it seems to have no neck at all.

In summer the range of the green heron is a wide one, extending from Central America to Canada; in winter the birds withdraw from the northern edge of the range to the southern United States. In this vast area the bird lives under a wide variety of conditions, in salt- and fresh-water marsh, and on the margins of lake, river and tiny creek.

The bird's food varies with the locality, but includes fish, frogs, tadpoles, aquatic crabs, crayfish and grasshoppers. When it locates a fish in shallow water it crouches low, its body held horizontally, its neck drawn in, and creeps stealthily up until the fish is within range of the quick thrust of its bill. Sometimes it stands and waits for its prey or jumps headfirst from its perch into deep water to seize a fish, then floats to the surface, swallows the fish, and flies ashore.

Though the nest of the little green heron is similar to that of many other herons, it is less gregarious and its nesting colonies are small. Sometimes only a single nest may be placed in the bushes along a marsh or stream.

Night Herons

Our two species of night herons differ from other herons in posture, the neck being pulled back so that its "S"-curve is hidden in the long feathers of the neck, giving the bird a round-shouldered appearance. The night herons' comparatively large eyes provide a clue to another difference in habits: they feed by night, except when the demands of the growing young force the parents to seek food both day and night. Otherwise their days are spent in roosts in shady trees. The striped, brownish young are very different from the conspicuous gray and black adults, a difference much more pronounced with the night herons than with other herons.

As dusk approaches, the black-crowned night herons (Plate 32) leave their roosts for their feeding places and most watchers see them as they fly from the nesting grounds to the feeding areas. Frequently as they pass overhead in the dusk they utter a hoarse cry which has earned them the name of "quawk herons."

They feed in salt- or fresh-water marshes, on reedy lakes or along the sides of streams. Sometimes they walk about hunting for their food, which consists largely of fish, but usually they stand quietly in their round-shouldered stance, waiting for their prey.

The biggest colonies of black-crowned night herons are not located in the southeast along with most of the big heron rookeries, but in the northern states. In the Barnstable colony near Cape Cod, thousands of this species nest in hardwood trees. Their nesting sites vary with the locality: in Maine they may be found, along with great blue herons, in spruce trees; in Oregon, 160 feet up in fir trees; on the Texas coast, on the ground among tufts of grass; in Florida, in mangrove, willow or cypress swamps, along with other herons.

The range of the species is wide, extending from South America to the northern United States, where it is migratory; it is also found in the warmer parts of Africa, Europe and Asia.

The yellow-crowned night heron (Plate 27) ranges from South America to Mexico and the eastern United States, withdrawing southward from the northern part of its range in winter. In our area it feeds along coastal mud flats as well as in inland marshes, crabs and crayfish bulking large in its diet. It hunts its food by day as well as at night, but in the hottest hours it gathers with others of its kind to rest in a shady tree. Its nests are sometimes placed singly in trees along a wooded stream, or several nests may be grouped together, forming a small colony. In the South, a few nests of yellow-crowned night herons are often built in the larger heron colonies containing a number of species.

Bitterns

Our two species of bitterns are herons that are adapted to living in reedy marshes and have taken over some of the habits of rails. Their plumage is cryptic and matches their background.

The American bittern spends much of its time prowling about among the reeds and grasses of its favorite marsh. There it leads a secretive, solitary life. But occasionally, especially in the half-light of dawn and dusk, it comes out into clearings and onto the edges of marshes. When the bird is alarmed it may spring into the air with a startled croak and fly away with wing beats faster than those of most herons. But if it is not too much alarmed it may also steal away on foot, or adopt its famous protective pose, standing upright, feathers closely compressed and bill pointed skyward, both its color and its shape making it very inconspicuous among the dead reeds in which it lurks. One observer has even seen a bittern in such a pose sway gently when a breeze swept across a marsh, as though the bird were one with the surrounding reeds.

Any small animal of the marsh, whether snake, mouse, fish or insect, apparently serves the bittern as food, but frogs seem to be preferred. Some of its prey it gets by waiting quietly in the concealment of the marsh; some it gets by stealth, holding its head low and carefully scanning the water and vegetation around it as it stalks slowly along.

The American bittern breeds over much of the United States and Canada, and winters from the United States south to Panama. Shortly after these birds return in the spring, they give the famous vocal performances sometimes colorfully described as "thunder-pumping" or "stake-driving." For many years, when bird study was in its infancy in this country, this strange noise was well known, but its source was not. Best described as a number of gulping or clicking notes culminating in a deep, guttural "pump-er-lunk," it can be heard a quarter of a mile away. This is part of the courtship performance, which also includes the display of white tufts of feathers on the shoulders.

Unlike most herons, the bittern constructs a solitary nest in the marsh, building it of dead cattails or other marsh vegetation, and placing it only a few inches above the water. The nest, with its four or five buff-colored eggs, is usually partly hidden by vegetation, through which the bittern makes little runways.

The least bittern (Plates 26, 28), our smallest heron, is almost rail-like in its habits. A shy, retiring bird, its life is spent in the fastnesses of cattail or reed beds. There it can wade or walk on floating vegetation and on mud flats, but it also travels by climbing through the reeds a foot or more above the water. From the water it gets fish, crayfish and aquatic bugs; from the reeds it picks dragonflies.

So retiring a bird is the least bittern that it is seldom seen except when flushed ahead of an intruder in the marsh. Then it flutters a short distance and drops back into the covering vegetation.

But the weak appearance of its flight is deceptive, for the least bittern ranges extensively from South America to southern Canada and migrates from the northern part of its range at least as far as the southern United States in winter. It arrives back on its breeding ground in April or early May. Then its love song is heard from the marshes—a soft, low "coo" repeated a number of times. In May or June the nest is built, usually a flimsy platform of dead reeds in the reeds, sedge or even in a bush. There four to six bluish-white eggs are laid.

To escape observation the least bittern uses two quite different protective poses around the nest. In one the bird stretches up, feathers closely pressed to the body, bill pointing upward, neck at an angle in simulation of a broken reed; in the other pose, the long neck feathers are fluffed out to their fullest, intensifying the color pattern of streaks on the neck and presenting the appearance of a composite of reeds and dark shadows.

CHAPTER 13

Storks and Wood Ibis

I
T IS unfortunate that the only member of the stork family occurring in the United States is called a wood ibis, for this name gives the erroneous impression that it is a true ibis rather than a stork. The best-known member of this family is the white stork of Europe, noted for its habit of rooftop nesting, its long migration to South Africa, and its place in childhood myth as the bearer of new life. Throughout the world there are about seventeen species of storks, most of them living in the warmer parts of the globe. They are large birds, measuring up to about four feet long, with long legs and necks, the neck being extended in flight, and long, heavy bills. Their plumage is black and white, or gray, and in several species the head and neck are bare of feathers and brightly colored.

The members of this family eat a variety of small animals such as mammals, reptiles, frogs, fish and insects, seeking their food by walking about in shallow water, marshes or dry fields.

Some storks are nearly voiceless but do make a loud, clattering sound with their huge mandibles.

Others are vocal only at nesting time. In nesting, some species gather in colonies while others nest singly. The nests are platforms of sticks and are sometimes added to year after year until they are enormous structures; they are located on a tree, cliff or village roof. In some species, after the plain white eggs are deposited in the nest the parents take turns at brooding, sometimes for as long as thirty days, until the down-clad young hatch out. Both parents share in bringing food to the nestlings and feed them by regurgitation.

Wood Ibis

The wood ibis (Plate 37) is the only representative of the large stork family in the United States. It is nearly four feet long and the adult has a naked, dark gray head and neck, and white plumage with large black areas on the wings.

Presenting a characteristic profile with its long, heavy bill slanting downward, the wood ibis is one of the common and conspicuous white birds about the ponds on the Florida prairies. There, in feeding, the flocks of wood ibis associate with the herons. But the wood ibis' usual method of hunting for food is very different from that of any heron. There is no standing, or any dashing about; rather the bird walks steadily and methodically back and forth through the water. Every step or so it thrusts its open bill down into the water and, while standing on one foot, moves the other up toward its open bill to frighten its prey out of hiding and into its mouth. When it catches something the bird swallows with a jerk of its head. Although its food is evidently mostly made up of small water animals, aquatic insects, tadpoles and fish, the wood ibis is, like most birds, an opportunist, and undoubtedly snatches up whatever it can. I have seen one trying to swallow a sunfish the size of my hand. While trying to swallow a thick-bodied snake, another bird was so pestered by companions who wanted to steal the snake that it flew off, dangling snake and all.

These birds evidently have little trouble getting a full meal, for they usually stop feeding by eight o'clock in the morning. They then stand together on a bit of higher ground, forming little groups of their own kind, even when surrounded by egrets. The flocks rest in trees wherever these are available. Sometimes, perhaps for diversion, flocks of the birds soar and circle high in the air, their long necks outstretched and their wings motionless.

The wood ibis nests in the isolation of big cypress swamps or of mangroves. It is one of the most gregarious of birds, and colonies have been estimated to contain as many as ten thousand nests, with a single cypress tree holding as many as thirty nests. The nests are made of sticks in heron style, and during the breeding season become completely covered with a whitewash of excrement. I have never heard the birds make a sound away from their nests, but in the colonies both young and old are very noisy and make a tremendous racket.

The chicks are at first covered with thick, woolly white down and they stay in the nest for some weeks. During this time they grow their first feathers and come to look much like the adults, except that their heads and necks are not bare, but are covered with feathers.

The wood ibis is a southern species, occurring from South America to Mexico and the southeastern United States. It is a permanent resident of the latter region, although after the breeding season some of the birds wander to California in the West, and even to Indiana in the Midwest and Massachusetts in the Northeast.

CHAPTER 14

Ibis and Spoonbills

IBIS and spoonbills belong to the same family, and except for the slender, downcurved bill of the ibis and the spoon-shaped bill of the spoonbills, they are much alike in shape, both being long-legged, long-necked birds, and have similar habits. The American species are birds of the marshes, mud flats and beaches, where they walk actively about hunting their food. Because many of the small animals they seek are buried in the mud or hidden in muddy waters, the birds do a great deal of systematic probing and sifting in the course of their daily search. When they have finished feeding they fly up and perch in trees to rest.

These birds are strongly gregarious and like to move, feed, rest and nest together. They fly with their necks and feet fully extended and flocks in flight often form long diagonal lines or "V's." Their flight is swift and direct. Like many other wading birds they nest in colonies on islands, in clumps of reeds, or in bushes or tall trees growing in water. The nests themselves are bowl-shaped, made of sticks if they are placed in trees, and of reeds or grass if placed among low vegetation. Both parents share in the nest-building and in sitting on the three or four eggs. After about three weeks the eggs hatch and the down-clad young emerge. The nestlings are

78]

fed by both parents, who bring food and regurgitate it for them. The small birds stay in the nest for some time but like immature herons, leave it and climb and wander about in the rookery before they can fly.

The ibis and spoonbills have not attracted the particular attention of man, either for sport or for plumes, although ibis were once classified as game in some states and although the roseate spoonbill suffered, apparently incidentally, in the days of the plume trade.

There are five species of this family in the United States. The adult white ibis, about two feet long, is white with a small black patch on its wing tips and with red legs, bill and face; the immature bird is dark brown with a white belly. The eastern glossy ibis, about two feet long, is of a glossy purple-and-greenish hue that looks black at a distance, while the white-faced glossy ibis is similar to the others except for a white area about the front of the head. The scarlet ibis is red; and the adult spoonbill, thirty inches long, is mostly whitish with pink wings, the young bird being whitish.

White Ibis

A flock of white ibis (Plate 36) feeding in a wet, grassy field gives an impression of great industry. Egrets nearby may be standing up, waiting for their prey, but the ibis are bent over, busily probing and poking in the muddy ground for theirs. The bulk of their food is crayfish but they also eat grasshoppers and beetle larvae. When startled during their feeding, they fly up and perch in a dead tree, and, if not further disturbed, stay there, preening and dozing. Their favorite feeding marshes may be some distance from the roosts where they spend the night, and the sight of these birds flying back and forth, morning and evening, is an impressive one. Their flight is swift and direct, with quick wing beats, interrupted by short glides in which the whole flock acts in unison.

The breeding range of the white ibis is from South Carolina to Texas and southward into South America. In our southeastern states it is a common bird, withdrawing southward only a relatively short distance in winter. The nesting colonies are often very large, one in the Big Cypress of Florida having been estimated to contain 100,000 birds. The nests, with their four bluish, brown-spotted eggs, are placed close to each other. Associated with the white ibis in the same rookeries may be thousands of the other marsh and water birds for which our southeastern states are famous.

Eastern Glossy Ibis

The distribution of the glossy ibis is peculiar. It is widespread in the warmer parts of the Old World, but in the New World it breeds only on certain islands of the West Indies and in a restricted area in the southeastern United States. In this country most of the birds nest on islands in Lake Okeechobee in Florida. One of the colonies there is said to contain about twelve hundred pairs of glossy ibis.

In many ways this dark-colored bird is very similar in its feeding and nesting habits to the much more common white ibis, with which it sometimes feeds. In Florida the glossy ibis allows itself to be robbed of its food by the much smaller boat-tailed grackle. The latter waits until the ibis finds a crayfish and then calmly takes the prize, the ibis making only ineffectual efforts to save its catch.

White-faced Glossy Ibis

The white-faced glossy ibis (Plate 35) lives in the country to the west of the eastern glossy ibis, ranging from Texas to Oregon, and south to Argentina. In the western United States it is a bird of the tule marshes, placing its bowl-shaped nest, with three or four bluish eggs, in clumps of the tule reeds. It nests in large rookeries along with herons and egrets. The various species do not scatter their nests indiscriminately through the rookery, but tend to form little groups or neighborhoods of their own.

The roosts or rookeries of these birds may be some distance from the marshes or the river margins where they feed, and they fly back and forth in flocks or in long lines. Often all the birds in a flock interrupt their flapping flight to glide for a few moments in unison.

Like the white ibis, the white-faced glossy ibis probes in the mud, seeking crayfish, angleworms and insect larvae, but like most large marsh birds it is an opportunist and also eats many other animals, such as grasshoppers, frogs and fish.

Scarlet Ibis

As one might guess from the brilliant plumage, the scarlet ibis is a tropical species. Its home is in South America and only occasionally has a wandering individual been found in our southern states.

Roseate Spoonbill

The roseate spoonbill (Plate 38) lives in Florida and the coastlands of the Gulf of Mexico, and also has an extensive range southward into South America. It feeds in shallow coastal waters and in fresh-water ponds by walking along and swinging its spoon-shaped bill back and forth through the water or mud. Any small fish, water insects, shrimp or prawn that comes between the mandibles in this methodical search is seized and swallowed.

The nests are generally placed on islands low in mangroves or in grass on the ground, but always in colonies and usually in association with other marsh and water birds. The spoonbill, however, appears to be much shyer at nesting time than the other birds amid which it makes its home.

The history of the spoonbills parallels in part that of the egrets. During the period between 1890 and 1910, they disappeared from Texas and nearly vanished from Florida. In Texas, they have returned; there are now a number of large breeding colonies there and the birds are increasing. In Florida, on the other hand, there is, despite protection, only one breeding area today—in Florida Bay—and the breeding birds show little increase. Each summer, however, a few flocks of roseate spoonbills, totaling several hundred birds, come north, perhaps from Cuba, to spend the summer in Florida, and there may be similar flocks of southern birds summering in Texas. It should be added that the European spoonbill, a white-plumaged, Old World species, has occasionally turned up in this hemisphere.

CHAPTER 15

Flamingos

FLAMINGOS (Plate 39) are fantastically exotic in appearance. They are pink in color, have bodies as big as geese, very long, thin legs with webbed feet, long, slender necks, more flexible than those of swans, and a short, stout bill which is bent sharply down in the middle. They are more often seen in flocks than singly, and the flocks may contain hundreds or even thousands of birds. A large flock of flamingos wading in shallow water looks from a distance like a pink band and may extend for a mile. In flight the birds arrange themselves in formations of long, curved lines, each bird with its neck fully extended in front, and its legs trailing behind. While flying, they utter loud, goose-like calls.

Extensive mud flats covered with shallow water, and brackish or fresh-water lagoons or lakes are the homes of the flamingos. There the birds wade about and feed on the abundant, tiny animals and plants. When a flamingo reaches down into the water to feed, the curious shape of its bill causes the top to point downward and the tip to point backward and upward. The bill opens and mud, water, tiny animals and plants are all taken into the mouth; then the bill closes and the mud and water are forced out, the food being retained by the fine plates which edge the mandibles and act as strainers. Sometimes the top of the bill is pressed into the mud; at other times the flamingo stirs up the mud with a dancing movement of its feet and thus makes it easier to sift. Karl Plath of the Brookfield Zoo tells me that this dancing habit in feeding is so deeply ingrained that flamingos in captivity may take a beakful of their food of shrimps, drop it into the water and then dance on it to make it float before they eat it.

Mud flats are also the nesting places of flamingos. Their nests, which are massed together in great colonies, are made of mud scooped up into truncated cones rising a few inches above the level of the water. A single chalky-white egg is laid in a hol-low in the top of each cone. These eggs are incubated by both parents in turn, the brooding birds folding their long legs under them as other birds do when on the nest. When the young hatch they are covered with down and soon walk about over the mud flats while the parents bring them food and regurgitate it for them.

Only one of the half-dozen species of flamingos found in the warmer parts of the world comes into the United States, and then only in small numbers which appear in Florida as occasional visitors. For several years a large flock of flamingos has been kept at the Hialeah race track near Miami. Some of the young birds raised there have been left full-winged and this probably accounts for the increasing number of these colorful birds seen in other parts of Florida.

The flamingo's real home is on the islands and shores of the Caribbean Sea. Though flamingos may be present in enormous numbers in one area, this may give a mistaken idea of their abundance, for the colonies, though large, are few and scattered. An additional problem in assessing the status of these birds is that they are erratic in their nesting. They often change the site of a colony and in some years they may not nest at all. This is sometimes the result of human interference, but non-breeding may also be caused by fluctuating water levels and by high water, after breeding has started, that floods the nests and destroys the colony.

CHAPTER 16

Swans, Geese and Ducks

PROMINENT among birds which have always held special interest and appeal for man are swans, geese and ducks. The migrating flocks of these birds in the spring and autumn exhilarate countless people as tangible evidence of the changing seasons; the pursuit of geese and ducks as sport has inspired what is almost a cult of wildfowling; tame waterfowl decorate ornamental ponds; and certain species have contributed domestic varieties to the poultry business.

This family is a fairly large one, containing about 145 species. Some of them are found in almost every part of the world, though they are most abun-

dant in the North Temperate Zone. These birds have rather heavy bodies, with short legs placed well back on the body, webbed feet, short tails, moderate-sized and usually rather pointed wings, and long necks. Except for the mergansers, whose narrow bills have toothlike edges, their broad bills are fluted at the edges. Essentially they are water birds, fitted for swimming and resting on the surface of the water, but some of them dive as handily as loons and grebes, some walk about on land while feeding, and some commonly perch in trees. When launching into flight, some species spring directly into the air, but others need a long running take-off from the surface of the water. Once they are awing, their flight is strong, steady and direct, and the flocks in which they travel often form lines or "V's."

In many species the drake is conspicuously bright-colored, the female dull. Moreover, during a period in late summer, many species assume an eclipse plumage and, while this is worn, all of the flight feathers in the wings moult out and then grow in together, so that the birds are flightless for a time. In the drake the eclipse plumage is duller and plainer than the breeding plumage and often resembles the plumage of the female.

In American species nests are found in a variety of places: on the ground, in holes among rocks, or in holes in trees. A large clutch of eggs is laid in a nest and the female usually plucks down from her breast to make a blanket for them. All of the sitting on the eggs is done by the female, but when the downy young emerge and start to walk about and swim, which they do within a day or so of hatching, the female in some species, such as the geese and the ruddy duck, is assisted in her care by the male. In other species the male deserts the female, and even leaves the vicinity of the nest by the time the female begins incubation.

Nesting mostly by fresh water in the temperate and northern latitudes, the American species must migrate in the winter. Some of them go to salt water, others retreat no farther south than is necessary to reach open fresh water, while a few migrate as far as South America. As the prairies and plains of the northwestern United States and Canada are noted for the number of nesting ducks, with ten to fifteen species nesting in a single marsh, so certain areas are noted for the abundance of wintering wildfowl: notably Chesapeake Bay and Currituck Sound on North Carolina's Atlantic coast, the lower Mississippi River and its delta, the Texas coast of the Gulf of Mexico, and the great marshes of the interior valleys of California. To get to such restricted wintering areas, birds from a wide breeding area may funnel into rather narrow migration routes.

Wildfowl have decreased enormously from the immense numbers present in Colonial days. Of course some of this decrease was inevitable. With the settling of the land, the plowing of the fields, and the draining of the marshes, the habitat of the birds was partly destroyed. But some of the decrease was not incidental. There were "market shooting" and "spring shooting" and big bag limits, and these, as gunners became more plentiful, played havoc with duck populations. There was also the factor of drought that in some years, in prairie areas,

completely cut off the crop of young ducks, and with no crop there could be little harvest.

Wildfowling nowadays supports a variety of enterprises, commercial and otherwise, not only of those who equip and cater to sportsmen but also those who work at maintaining the supply of ducks. Notable among the latter are the government agencies that gather data so that open seasons and bag limits can be properly adjusted; and the agencies, public and private, that are reclaiming marshes and lakes, reflooding areas that should never have been drained, and establishing systems of refuges and preserves. With short "open seasons," small bag limits, plentiful, safe and strategically placed resting areas on migration routes, protection on wintering grounds, and adequate marshes preserved for breeding areas, the steady depletion of our duck populations has been checked.

Although the habits and appearance of the members of this family vary considerably, several patterns emerge, permitting the grouping of the species into a few categories: swans, geese, tree ducks, pond ducks, the wood duck group, pochards, sea ducks with their subdivisions, and the ruddy duck group.

Swans

The largest members of the waterfowl family form a closely related group of birds called swans. Compared with their nearest relatives, the geese, swans have longer necks, shorter legs, larger feet, and spend more of their time on the water. The species in the northern hemisphere are all white; the single Australian species is all black, while the South American one is white with a black neck.

We have only two native species of swans in America. One, the whistling swan, nests in the Arctic; the other, the trumpeter swan, nests in the Temperate Zone, but both have similar habits. They are most at home in water and swim about with their necks held rather stiff and straight. The bulk of their food is aquatic vegetation, which they get by reaching underwater with their long necks or by tipping like a mallard duck. They rarely dive for food. On land they walk easily; when they fly it is with neck fully extended and with wings beating slowly and powerfully. Except during the breeding season they are sociable birds, gathering in flocks. In flight these flocks travel in diagonal lines or in "V" formations.

In the spring each pair, which mates for life, selects a territory and collects a mass of vegetation into a nest on an islet or at the edge of a pond. There the female incubates the eggs for thirty-five to forty days, while her mate stands guard. When the youngsters, called cygnets, hatch, they are densely clad in down of a pale gray and white, and soon swim about under the care of both parents. During their first year there is much grayish brown in their plumage and it is several years before they become adult. The fully mature birds are completely white. If a reddish-brown color sometimes tinges their feathers, it is only a stain caused by iron-impregnated water.

Despite the similarity between these two species of swans, they do differ in size, range and habitat.

Trumpeter Swan

The trumpeter (Plate 43) is the largest of all swans, having an average weight of thirty pounds and a wingspread of about ten feet. It also differs from the whistling swan in having a completely black bill and a low, trumpet-like voice (correlated with its elaborately coiled windpipe), in preferring the Temperate Zone, and in being fairly sedentary. Its home is in western North America, where during the nesting season each mated pair pre-empts a small lake or part of a large one and vigorously protects it against all other swans. After the nesting season the birds gather into flocks and spend the winter in places where warm springs or strong currents keep the water from freezing, or they move just far enough south to find open water. These birds migrate no farther than necessary and favor inland waters, rarely venturing to the coast.

The trumpeter swan has often been in the news because of the danger of its joining the dodo and the great auk in the limbo of extinction. In Indian days it ranged widely in North America, but with the coming of the white settler it was forced to withdraw from much of its former range. Its size, relative tameness and preference for inland waters in winter have also made it particularly vulnerable to gunners. By 1935 there were thought to be only seventy-three trumpeter swans living in the United States, and a few more in Canada. By 1954, however, there were 642 in the United States, chiefly in Wyoming and Montana, probably about the same number in western Canada, and as many more in southern Alaska. There is therefore much hope that the trumpeter swan, living in protected areas and with encouragement that includes feeding in winter, will not disappear.

Whistling Swan

Our only common swan is the whistling swan. It is distinguished from the trumpeter by its smaller size (it rarely reaches twenty pounds in weight), sometimes by a yellow patch at the base of the bill in front of the eye, and by a high, bugle-like voice correlated with the simpler coiling of its windpipe. It is a highly migratory species, nesting on the tundra near the Arctic coast from Alaska to Hudson Bay and wintering along our Pacific and central Atlantic coasts. In the interior of the continent we see the whistler only in migration, when flocks of these great white birds pass high overhead or rest far out on open water. One strange hazard threatens them. During their spring migration, numbers of them rest on the Niagara River and sometimes on foggy nights many are swept over Niagara Falls and killed. The migrating flocks break up as they approach the Arctic and pairs arrive singly at their nesting sites. They then raise their families, and by late October they gather again into flocks that may number hundreds of birds, and start southward.

Mute Swan

Originally the mute swan (Plate 40) was brought from its home in Europe or Asia to decorate the ornamental waters of gardens and estates in America. Here some lived a life of partial freedom and a few escaped and have established themselves in a wild state, as, for example, on Long Island.

Though the mute swan, like our two native swans, is all white in plumage, it is easily distinguished by its pink bill with a black base, and by a number of distinctive habits. Its long, gracefully curved neck and the way it holds its wings, with elbows raised, make it an embodiment of grace. As its name suggests, it is usually silent, but it does have a voice and upon occasion it gives a hiss and an explosive snort or trumpeting call. When kept on a small pond it can be very ill-tempered at nesting time, though it is sociable at other seasons. When nesting, it will sometimes attack and kill other birds such as ducks, and may even be dangerous to children, delivering severe blows with its wings.

The whooper swan of Europe and Asia rarely visits this hemisphere and then only in Greenland.

Geese

Though a number of big ducks in various parts of the world are called geese, the name is properly applied only to the group typified by the gray goose of Europe and the snow and Canada geese of America. The geese, which include about twelve species, are all of the northern hemisphere, many of them nesting only in the far north and all of them wintering in temperate regions.

[continued on page 105

84]

39. *Flamingo*

[CY LA TOUR]

40. *Mute Swan*

[ALLAN D. CRUICKSHANK:
NATIONAL AUDUBON]

41. *Canada Goose*

[ALLAN D. CRUICKSHANK:
NATIONAL AUDUBON]

42. *Canada Goose*

[ALLAN D. CRUICKSHANK:
NATIONAL AUDUBON]

44. *Brant*

[ALLAN D. CRUICKSHANK: NATIONAL AUDUBON]

45. *White-fronted Goose*

[HELEN CRUICKSHANK: NATIONAL AUDUBON]

46. *Emperor Goose*

[CY LA TOUR]

47. *Blue Geese*

[EDWARD PRINS]

48. *Ross's Goose*

[CY LA TOUR]

49. *Snow Goose*

[CY LA TOUR]

50. *Canada Geese*

[HUGO H. SCHRODER]

51. *Snow Geese*

[W. F. KUBICHEK: FISH AND WILDLIFE SERVICE]

52. *Pintail* (*drake*)

[PAUL J. FAIR]

53. *Blue-winged Teal* (*drake at left*)

54. *Baldpates* (*drakes*)

[PAUL J. FAIR]

55. *Baldpate* (*drake*)

[PAUL J. FAIR]

56. *Gadwall*

[EDWARD PRINS]

57. *Black Duck*

[EDWARD PRINS]

58. *Mallard* (*drake*)

[ALLAN D. CRUICKSHANK:
NATIONAL AUDUBON]

59. *Mallard* (*drake*)

[MARTIN IGER AND
SPORTS ILLUSTRATED]

60. *Mallard* (*drake*)

[ALLAN D. CRUICKSHANK: NATIONAL AUDUBON]

61. *Fulvous Tree Duck*

[VAN NOSTRAND]

62. *Redhead*

[HAL H. HARRISON: NATIONAL AUDUBON]

63. *Pintail (drake)*

[CY LA TOUR]

64. *Wood Duck* (*drake*)

[EDWARD PRINS]

65. *Wood Duck at nest-hole*
(*female*)

[MASLOWSKI AND GOODPASTER:
NATIONAL AUDUBON]

66. *Ring-necked Duck*

[ALLAN D. CRUICKSHANK: NATIONAL AUDUBON]

67. *Lesser Scaup Duck*

[HELEN CRUICKSHANK: NATIONAL AUDUBON]

68. *Common Eider*

[JOHN MARKHAM]

69. *Dusky Grouse* (*female*)

70. *Spruce Grouse* (*young*)

71. *Prairie Chickens
on display grounds*

[CHARLES W. SCHWARTZ]

72. *Rock Ptarmigan in winter
plumage (brown summer
feathers still visible)*

[CHARLES OTT: NATIONAL AUDUBON]

73. *Wild Turkey gobblers strutting*

[ALLAN D. CRUICKSHANK: NATIONAL AUDUBON]

74. *Willow Ptarmigan in summer*
   (male at right)
   [TOM MC HUGH]

75. *Sage Grouse displaying*
   [JOE VAN WORMER]

76. *Ruffed Grouse on drumming log (male)*
   [ELSA AND HENRY POTTER: NATIONAL AUDUBON]

77. *Mearns's Quail*

78. *Quail (young)*

79. *California Quail*

80. *Bobwhite Quail*
(*male at right*)

[HERBERT LANKS : SHOSTAL]

81. *Gambel's Quail*

[WILLIS PETERSON]

82. *Chukar Partridge in flight*
[CY LA TOUR]

83. *Chukar Partridge*
[CY LA TOUR]

84. *Ring-necked Pheasant in flight*

[MARTIN IGER AND
SPORTS ILLUSTRATED]

85. *Ring-necked Pheasant*

[CY LA TOUR]

86. *Wild Turkey*

[ALLAN D. CRUICKSHANK:
NATIONAL AUDUBON]

[*continued from page 84*

Flocks of these birds are noted for the spectacle they present in their seasonal migrations. Geese travel in big, noisy flocks, often high in the air and usually in long lines or "V" formations. They travel both by day and by night, and at night only their trumpeting, honking, or cackling calls tell us of their passing. On the wintering grounds, marshes, lakes, or in a few cases, seacoasts, flocks of most of these species spend the night and the midday hours on the water or on some sandbar or marsh. In the early morning and evening they fly to nearby fields, where they walk about, grazing on green vegetation, grubbing out roots, or eating grain, seeds or berries. Correlated with these terrestrial feeding habits are their comparatively long legs, placed well forward, and their small feet.

Geese ordinarily pair for periods of years, if not for life, and their lives may be long, individuals nearly fifty years old having been reported. When the birds arrive on their breeding grounds the flocks break up and each pair selects a nesting site. The guarded area around each nest is small, so that a favorable habitat may contain many nests which form loose colonies. The nests are crudely lined hollows, usually among vegetation, and there the female lays a clutch of three to eight whitish eggs. The male does not help her incubate the eggs, but stands guard, and when the young hatch, after from twenty-four to thirty days of incubation, both parents accompany them to water and share in their care. In the autumn these family groups join others to form large flocks, though the families retain their identity within the flocks until the next spring. This clannishness among geese has given rise to many local varieties because of inbreeding and has helped pose many puzzling problems in classification, such as the number of species of Canada geese.

Several species of wild geese still extant have provided the ancestry of our domestic geese. Thus the common gray goose is a descendant of the graylag of Europe; and the Chinese goose, the male of which has a knob at the base of its bill, is a descendant of the swan goose of Asia.

In America we have six common species of geese, as well as others that occasionally wander to this country. The sexes are alike in color, though the young of some species are duller than the adults. The Canada goose, varying in length from twenty-six to forty-three inches, has a black head and neck, with a white band on the chin and cheeks. The brant, about twenty-six inches long, also has a black head and neck, but with only a small patch of white on each side of the neck. The barnacle goose, about twenty-six inches long, has a black head and neck, but the whole face is white. The Emperor goose, about twenty-eight inches long, can be distinguished by its white neck and the white top and sides of its head, with black chin and throat. The adult white-fronted goose, about thirty inches long, is gray-brown, with a white patch about the bill and scattered black patches on the gray underparts. The bean goose is gray-brown and without distinctive markings, and is very similar to the young white-front. The snow goose, varying from twenty-four to forty inches in length, is white with black wing tips, and the blue goose, a color phase of the snow goose and about twenty-eight inches long, is slate-colored, with a white head and neck. The Ross's goose is white, with black wing tips like a snow goose, but is smaller, being about twenty-three inches long, and has a relatively smaller bill.

Canada Goose

Despite the name, some Canada geese (Plates 41, 42, 50) nest in the United States and most of them spend the winter here. The Canada goose once nested as far south as Tennessee, but this was before heavy settlement restricted its range. In recent years these geese have been kept in partial liberty in many localities in the United States and now breeding birds are again found in some of the southern localities from which they have so long been absent.

Canada geese live under a variety of conditions. In summer they nest by prairie sloughs, by sedge swales in muskeg and spruce country, or on Arctic tundra. In winter some live on the seacoast, where they feed on eelgrass, others on inland lakes, while many join the great throngs of waterfowl on the marshes bordering the Gulf of Mexico and in the valleys of the interior of California. In the inland wintering places, fields of stubble or of sprouting grain are their favorite feeding places.

To many people wild geese mean the Canada geese that fly in wedge formation high over town and country in spring and fall, honking as they fly. To the wildfowler, the Canada goose, or "honker" as he may call it, is one of the noblest of feathered game, the equal of the turkey gobbler. To him the variety in the size of the geese he gets is bewildering. Some of them may be little larger than a mallard duck, others may weigh twelve pounds or more. Southern-nesting Canada geese are large, those that nest in the far north are small, and birds of intermediate size nest in the areas in between. In addition, the birds of the eastern and central parts of our country have much gray on them, but those from the far West, both large and small, are brownish. There is no consensus as to how many species should be recognized and in the present state of knowledge it seems the safest course, because it is the simplest, to call them all subspecies or local varieties, whether they are big Canada geese or the small, "cackling" geese.

Brant

Brant are the most northern of geese. They nest on the lands all around the Arctic Ocean, and on its islands. In North America there are two geographical varieties, that is, subspecies, which are so different that they have often been considered separate species. One, the Atlantic brant, which has whitish underparts, nests in the eastern Arctic from Greenland to west of Hudson Bay, and winters on our central Atlantic coast. The other, the black brant (Plate 44), nests in the western Arctic from Victoria Island to Alaska and migrates to our Pacific coast for the winter.

The birds gather in big flocks to migrate, flying in long lines or irregular bands. Some follow the coast on their journeys, as do most of the black brant of the western Arctic on their way to the Pacific via the Bering Sea; others, like some of the pale eastern birds, may make long cross-country journeys, such as the Hudson Bay—Gulf of St. Lawrence crossing. In its winter quarters the brant is a salt-water bird and the flocks gather on tidal flats to feed. When the tide is high they may sit quietly on the water, but when the tide falls and the beds of eelgrass, their favorite food, are exposed, the birds begin to feed. They may even tip up like mallard ducks to reach the bottom, but they rarely dive.

In the spring the flocks move north, forsaking their gregarious habits and their salt-water habitat. The pairs build their nests on the tundra near fresh-water ponds, or on islands, and for a time they feed on the plants of the tundra, grazing like other geese. But as soon as the gray and white offspring are hatched the parents lead them to the sea.

The related barnacle goose breeds in lands bordering the far North Atlantic, northeastern Greenland, Spitsbergen and Nova Zembla, and winters in northwestern Europe. Few individuals of this species have strayed to North America.

Another species, the Emperor goose (Plate 46), is restricted to the coasts of the Bering Sea and its islands. Even within this area it migrates, breeding chiefly in the north and wintering as far south as the Aleutians. It is a bird of salt water, feeding along the sea beaches, where it eats seaweed, shellfish and other marine animals. When breeding time comes these birds make their nests on islets, along the beaches above the reach of tides, or by inland lagoons, but ordinarily not more than a few miles inland. When breeding on the tundra they may graze on grass, but even at this time some birds may fly to join others at favorite salt-water feeding places.

White-fronted Goose

The white-fronted goose (Plate 45) is one of the common geese that migrate through our western states, feeding on stubble fields in autumn and on sprouting grain in spring. The birds winter in the vast marshes from Louisiana to Texas and in California and Mexico. In these winter quarters the flocks join aggregations of wintering waterfowl that are impressive because of the sheer abundance of birds. In summer the nesting grounds of the American white-fronts are on the tundra of the western American Arctic; this species also lives in the Old World.

A mystery still surrounds one group of white-fronted geese—the large, dark birds sometimes called tule geese. These are known only from California, where they winter, and from their migration path, which has been traced as far north as Alberta. They have not been seen farther north, where presumably they nest. This recalls the state of our knowledge of the Ross's goose before 1938, when that bird's nesting area was found on barren islands in the Perry River region.

In California the tule goose behaves somewhat differently from the ordinary white-front. It gathers in smaller flocks, perhaps because the overall number of these geese is smaller. It has a harsher voice, and spends its days feeding in openings in the marshes rather than on grainfields and grasslands like the other white-fronts. We know nothing of its nesting grounds. Until these are found and its relationship with the white-front is studied at breeding time, the possibility remains that it is a separate species, but for the time being it seems best to consider it a geographical variety of the white-front.

The pink-footed goose, a race of the bean goose, nests in eastern Greenland.

Snow Goose

All the snow geese (Plates 49, 51) belong to one

species, though they have at times been divided into three because of variations in color and size. One of these so called "species," the greater snow goose, a large white bird that breeds in northwestern Greenland and adjacent Canadian Arctic islands, is a northern subspecies; another, the lesser snow goose, breeding from Baffin Island west to Siberia, is a smaller subspecies; and the third is a slate-colored bird which occurs in the eastern part of the range of the lesser snow goose and has been called the blue goose (Plate 47). The blue and the lesser snow geese are identical in size and habits, intermingle in their breeding colonies, and interbreed. There is little doubt they represent only different color phases of the same kind of bird.

The migration of the greater snow geese follows a narrow path. From the high Arctic summer range where they breed on the tundra, they migrate south to congregate at St. Joachim, on the St. Lawrence River about twenty-five miles east of the city of Quebec. The whole population, which now numbers about 42,000 birds, stays there from mid-September until the freezing of the inshore waters forces them south. They then go to their wintering grounds on the Atlantic coast, which extend from Chesapeake Bay to North Carolina. On their way north in the spring the flocks stop again for a few weeks at St. Joachim.

The lesser snow goose is similar to the greater snow goose in habits, nesting on the marshy tundra in loose colonies and feeding on the grass and grass roots growing there. But its colonies are much larger, for the lesser snow goose is much more numerous; indeed, it has been said to be the commonest North American goose. Its migration pattern is different, too, for it travels mostly west of the Great Lakes, and the birds winter in California, where all-white ones are found; in Texas, where a few blues are mixed with the white ones; and in Louisiana, where mostly blue birds are found. On the great marshes of these southern states the large flocks of lesser snow geese mingle with those of Canada and white-fronted geese in spectacular congregations.

Ross's Goose

Until 1938 Ross's goose (Plate 48) was known only as a bird that wintered in California, traveled a narrow migration route that went up through Washington and Alberta and disappeared into the great northland. Nests and eggs of captive birds had been seen, for birds had been caught in California and shipped to European aviaries where they had bred, but no one knew where the wild Ross's geese nested. Then, in 1938, Angus Gavin, a Hudson's Bay Company post manager stationed on Queen Maude Gulf, made the discovery—Ross's geese were nesting in the nearby Perry River area. Eleven years later an American scientist, H. C. Hanson, led a party to study the birds there. They found the geese nesting on tundra-covered islands on a lake about twenty-five miles from the coast, and they counted 260 nests in this colony. Later, airplane surveys were made but no additional colonies were found. It had always been known that Ross's goose was restricted in distribution and small in numbers, but when it was realized that there were less than two thousand—about the same number as of the trumpeter swan, long considered to be threatened with extinction—the necessity of protecting these birds became evident.

Very little has ever been recorded of the habits of the Ross's goose in California, though it was commonly shot for the market there in the early days. Apparently its habits are much like those of the snow geese with which it feeds on the stubble fields.

Ducks

The word duck is often used to include all the birds of the family Anatidae that are not swans or geese. This is a matter of convenience, predicated on lack of knowledge. Actually the "ducks" contain a number of groups of water birds that are as distinct from each other as they are from geese and swans. Because of this, each of these groups that live in North America, tree ducks, pond ducks, the wood duck group, pochards, sea ducks, and the ruddy duck group, is introduced individually in the following pages.

Tree Ducks

The tropics, poor in nesting ducks compared with temperate and Arctic lands, are the headquarters of the tree or whistling ducks. This group comprises about eight species whose range extends only a little beyond the subtropics, and only three of which reach the United States. The tree ducks are so named because some of them roost in trees, but since this habit is even more characteristic of such other ducks as the muscovy, the use of the name "whistling ducks," referring to the fact that their calls are whistled cries, has recently gained favor.

The favorite habitats of these ducks vary from grassy marshes to lakes and ponds in wooded country and to wooded swamps and mangroves. All of them live in flocks most of the year, separating only to nest. The flocks of some species rest during the day on mud flats, sandbars, islands or floating logs, or perch in trees, and feed by night. Others feed by day and gather at night to sleep in favored roosting trees. They are not at all shy and when forced into flight will fly with slow, noisy wing beats, the flock meanwhile giving out a chorus of whistled notes. Though they are conspicuous birds and often quite common, strangely enough the details of their lives are better known from observation of captive birds than of wild ones. In feeding, they may graze on green vegetation or seek their food, which is largely vegetable, in water. They dive readily. One species in the West Indies feeds on the fruit of the tall palms on which it perches.

On land these ducks walk easily on their long legs and have an upright, gooselike pose, with their necks held straight. They resemble geese, too, in that the sexes are alike in plumage, having only one moult a year, as well as in some details of courtship and nesting. The nest may be placed in a variety of locations: on the ground among concealing vegetation, in a fork of a tree, or in a hole in a tree trunk; and a wide variation in nest sites may be found in a single species. The nest is a substantial one, but is unique among waterfowl nests in having no lining of down, presumably because of the influence of the tropical environment. In this nest a large clutch of white, rather round eggs is laid, up to fifteen and even twenty eggs having been recorded in a nest. The male as well as the female shares in the task of brooding the eggs, as with the black swan, and after from twenty-seven to thirty-two days of incubation, the young hatch and are cared for by both parents—another gooselike trait.

Two species of tree ducks reach their northern limits in the southern United States. One is the black-bellied tree duck, a tropical American species that summers in southern Texas. It is nocturnal in habits, spends the day sleeping on the edge of shallow water or perched in trees, feeds commonly on the grain in cornfields, and nests on the ground or in trees. The other species is the fulvous tree duck (Plate 61), which has a wide but broken range, including the southern United States (California to Louisiana), Mexico, South America, Africa and India. It occupies a wide variety of habitats but seems to prefer open country. It is nocturnal and usually nests among reeds. A third species, the white-faced tree duck of South America and Africa, has been recorded as an accidental visitor in the United States.

The size and color of the tree ducks are as follows: the black-bellied tree duck, about twenty-two inches long, is a rusty-brown bird with a black abdomen and big whitish patches in its black wings; the fulvous tree duck, about twenty inches long, is buff brown with a dark brown back and whitish stripes on its flanks; and the white-faced tree duck is a reddish-brown bird with belly and the back of its head black, and the front half of its head and a patch on its throat white.

The shelducks belong to a group of large, showy ducks of the Old World. They need be mentioned here only because a few individuals of two species, the common shelduck (or shield-duck) and the ruddy shelduck (or sheldrake), have strayed across the Atlantic to the United States.

Pond Ducks

Grassy or reedy fresh-water marshes, ponds and lakes are the favorite summer and winter homes of pond ducks. The prairies, with their numerous sloughs, are the summer headquarters and principal nurseries of most of these ducks, as they are for a host of other water birds. Not all our pond ducks—they are also called dabbling, river or surface-feeding ducks—are restricted to the prairies. Some also nest elsewhere and a few species such as the black ducks live only in the eastern and southern states. But the prairies are supreme in the abundance of both species and individuals of pond ducks. Thousands upon thousands of ducks can be seen there at one time, and on little islands in the sloughs one must walk carefully to avoid stepping on their nests.

Male pond ducks may have very distinctive, bright-colored plumage, but the females are much more alike; in general pose, habits and habitats, they are all very similar. Some students, impressed with differences between the species, have divided these ducks into many genera, but others, noting their similarities, have decided that they are best grouped into one comprehensive genus, *Anas,* of which the best known species is the mallard.

Before we consider these ducks in detail, it will be well to put them in their proper setting. Pond ducks as a group are distributed over most of the land surfaces of the globe, but the North Temperate Zone is richest in the number of species. Eleven species nest in America: the mallard, the three black ducks, the gadwall, baldpate, pintail, green-winged teal, blue-winged teal, cinnamon teal and shoveller. Several of these, such as the mallard, pintail, gadwall and shoveller, we share with Europe and Asia. We have a few species peculiar to North America, such as the blue-winged teal and the black ducks, and one, the cinnamon teal, which we share with South America.

Pond ducks are rather trim birds that waddle competently, float high on the water, and swim well, but rarely dive unless flightless or crippled. They flush easily and with a bound that takes them straight up from the water on whistling or clattering wings. Once awing, their flight is usually swift and direct, with rapid, steady wing beats. Their speed of flight has often been overestimated, and 40 to 65 miles per hour probably covers the speeds of most of these ducks, unless they are helped along by a strong tail-wind. Pond ducks are gregarious creatures and except when actually nesting they consort in flocks. These flocks in flight sometimes form "V's" or lines but more often have no definite arrangement.

The food of the pond ducks is largely vegetable: aquatic plants and their roots and seeds, together with a small miscellany of animal matter, notably mollusks and insects—which last are particularly important to the shoveller. Seasonably, of course, this diet varies, as when the mallard goes to the stubble fields for waste grain, or to sprouting wheatfields to eat the tender, green shoots and to grub out roots, or when the black duck goes to the coast in the winter for shellfish. When feeding in water, pond ducks often swim along skimming the surface with their bills or reach down into the water as far as their necks will allow. Wherever the water is deep, they tip up in a characteristic action, bodies vertical, tail sticking straight up, and feet paddling now in the water, now in the air, as they reach toward the bottom for food.

Since most of our pond ducks are birds of temperate and low Arctic breeding grounds, they must migrate to escape the freezing of the pools. Some of them, such as the black duck, stay far north but seek the open water of the coast; others, such as the shoveller and the blue-winged teal, are summer ducks, moving northward late and leaving again before the cold sets in. The length of their migrations varies. Such ducks as the green-winged teal and the black duck seem to go just far enough to find open water, while others, such as the blue-winged teal, often winter as far south as South America. As the prairies are the principal nurseries of the pond ducks, the Gulf of Mexico coastal states, the lower Mississippi Valley, and the interior California valleys are their chief wintering grounds.

Pairing often takes place on the wintering grounds or on the migrations northward, so that when the flocks arrive on their breeding grounds they may be composed of birds already paired. The usual courtship of pond ducks starts with a male swimming about a female or resting on the water with other males. He fluffs out his head feathers and draws his head down on his back, raises his tail, and shakes both tail and head repeatedly. Following this he raises his head and tail with quick, jerky motions, stretches his head out low over the water, and swims rapidly about. Or the drake may stand up in the water, and with a rapid jerk pass his bill from the water up over his breast, producing a jet of water. The final phase of the courtship, that in which the pairs are formed, comes when the male swims about with his head slightly turned and raised, the female moving along at his side, quacking and with head lowered or stretched out over the water.

Even more spectacular than the performances on the water are the courtship flights in which a party of several males is led by a female in a chase over a marsh. Once pairs are formed, elaborate courtship ceases, but just before actual mating takes place, each bird of a pair puts on a display for the other, bobbing its head up and down. With minor modifications, similar displays are given by other pond ducks.

Upon arrival at the nesting place, the female chooses a territory containing shallow water in which the couple can feed, and a muddy beach or point, a mat of reeds, or an old muskrat house on which she and her mate can rest and preen. She also chooses the actual nest site either nearby or some distance away, usually on dry ground and concealed among vegetation. The nest is simply a hollow in the soil with a lining of dead grasses. When the eggs are laid, the duck uses down from its breast as an additional lining for the nest. When she leaves the nest she pulls this down up from the edges and over the eggs like a blanket. The eggs are whitish, tinged with buff or greenish blue. A full clutch contains from eight to twelve eggs, but the number of eggs laid is variable and more than one female may lay in one nest.

The care of the eggs and the young is typically the province of the female pond duck, though there are a few records of drakes with broods. Ordinarily the male leaves the female and the territory by the time she starts to incubate the eggs. The drakes then gather in parties or large flocks in favorite marshes to feed and loaf, awaiting the moulting period. This moulting period is peculiar in that, except for the wing feathers, there are two moults. First, the drake loses his gaudy plumage and assumes a dress, called the eclipse plumage, similar to that of the female, and at the same time moults all his flight feathers at once. He then stops loafing conspicuously in the marsh and hides in the reeds, so that the marsh seems comparatively deserted. Not until the wing feathers are grown again do the birds come out of hiding, band together in flocks and start to undergo another moult, slowly regaining their bright feathers and becoming conspicuous again, flying about or even starting to migrate.

Meanwhile the female has been brooding her eggs. After twenty-one to twenty-five days they hatch and the downy young emerge. The duck then leads them on foot to the marsh or pond, and the family stays together, swimming about in the water and waddling about on the mud in search of food. When danger threatens, the young generally hide in nearby vegetation while the female gives a broken-wing or injury-feigning display, flopping about as though she were hurt. This is a ruse to draw the enemy away from the brood, and has actually been seen to work effectively with a marauding coyote. The fledglings are able to fly at from seven to nine weeks of age. About the time they learn to fly the female goes through a moult that leaves her flightless for a period. Her family cares have necessitated a delay in this, so that she moults a month or so later than her mate—who deserted her when family responsibilities started.

Among the ranks of the pond ducks are found some of the finest of the wildfowler's game: the large green-headed mallard, the spritely pintail, and, in the east, the black duck. The small teal, with their speedy, twisting flight, present a special test for the gunner. The hours just after dawn and those just before dark are the true wildfowling hours. Then the ducks are stirring, leaving the safety of the big marshes to go to their feeding places. It is then that the sportsman in his blind on the stubble, in the passes, or on the edge of the marsh, can hope for a chance to make a score. The hunting of waterfowl has brought about a change in the birds' habits. When undisturbed many ducks feed by day and sleep in the marshes by night, probably their original pattern of behavior. But when they are much hunted they quickly learn to feed at night and to spend the daylight hours not in the marshes, but on wider, safer expanses of water. Yet this pattern can be quickly changed again, as in the case of the wild ducks that become tame and drop into many a city pond

or protected area even during the hunting season. Sometimes at nesting time, too, wild ducks can become very tolerant of human beings, as, for example, has the mallard that nests on the grounds of the Chicago Natural History Museum and later leads its brood across a busy city parkway to the waters of Lake Michigan.

The pond ducks vary in size from about fourteen to twenty-five inches long, with the females slightly smaller than the males. The females are generally dull-colored birds with a pattern of brownish streaks; the drakes usually show some contrasting colors in bold patterns. The black ducks, measuring about twenty-five inches long, are exceptions, the duck and the drake being alike and both looking like a dark version of the female mallard. Also exceptional are the male and female gadwall, which are about twenty inches long and are both plain, grayish birds with a white speculum or patch in the wing.

The drake mallard, about twenty-five inches long, has a green head and a white ring around its neck; the baldpate, about twenty inches long, has a grayish head with a white crown and green patches on its cheeks. The European widgeon, the same size as the baldpate, has a reddish-brown head with a buff-white crown; the pintail, a slender duck with a long pointed tail that helps give it a length of about thirty inches, has a white line up the side of its neck and head. The blue-winged teal, about sixteen inches long, has a white crescent in front of its eye and a large, pale blue patch on the front part of the wing. The cinnamon teal, about seventeen inches long, is generally cinnamon brown and also has a large, pale blue patch on the front edge of the wing. The green-winged teal, the smallest species, fourteen inches long, has a reddish-brown head with a green patch on each side and a white bar in the front of the wing. The shoveller, about twenty inches long, has a spoon-shaped bill, a dark green head, white breast and chestnut flanks and abdomen.

Mallard

The beauty of the wild mallard's plumage (Plates 58, 59, 60) and the grace of its form are perhaps not adequately appreciated because of our familiarity with its coarser and heavier barnyard descendants. The mallard has been the ancestor of all the varieties of domestic ducks except the muscovy. These mallard descendants include such diverse varieties as the giant, mallard-like Rouen and the white Pekin, the Indian runner, the dark

Cayuga, the small, black East Indian ducks, and the call duck. The mallard is not only important historically and economically, but sportsmen have also placed it near the top of their list of preferred game birds because of its wide distribution, abundance, size, and wariness, and its excellence as a table bird.

The mallard's adaptability is great. It nests from tree line at the mouth of the Mackenzie River in the Arctic to the hot, dry country of northwestern Mexico and throughout much of Europe and Asia. In North America it is absent only in the east, where its place is taken by its close relative, the black duck. When northern waters freeze, the mallards move south, some of them as far as southern Mexico. In the United States their main winter stronghold is the lower Mississippi Valley and the adjacent marshes in the states bordering the Gulf of Mexico. Their wintering range, however, is wide and some of the birds, by living on salt water, are able to winter as far north as southern Alaska.

Naturally this wide range and the diversity of habitats result in a great variety of diets. When the mallard lives and feeds on ponds and marshes, aquatic vegetation and seeds are important; in grain and rice fields, grain is its principal food; and in the uplands it eats seeds, berries and nuts. It also takes many insects and other invertebrates, and when it winters on salt water, may feed chiefly on marine organisms such as shellfish and crustaceans.

Black Ducks

East and south of the mallard's range in North America are three species of black ducks that are very closely related to the mallard: the northern (Plate 57), the mottled, and the Mexican black duck. The males and females of these species are very similar to each other and to the female mallard, except that they are darker brown, whence their name.

The northern black duck is the common fresh-water duck from Quebec to North Carolina. In the Midwest its counterpart is the mallard. The black duck is a bird of the fresh-water ponds and marshes and brackish waterways. With the coming of autumn these birds gather into flocks and some of them go as far south as Florida, but many of the northern birds move to the salt marshes of New England and Nova Scotia. There during the hunting season they spend their days on salt water or on inaccessible mud flats and come to feed at night in the marshes or on the stubble in the grainfields.

When they feed on salt marshes they sometimes make journeys to the mouths of streams or to ponds for fresh water.

The Florida black duck, Florida duck, or mottled black duck lives the year round in the lowlands of the states bordering the Gulf of Mexico, inhabiting everglades and river marshes, lakes and lagoons. Apparently it tends to stay in pairs the year round; certainly the flocks into which it gathers are small, and rarely are more than a dozen of the birds seen together. Since there is a more abundant animal life in the southern marshes in which it lives, its food consists more of animal material than does that of its more northern relatives. Nearly half of its diet is shellfish and insects, the other part being made up of seeds, leaves, stems and plant roots. Among the vegetation the mottled black duck favors is the rice plant, and it is even said to have damaged rice crops in Louisiana.

On the upper reaches of the Rio Grande and southward into Mexico lives the Mexican black duck, or New Mexican duck. In the United States it spends the day on the mud flats of the Rio Grande and at night flies to swamps, ponds, and flooded alfalfa fields or grainfields to feed. When feeding it tends to stay in flocks of its own kind, mixing little with other wintering waterfowl.

Gadwall

The writer has watched the gadwall (Plate 56) on its nesting grounds on the Canadian prairies and on migration in the Midwest, and it has struck him as a truly elegant bird. Mallard-like in shape, but lacking the bold, gaudy patches of color that adorn the drakes of most of the surface-feeding ducks, the gadwall drake has a quiet plumage of finely patterned grays and blacks. But both drake and duck have one ever-present color characteristic, a white speculum—as the patch on the inner flight feathers of ducks is called.

In some reference books the gadwall is recorded as a rare or uncommon duck, except locally, despite a breeding range that includes temperate Europe, Asia and the western two-thirds of North America. On checking, one finds that it is a common nesting bird from western Minnesota to the Canadian prairies and eastern Oregon and New Mexico, and sometimes its numbers are reported as being greater than those of the abundant mallard. In recent years it has begun to nest commonly at scattered points in the East, as, for example, in a pond near Jones Beach on Long Island. The sportsmen whose sharp eyes have distinguished between the early-autumn and the late-migrating mallards and have even given different names to these seasonal aspects of the same bird, seem to have overlooked the gadwall, including it with the female baldpates and pintails and calling them all "gray ducks," or widgeon. Despite this error, the outline of the gadwall's life story has become fairly well known in recent years. The gadwall is one of the later spring arrivals on its nesting marsh. After its arrival the marvelous grace of its courtship flights, in which as many as a dozen males may pursue one female, has been much admired.

Reporting on the gadwall's nesting, one ornithologist tells of twenty-three nests found on an island about 350 yards long in Crane Lake, Saskatchewan. These nests were associated with those of some fourteen other species of ducks, and perhaps 150 pairs of ducks in all were found nesting on the island. These nests were probably concentrated on this site because it was an island and seemed relatively safe from predators. The next year a coyote came to live on the island, and only three nests escaped being robbed.

Not only do the gadwalls nest late but they leave the northern marshes early for their wintering homes in the southern states and Mexico. Many gadwalls have been banded, and of these bands more than a thousand have been recovered. The records taken during the autumn or winter of the year the birds were banded, show that most of these prairie-bred birds winter in the Mississippi Valley, Texas and Mexico, whereas birds from western Alberta and Oregon tend to winter in California. Since this bird nested largely in areas suitable for agriculture, the species suffered greatly as the land became settled and the wide marshes, its favorite summering grounds, were drained for farming.

Baldpate

The baldpate or American widgeon (Plates 54, 55) is rather more graceful, dainty and active than many of our dabbling ducks. It is often the first to take alarm among the marsh ducks, and flocks of baldpates taking wing with whistled calls may startle other ducks into flight. Of course baldpates are not always in flocks, for their habits vary with the seasons. In late spring they nest over a wide range in the western part of our continent from Colorado to Alaska. They stay in pairs, holding a territory on the edge of some marsh, while the female builds her nest, hiding it among the vegetation on nearby dry ground. On the duck marshes of the prairies these birds may be common; in the

marshes of the north they are likely to be scarcer and their nests scattered. Thus in Delta marsh in Manitoba, baldpates are uncommon as breeding birds, but in June crowds of drakes pour into the marsh and in July, when they are moulting, they are the commonest ducks in this duck-rich marsh. In late July, an investigator once flushed three hundred moulting, flightless ducks, mostly mallards, baldpates, and pintails, from their hiding places on one tule island less than a quarter of an acre in size. By mid-August the drakes have grown their wing feathers again, recovered their powers of flight and moved on. They start south early and are joined later by the females and the fledglings of the year.

Though entirely a western-breeding duck, the baldpate in migration spreads out to the Atlantic as well as to the Pacific coast and winters from southern Alaska, Chesapeake Bay, and our central southern states south to Panama. On their winter grounds they live in marshes and lagoons and even on tidal flats, where most of their food continues to be aquatic vegetation. In addition to dabbling and tipping up like other dabbling ducks, baldpates have another method of feeding. They consort with diving birds, such as canvasbacks and coots, which regularly dive for their food, and as these birds bring aquatic vegetation to the surface the baldpates snatch it from them.

Pintail

In shape the pintail (Plates 52, 63) is the most slender and graceful of our pond ducks, and the slenderness of the long neck of the drake pintail is accentuated and balanced by his elongated central tail feathers. It is true that this long neck would seem to give the pintail an advantage when reaching underwater for its food, but actually it feeds in much the same way as does the mallard with its shorter neck. Like the mallard, the pintail is an early migrant, pressing northward as soon as the ponds are free of ice, and the pairs, already mated when they arrive, soon select their nesting territories. These may be on prairie marshes or on tundra ponds in the Arctic, for the pintail has a wide north-to-south range west of the Great Lakes. It also breeds throughout Asia and Europe.

The pintails not only arrive early but finish breeding quickly, many of them leaving long before the ice forms. Some of them have far to go since they winter in Central America as well as in the United States as far north as southern Illinois and Maryland.

In a study of pintail migration, about 175,000 pintails were banded by 1949, and the preliminary study of some 30,000 returns has given us some interesting information. In particular there is the suggestion that this duck has a circular migration route, many of the northern birds migrating south through the prairies, across to California and then to the coast of the Gulf of Mexico in the winter, and in the spring returning to their breeding grounds by way of the Mississippi Valley.

Wildfowlers have often rated the pintail third in importance after the mallard and the black duck. Thus it has had to withstand much hunting. Also, much of its original summer home on the prairie has disappeared as the land has been plowed and drained. Nevertheless, the more northern-breeding population has produced a reserve of birds that has helped to keep up the numbers of this species.

Green-winged Teal

The smallest of our pond ducks, the green-winged teal, is also the most agile awing, wheeling, turning and twisting like a shore bird as it darts low over a marsh. The teal has become a by-word for swiftness of flight, and speeds up to 160 miles per hour have been estimated. As with the blue-winged teal, the small size of the green-winged species has undoubtedly contributed to the illusion of its speed, and probably it would need a stiff wind behind it to attain half the speed attributed to it. The telephone and electric wires that crisscross the country are hazards to many birds, but of the birds that this writer has watched only two have actually struck such wires, and both were green-winged teal—one on the Canol Road in the Yukon territory and the other in Indiana.

The green-winged teal is a hardy bird, migrating northward early and leaving late for its wintering grounds. Although its main breeding grounds are on the western prairies, around ponds and marshes, it also nests as far north on the tundra as Alaska, and a few nest as far east as the Gulf of St. Lawrence. Many of these teal winter in the coastal marshes as far north as British Columbia in the west and Maryland in the east, and in marshes in our central states, while others go as far south as Mexico and there winter inland on fresh-water marshes. The cross-country traveling that ducks do, cutting across the usual migration routes, is illustrated by the flight of a green-winged teal that was banded in California and three years later was shot in Labrador.

Blue-winged teal

The blue-winged teal (Plate 53) is known as one of our "summer ducks," a name it has earned by migrating northward later than most ducks and by leaving again for the south early in the autumn. Its breeding range is largely in the Temperate Zone. At one time the potholes, marshes and sloughs of the prairies, about equally divided between the United States and Canada, were the summer homes of the bird. Its numbers contributed substantially to the clouds and swarms of waterfowl that the early settlers reported finding on the plains. But in this Temperate Zone range lay a hazard to the species, for the land where they nested was arable. The blue-winged teal, like the gadwall, has suffered acutely from the advance of settlement, especially from the plow that destroyed the prairie and the drainage that dried out marsh and slough. At present a large proportion of blue-winged teal come from Canadian breeding grounds, where settlement has advanced more slowly than in the United States.

Most of these teal migrate before frost drives them out, many of them being fortunate enough to leave the north before the shooting season starts. The progress of the main flocks to wintering grounds that extend from the states bordering the Gulf of Mexico to South America has not been timed. One would expect a leisurely migration, the birds stopping to feed on their favorite water plants in inviting marshes, but a surprising haste is indicated from some banding records. One of the fastest long-distance flights on record was made by a young blue-winged teal that was banded in Alberta, on the Athabasca Delta, in the second week in September and was taken in Venezuela, 3,800 miles away, exactly one month later. This bird thus averaged 125 miles a day. Records for the blue-wing of flights of over 2,500 miles are common; and there are quite a number of records of flights of from 2,300 to 3,000 miles being made within a month. The bird's normal flight speed, however, is only from 35 to 45 miles per hour, much less than the 130 miles an hour that has been attributed to this species.

Cinnamon Teal

Though many pond ducks are primarily western birds during the breeding season, most of them spread eastward to the Atlantic coast as well as west to the Pacific coast in migration. Not so, however, the cinnamon teal. This species is a close relative of the blue-winged teal and takes its place on the Pacific coast. It ranges eastward only to the Rocky Mountains, and its breeding range overlaps that of the blue-wing only where the range of the latter extends west of the mountains.

Like the blue-wing, the cinnamon teal is an American species extending from British Columbia to Mexico, west of the Rockies, while there are isolated populations of cinnamon teal that live the year around in South America. The birds of the United States winter from California and New Mexico to South America. Though the male cinnamon teal and blue-winged teal are very different in color, their close relationship is shown in their structure and size, and the females of the two species are almost indistinguishable.

Shoveller

The spoon-shaped tip of the shoveller's bill is its distinctive mark; in addition, the drake shoveller is perhaps the most boldly and gaudily patterned of any of our pond ducks. Its pose as it swims on the water is distinctive, too, for as though weighed down by its huge bill, it carries its head lower than do other pond ducks, the bill tip barely clearing the surface. The fringe of plates on the broad bill of the shoveller is better developed than that in other pond ducks and serves as a strainer to separate its food from water and liquid mud. Because of this the shoveller spends much of its time feeding at the surface, sieving out its food from the edges of the ponds and marshes where it lives both summer and winter. This indiscriminate sieving may explain why it takes in a larger percentage of animal food, especially mollusks and insects, than do most of its relatives, and it may also explain its frequent leanness—a characteristic that gives it a poor reputation with many sportsmen.

In the United States its main breeding grounds are on the western prairies, but we also find it breeding north to the Alaska tundra and, in addition, widely throughout Europe and Asia. It is one of the less hardy ducks and tends to migrate north late in the spring and south early in the fall. In the Americas the shoveller winters from the southern United States to northern South America and shares with the pintail the distinction of being the only duck that regularly migrates in winter to the Hawaiian Islands.

Pond Ducks—Casual Visitors

In addition to the eleven species of pond ducks that nest within our borders, five species occur here as casual or accidental visitors. The most common of these is the European widgeon, a native of Europe and Asia. This duck has been recorded here more than six hundred times. In 1944 an analysis of the records indicated that in the autumn there is a southward migration of these birds down our Atlantic coast and another on our Pacific coast, and that in the spring there is a northward migration up the Mississippi Valley along with other waterfowl. Some of these records were of individual birds, but others were of pairs and small parties, often traveling with their close relative, the baldpate. From this data an American breeding population in the far north was postulated. On the other hand, seven European widgeon taken in America had been banded in Iceland, so the American birds may come from there.

Another pond duck which appears occasionally in the continental United States is the European teal. This bird is a close relative of our green-winged teal, but occurs mainly in the Old World. It also has an outpost in the Bering Sea, however, nesting commonly in the Aleutian Islands and being resident there. Occasional individuals are also found in the eastern part of the United States. These are probably visitors from Europe. There are three more pond ducks whose occurrence in America is accidental: the Bahama pintail of South America and the West Indies; and the falcated and the Baikal teal of Siberia.

Wood Duck Group

The drake wood duck (Plate 64) is an ornamental bird that is as beautiful as its near relative, the mandarin duck of eastern Asia. Though often grouped with our pond ducks, the wood duck seems more nearly related to a group of perching ducks of the tropics which includes such an assortment of members as the muscovy duck, the comb duck, and the pygmy goose. As one might expect of a bird with tropical relatives, the wood duck does not range far northward. It lives mostly in the United States. Since its favorite haunts include woodland ponds and streams, it is naturally absent from the prairies where most of the pond ducks nest, and its range is divided: some of the birds live in eastern woodlands, some in the West from British Columbia to California. The individuals which nest in the more northern areas winter on wooded ponds and in swamps in our southern states.

The drake wood duck is about twenty inches long, has iridescent green in the wings, chestnut in the breast and neck, and a distinctive head pattern. The head and the full, drooping crest are iridescent green and purple. It has a white throat, one white bar extending upward behind the eye, another extending from the throat toward the nape, and two white lines in the crest.

Despite this ornamental plumage the courtship display of the wood duck is simple: the drake raises his crest, arches his neck, and bows, meanwhile uttering soft, whistled calls. When paired, the mated birds leave the flock and fly through the woodlands looking for a nesting site, typically a natural hollow in some large tree, often far above the ground. No material is brought to line the nest. The ten to fifteen whitish eggs are laid on whatever rubbish is in the cavity, but as laying progresses, the female makes a typical duck blanket for the eggs with down plucked from her breast. During the house-hunting and egg-laying periods the male accompanies the female, following her, and while she is in the nest hole laying her daily egg, waits nearby, perched on a large branch of a tree. During their leisure time the pair, sitting on a log or a bough, preen and loaf.

When the female starts brooding the eggs, the male leaves her for good. Joining other males, he goes through the eclipse plumage stage, becoming duller and more like the female. He also moults all of his wing quills at once and is flightless for a time.

The downy young wood duck hatch after about thirty days. Then comes the problem of their getting to the ground from the nest hole, sometimes as much as sixty feet up in a tree. At one time the opinions about this differed, but recent observations have shown that the nestlings simply jump out, fall so slowly and land so lightly that they are unhurt, and can at once follow the female to water.

The early records indicate that these ducks were once amazingly abundant, but most of their breeding range was near settled areas, and great numbers of them were killed in spring and fall shooting. Moreover, the cutting down of the forests and thus the destruction of their nesting sites left many of them without breeding places and this was just as effective as direct killing in reducing their numbers. With the aid of special game laws and management practices (which includes putting up nesting boxes with oval openings three inches high by four inches wide), these charming birds have made a good recovery in numbers.

Though woodland ponds are their favorite sleeping and resting places, the wood ducks get part of their food of aquatic vegetation, seeds and nuts, and a few insects and spiders, from woodland waterways and their margins. In the autumn the flocks visit nearby marshes to feed and there they meet the pond ducks. From these other ducks they are distinguishable not only by their distinctive coloring, but also by a rather long, broad tail, and the fact that the head is held in flight with the bill pointed downward.

Pochards

Since the redheads, canvasbacks, ring-necks, scaups and their relatives form a closely-knit group of diving ducks for which we have no common name, it is convenient to call them by the familiar European name of pochard. This is a widely distributed group of about fourteen species, five of which are a regular part of the bird life in the United States. In form, pochards are short and heavy-bodied, with a relatively large head and with large feet placed far back and to the sides. In habits they differ considerably from the pond ducks. Although they swim well, they seem to float low on the surface, with the tail dragging in the water, and they get their food, largely aquatic vegetation, by diving and swimming underwater for it. When they take to flight they do not spring up like a pond duck but take a running start, pattering for a short distance over the surface. Once awing, their flight is strong and direct, with more rapid wing beats than the pond ducks. They rarely come ashore except at nesting time, and when they do, they walk clumsily.

Like that of the pond ducks, the breeding headquarters of the pochards is in the western and northern prairie country, though the ring-neck also breeds east to the Atlantic coast, while the greater scaup is mainly an Alaskan breeder in this hemisphere. When the birds arrive on their nesting grounds in the spring, only a few of them are already mated. Most courtship takes place in the north. The displays in this courtship seem somewhat simpler than those of the pond ducks. Several head postures are most characteristic: in the canvasback, for example, they include throwing the head backward until the crown touches the back and the throat points skyward, and then bringing the head back to the normal position, the bird meanwhile uttering low notes; stretching the head and neck upward; and a crouching, threatening pose. When several males are displaying before a female she may spring into the air and lead them on a courtship flight similar to that of the pond ducks but usually less graceful.

Once the pair is formed, the behavior pattern follows the broad outline of that of the pond ducks, but with modifications. The male accompanies the female while she is choosing a territory—which may be only an area of open water, for the diving ducks do not need a resting place on land—and also stays with her while she chooses a nest site. While the female is laying her eggs, the male waits nearby for her to rejoin him, but by the time incubation starts he severs his relations with her and she continues her nest duties alone.

The nests of the pochards are of two types: that of the ring-neck and the scaups is located, like that of the pond ducks, in a hollow scratched in the ground; that of the canvasback and the redhead is a substantial nest of dead reeds placed above water or mud in standing reeds. A full clutch generally comprises from seven to fifteen eggs, usually olive or buff, and darker in color than those of most pond ducks. The clutch is not only subject to individual variations in size, but may include eggs from more than one female which have been laid in the same nest. The redhead is especially prone to do this, even laying in the nests of other species. Nests with mixed clutches are not uncommon and one nest was reported to have contained sixteen eggs, as follows: redhead, five; canvasback, two; mallard, five; shoveller, four. The female sits for from twenty-two to twenty-four days, when the downy young emerge. This is usually somewhat later in the season than the hatching of the early-nesting pond ducks. The female leads her brood to open water, where the fledglings feed at the surface for a week or two, and then begin diving for their food like the adults. Sometimes a brood is augmented by lost or strayed fledglings from other broods until it may be twice its original size. After some two or two and a half months—somewhat longer than with the pond ducks—the young diving ducks reach the flying state. Unlike the pond ducks, the female pochards abandon their offspring some time before they can fly, and go through their moult, losing their wing quills and becoming flightless for three or four weeks.

The broods of diving ducks are raised in open water and ordinarily do not seek the protection of vegetation when danger threatens, nor does the female use the broken-wing ruse for decoying enemies from nest or eggs as often as does the pond duck. The broods of flightless young pochards, left to their own devices, tend to gather together in large bands on open water, and once they gain their wings begin to move about from marsh to marsh. Most of them do not migrate at this time, but seem to await the mass fall exodus from the north. The migrating flocks may be large, moving in long, wavy lines, blunt-angled flocks, or compact masses.

To go back to the male who abandons the female as she starts incubation: he then joins others of his sex in flocks on areas of open water. Sometimes birds from a considerable area gather on the favorite lake. They moult there on the open water, and do not seek the concealment of the marshes during the few weeks when they are flightless; rather the number of birds increases until the flocks or rafts contain thousands of birds. A few females, perhaps non-breeders, join these flocks, but most of the females moult later, having been delayed by family affairs, and seem to spend their flightless period skulking in the marshes.

Finally, full-winged, the birds start south, and a variety of migration patterns emerges. For the most part the ring-neck goes down the Mississippi Valley; the canvasback and the redhead go to both coasts, the canvasback especially favoring estuaries where the water is fresh from inflowing rivers, while the greater scaup winters in salt water off both coasts and the lesser scaup is widespread in our southern states.

Except for the ring-neck, the great rafts of these birds that gather on the waters of their wintering grounds are characteristic. In these flocks the harsh, churring calls of the females are sometimes heard, but the males are usually silent at this season. These wintering birds continue to feed by diving in water up to about ten feet deep, their dives usually lasting less than half a minute. Most species dive for aquatic vegetation, among which wild celery is a favorite, especially of the canvasback. The tastes of the greater scaup differ somewhat; when on the coasts it feeds almost entirely on shellfish, especially young mussels.

The wintering grounds of scaup, canvasback and redheads are among our most famous wildfowling areas, especially the stretch of coast from Chesapeake Bay to Currituck Sound in North Carolina. Normally most of these ducks feed in the morning and late in the afternoon, but in areas much shot over they have changed to night feeding, which allows them to visit their feeding places in peace and to rest far out on open water during the day. The characteristic picture of a wildfowler after pochards is that of a gunner crouched in a blind on some point, his decoys anchored just right, hoping for weather rough enough to make the canvasback forsake their safe offshore resting places, swing by his point, and come to his decoys.

116]

The males of this group are fairly easily recognized. The male canvasback, about twenty-four inches long, has a white back and a reddish-brown head with a long, sloping forehead. The redhead, slightly smaller, has a gray back and a reddish head with a sharply rising forehead. The greater scaup, about twenty inches long, has a black head and a gray back so pale that in the distance it appears white. The lesser scaup is similar but smaller, being about eighteen inches long. The ring-necked duck has a black head, black back, gray flanks and a white triangle pointing up from the breast in front of the wing. The females are generally duller, but the two female scaups have one distinctive characteristic—a white patch in front of the eye.

Redhead

More than any other of our ducks, the redhead (Plate 62) has the habit of depositing its eggs in other ducks' nests, not only in the nests of its near relative, the canvasback, which builds a similar, substantial nest of dead reeds above the water in dense vegetation, but also in the nests of such other species as the scaup and ruddy duck, mallard and shoveller. This recalls the habits of a South American duck that habitually lays its eggs in other ducks' nests and seems to be well on the way to becoming as much of a social parasite as the cowbird.

In breeding season and in winter the redhead lives in much the same areas as the canvasback. But in winter the big flocks usually separate and the redhead's greater tolerance for salty water in the estuaries and coastal bays often keeps the two species in different though adjacent areas. The curiosity common to many birds is well illustrated by the success of a method called tolling, often used in earlier days to decoy swimming flocks of redheads and canvasbacks within range of a wildfowl gunner on the shore. This was done by training a dog to run about and play, partly concealed, at the water's edge. This would attract the ducks' attention and they would come swimming in to see what was happening. Under the direction of the hidden gunner, the dog showed himself less and less as he moved about, and this would tempt the birds to come closer until finally they were within range. Similarly a rag, waved above a concealed hunter, may sometimes so intrigue swimming ducks that they will swing within shotgun range of the shore and the blind.

Ring-necked Duck

Until recent years the ring-necked duck (Plate 66) was considered a rare and little-known bird. When J. C. Phillips published *A Natural History of the Ducks* in 1923, he mapped its chief breeding range as a narrow band extending from just west of the Great Lakes to Athabasca in Northern Alberta. Now we know that the bird also breeds from Maine to British Columbia and in the West occasionally to California. This misconception was the result of at least two factors. The sportsmen and gunners whose records supplied us with much of our early information concerning the status of ducks often confused the ring-neck with the scaup. In addition, the ring-neck actually seems to have become more common and to have extended its range in recent years, especially in the Northeast.

Fresh-water ponds and smaller lakes are the ring-necked duck's haunts both in summer and winter, so that in winter it must move south. Unlike many of our waterfowl of the interior, the ring-neck does not spread out to our coasts in migration but funnels down the Mississippi Valley to its main wintering grounds in the United States, the states bordering the Gulf of Mexico.

In the spring the ring-neck migrates north in small flocks. Pairing evidently takes place late; the many flocks I have seen each spring on the shallow, weedy ponds of the Midwest show little evidence of courtship or of mating. Apparently this is delayed until they reach their breeding grounds, where the female builds her nest on swampy ground near the water.

Canvasback

Today the bird watchers outnumber the wildfowl gunners. Nevertheless, it is appropriate to introduce the canvasback from the sportsman's viewpoint. This bird, the most famous of wild ducks, remains the epicure's first choice as a table bird. Gone are the days, however, when a pair of canvasbacks brought up to eight dollars in the New York or Boston market. The sportsman, too, no longer regards a large bag as essential to a successful day's shoot, being content if he can get a brace of canvasbacks.

The prairie marshes, especially those of western Canada, are the nurseries of most canvasbacks. Like the redhead, they there build a well-constructed, substantial nest among rushes over water. The canvasback's stay in the marshes is a long one, for it is a hardy bird, migrating north early, and leaving late in the autumn. The most famous of its wintering places are on our Atlantic coast from Maryland to North Carolina on such waters as

Chesapeake Bay and Pamlico Sound, where they outnumber all other species. There the rivers, flowing into deep bays, fill the inner reaches with brackish water, more to the taste of the canvasback than salt water, and there the wild celery flourishes. There are other important wintering areas for this bird on the Gulf of Mexico coast and on the Pacific coast south into Mexico.

Greater Scaup Duck

As our knowledge of waterfowl has increased and become more precise, it has become evident that we know less about where the greater scaup nests in North America than we thought we did. It is a widely distributed breeding bird in the far north of the Old World, but in the New World definite breeding data outside the Alaska area are scant and mostly doubtful. Some earlier records failed to differentiate the greater from the lesser scaup, or the greater scaup from the ring-neck. A further complication is the fact that the greater scaup present in an area during the summer are not necessarily breeding birds. Numbers of non-breeding birds spend the summer in coastal areas far from any known breeding locality.

In migration and during the winter the greater scaup is a common species on our Atlantic coast, especially off New England, in the eastern Great Lakes area, and on the Pacific coast. Thus it follows a long migration route. No birds banded on their breeding grounds have been recovered. There have, however, been some long-range recoveries of birds banded on their wintering grounds. Individuals banded in Oregon have been recovered in New York, and others banded in New York have been found in Washington and in British Columbia.

Away from the breeding grounds most of the greater scaup go to salt water. There they feed largely by diving for small shellfish, a change from their largely vegetable diet of the summer. On our coasts the greater scaup are very gregarious birds, gathering in rafts of thousands. This habit has earned them one of their local names, "raft" duck, which they share with such other ducks as the redhead and canvasback. In summer the greater scaup also nests in loose colonies. In the Old World, their many nests built near together in little hollows in the ground have been compared to the colonies of eider ducks.

Lesser Scaup Duck

The lesser scaup (Plate 67) is much commoner and more widely distributed than the greater scaup.

Like many of our ducks, it nests in the West, chiefly on the prairies of our northwestern states, in Canada, and northward through the Mackenzie Valley to the Arctic Ocean. In winter it is widely distributed over the southern half of the United States, on smaller fresh-water ponds that stay open all winter, and also on the coasts. The greatest wintering concentration of these birds is in the area bordering the Gulf of Mexico from the Mississippi River delta to the mouth of the Rio Grande.

These little "bluebills," as they are also called, leave the northern marshes with the freeze-up. One mass exodus from a Manitoba lake was described as a spectacular sight, with the flocks of birds awing in the evening, as the flight started, recalling starlings. Groups of from forty to three hundred birds were everywhere, as far as the eye could see, and when darkness fell and the birds were no longer visible, they could be heard passing overhead.

Besides the five species of the pochard group occurring in North America, there are three more species that have been recorded, as stragglers out of their normal range, on rare occasions. These are the common pochard, Baer's pochard, and the tufted duck, all from the northern part of the Old World.

Sea Ducks

The species comprising the group called sea ducks present a variety of contrasts in habits and habitats. In general, however, they are heavily-built diving birds living on animal food and spending part of the year on salt water. They are a northern group which we share with the Old World. Almost all of our sea ducks breed north of the United States on fresh-water ponds of the tundra, northern forests and prairies. In winter, most of them come within reach of our bird students, but some never move south of the Bering Sea area. A few winter on our larger lakes, but most species migrate to coastal waters. Some of them, but not all, then gather in large flocks. Clumsy in walking, they sleep on the water and rarely come ashore. Some species need a long, running take-off to get on the wing, but others rise easily. In late winter, while still in their winter quarters, the sea ducks begin their courtship displays of head postures, chasing and diving, accompanied by whistling, cooing, or grunted calls. As a group these birds are normally rather silent, except for old-squaws, which talk constantly. In the nesting area the female seeks out a site on the ground, among rocks or in a hollow tree, according to the species. Here she lays her clutch of from four to ten eggs, which may be olive, buff, pink or pale green. After about four weeks' incubation the downy young hatch. Those in holes in trees jump to the ground or into the water and the female alone tends them. By the time incubation has started, her mate has left her, gathering with groups of his own sex and moulting into dull eclipse plumage. In this stage the males of at least some species are flightless, but they can fly again long before the female moults.

Sea duck males are easily recognized, most of them having very distinctive color patterns; but some of the females are less easily identified. The drake goldeneye, about twenty-three inches long, is a black-and-white duck with a black head. The common goldeneye has a round white spot in front of its eye. The Barrow's goldeneye has a triangular or crescent-shaped spot in front of its eye. The females are smaller, and grayish and white in color, with brown heads.

The bufflehead is a small black-and-white duck, about thirteen to fifteen inches long, the drake having a big white patch that extends from eye to eye across the back of the otherwise black head, the female having a small white ear patch on its black head. The old-squaws are also small black-and-white ducks, the drake having long, pointed, central tail feathers and in winter a dark brown patch on each side of its white head.

The harlequin duck, about sixteen inches long, is slaty in general color and the male has an elaborate pattern of white marks including a white crescent in front of its eye, a white ear spot with a white line back of it, and a more or less complete white collar around the lower part of its neck. The female is a brownish bird with three white spots on its face. The extinct Labrador duck has black underparts and back, white wings, and black-and-white head.

The male eiders are also predominantly black-and-white birds. The Steller's eider, about eighteen inches long, has buff-brown underparts, black-and-white upperparts, and a white head with patches of green. The common eider, about twenty-six inches long, has white upperparts and breast, black underparts and crown, and green patches on the sides of its head. The king eider, about twenty-five inches long, is mostly white in the forepart, from the foreback and breast to the head, with a bluish wash over its crown and green in its face. The back part of its body is mostly black. Conspicuous, fleshy, orange-colored projections run from the bill onto each side of its forehead. The spectacled eider, about twenty-two inches long, has mostly grayish-brown underparts, the upperparts and neck being predominantly white; top and sides of the head are green, with a large, black-edged, white area around the eye. The female eiders are dull brownish and barred.

The drakes of the three species of scoters are from twenty to twenty-three inches long and are mostly black. The common scoter has an orange area on the base of its bill. The white-winged scoter has a conspicuous white patch in the back edge of the wing. The surf scoter has a white patch on the top of the head and another on the back of the head. The female scoters are dull brownish-black birds.

Goldeneyes

The two goldeneyes and the bufflehead form a group of very closely related species in which the male is pied black and white and has a rather large head. Their summer homes are largely on the wooded ponds and lakes in the northern part of this continent. Typically they nest in holes in trees, from which the young, after hatching, jump, and fall to the ground or into the water. They winter on both of our coasts and on inland waters, some of them remaining as far north as they can find open water. They seldom gather into large flocks, but usually move and feed in parties of a dozen or so. They feed by diving for their food in shallow water or near shore, living largely on such animal matter as crustaceans, mollusks and insects. When they flush they get into the air more quickly and more easily than most sea ducks. Though some are shot, in general goldeneyes are not highly regarded as game birds, because they are small and less abundant than some other ducks. Nesting for the most part north of settlement, goldeneyes and buffleheads are seen by most bird watchers only when they come south, and are thus true winter ducks.

Common Goldeneye

When the common goldeneye, or the American goldeneye as it is sometimes called here, springs into the air, it usually flies high above the water and its wings make a whistling noise louder than that of any other duck. Thus it has earned the name of "whistler." In the United States the species winters on both coasts, on some of the Great Lakes and, less commonly, on unfrozen rivers. As spring approaches and migration northward is about to begin, the male courts the female by fluffing out its head feathers, stretching its head forward and then throwing it backward until the crown touches the rump, and by kicking up spurts of water. Soon the birds move northward to their breeding grounds on ponds and lakes in the northern forests from Maine and Newfoundland to Alaska, as well as across northern Europe and Asia.

Barrow's Goldeneye

The Barrow's goldeneye is so similar to the common goldeneye that, aside from a triangular instead of a round white patch in front of the eye of the full-plumaged drake, there are few characteristics by which to distinguish between the two. They are similar in habits, too, but very different in distribution. The Barrow's goldeneye breeds only in several widely separated localities: in the mountains of the western United States and Canada, on the Labrador coast, and in Greenland and Iceland. This range is mostly outside of the chief breeding range of the common goldeneye. Where there are trees with cavities in them the Barrow's goldeneye nests in these hollows, but north of the tree line it makes its home among rocks or even on the ground under bushes. In winter some of the Barrow's goldeneyes of the western mountains move to the Pacific coast or southward to unfrozen streams, while some of the Labrador birds move south on the Atlantic coast as far as New England.

Bufflehead

The bufflehead is a plump little black-and-white bird that floats buoyantly and is continually hopping up from the water, flying a short distance, and dropping in again with a splash. At the end of the winter, while still on its wintering grounds, the male begins to display, puffing out its head feathers, cocking up its tail, reaching its head out over the water and then tossing it backward, and engaging in short flights and chases. On its breeding grounds, extending from central Canada to Alaska and our northwest states, the pairs settle on little woodland ponds and lakes, where the female can find a hole in a tree in which to nest. In winter it moves south along inland waterways far enough to find open water, and to our coasts from Alaska and Maine southward.

Old-squaw

The old-squaw's home is in the Arctic, where it nests on all the land fringing the Arctic Ocean, and on the islands therein, in both hemispheres. Sometimes it nests by the salt water, sometimes near tundra ponds. Only the few people who live in the far north know the bird as a breeding species. Most of us think of it as a winter duck that lives on the coasts as far south as the states of North Carolina and Washington, and on the Great Lakes. Most ducks seem stolid creatures, but not the old-squaw. It is a lively, restless bird, feeding in open water and rarely coming to land, moving about in irregular flocks or in long, straggling lines, the flocks twisting and swirling as they go, continually settling and rising again, and always the males are calling. These calls have given them their New England name of "cockawee"; the names "old-squaw" and "old wife" come from their fancied resemblance to a group of women chattering.

The old-squaw dives to get its food, chiefly mollusks and crustaceans, and has been recorded as descending to such astonishing depths as more than two hundred feet below the surface. On the Great Lakes, where commercial fisheries may use nets up to eight thousand feet long, the old-squaws caught and drowned in a single net at one haul have numbered over a thousand, and in New York State single hauls of five to six thousand have been reported.

Harlequin Duck

The harlequin ducks are interesting birds whose vivid, parti-colored plumage has given them their name. Along our northeastern coasts they are sometimes called "Lords and Ladies." Their summer haunts are almost unique among ducks: mountain streams near which they nest, under bushes or in hollows among the rocks. The range of the species is wide but discontinuous, like that of the Barrow's goldeneye; one population of harlequins nests in the mountains of western North America, others in Labrador, Greenland and Iceland. In winter the eastern birds move south along the Atlantic coast only as far as Maine, while most of the western birds move to the Pacific coast. There they frequent the wildest, rockiest shorelines available, where the rollers break into surf on headlands, islets and hidden reefs. The harlequins feed by diving, being equally at home in the waters of rapid streams, where they seem to prefer the vicinity of waterfalls, and the tumbling waters of the ocean surf. In fresh water, insect larvae are probably important in their diet, but in salt water crustaceans and mollusks form their chief food.

Labrador Duck

The last Labrador duck seen alive was shot on Long Island, New York, in 1875. The species evidently bred in a very restricted range in the extreme northeastern part of our continent, wintering in an equally restricted range south along the Atlantic coast to New Jersey. Probably man's activities on the breeding grounds, as well as in its wintering range, exterminated it. In 1952 there were only fifty-one known museum specimens of this extinct bird.

Eiders

Eider ducks are big, stout sea ducks of far northern waters. In the summer they come south only as far as Maine in the United States, and in winter usually only a little farther. The drakes of all four species are conspicuously black and white and have a peculiar green color on the head. Three species reverse our concept of the usual color pattern of animals, the black of their abdomens contrasting with the pale color of their upperparts. The females are duller: brown, or barred brown and black. The ranges of the four species offer interesting contrasts. Two of them are restricted to the Bering Sea area; the two others are circumpolar, one of these nesting by salt water, the other by Arctic ponds. They all winter on the sea, usually in flocks, and dive for their food, which is chiefly mollusks, crustaceans and echinoderms.

Steller's Eider

The normal range of the Steller's eider is limited, including only the shores and islands of the Bering Sea and the adjacent Arctic Ocean. It breeds in the more northern areas and withdraws southward in winter. Strangely enough, some individuals winter off the north coast of Scandinavia, far from any of their known breeding areas. It makes tundra ponds its summer habitat, nesting on nearby flats, while non-breeding birds may frequent shallow bays and river mouths. But in winter the flocks feed off rough, rocky coasts and icebound shores, diving for mollusks and crustaceans.

Common Eider

The common eider (Plate 68), the largest of our ducks, is circumpolar in distribution, nesting along all the lands that fringe the Arctic Sea. On the Arctic Islands and in the Atlantic it extends its nesting range southward as far as Maine and the British Isles. Truly a sea bird, it is rarely found on fresh water. Not only does it spend the winter on the sea, but it almost always nests by salt water (typically in colonies on offshore islands where the nests are safe from predation by the Arctic fox), and it is to the sea that the young go. What care the young eiders are given is uncertain. Only the female incubates the eggs, and she has often been accused of being a bad mother. However, the fledglings some-

times seem to make their way independently to the sea, and there join any female who will look after them.

The blanket of down, pulled piecemeal from the female's breast and matted into a lining for the nest, is a common feature of most ducks' nests. That of the eider duck has assumed especial importance to man as an article of commerce. Its elasticity, lightness, and insulating quality make it a fine filler for comforters, sleeping bags and padded jackets. In the Old World, especially in Norway and Iceland, the birds are protected and have become very tame. The colonies in which they breed are preserved and improved and each year a crop of down is harvested. The female replaces the nest lining once and even a second time if two crops of the down are taken, and this does not seem to hinder the successful hatching of the eggs. Attempts have recently been made to introduce this industry into the American northland.

Even in winter the common eider ducks do not come far south, most of them rarely passing beyond the Aleutians or the New England coast. The birds that in other areas are called Northern, Hudson Bay and Pacific eider are only local varieties of the common eider and have similar habits. In winter they live at sea, usually in sizable flocks, and dive offshore for their food, of which mussels form an important part. Like scoters, eiders used to be commonly hunted along our northeastern coast, but in bad weather it necessitated rough boat work.

King Eider

The king eider is also a circumpolar species, but presents some interesting contrasts to the common eider. Both are widespread nesters on our Arctic coastal land, but in the Old World Arctic the king eider is abundant only in certain highly localized areas. Unlike the common eider, it nests not by the sea but by fresh-water ponds in the barrens, and it is to these ponds that the king eider takes its young. Though it does not nest so far south in the Atlantic as the common eider, big flocks of both birds occupy about the same range in winter, though of the two it is usually the king eider that is recorded on inland waters such as the Great Lakes. The common eider feeds in waters of moderate depth, up to thirty feet perhaps, but the king eider is said to go regularly to depths of sixty feet in search of shellfish and crustaceans, and one extreme dive of 180 feet has been reported.

The king eider, like the common eider, is very abundant in summer in the New World Arctic. Its migrations reflect its liking for the sea. These northern birds cannot fly directly to their southern goal without going overland. So across the immense stretch of the northern continental coastline the migration is approximately east and west, the birds going to Davis Strait or to Bering Strait before turning south. Along the western Arctic coast the long lines of migrating eiders are especially conspicuous. In the spring the flocks coming up through the Bering Strait turn eastward, even flying on a southeastern course, to get, for example, to their breeding grounds on Coronation Gulf. The migration continues well into June, and by July flocks are returning "south" again, following a northwest course to Bering Strait. It would seem that the species barely reaches its nesting grounds before the return migration starts. The males that have finished their share in reproduction probably leave their mates and the nest and go at once to the Bering Sea to join other males, and there go through their moult.

Spectacled Eider

Like the Steller's eider, the spectacled eider nests in the northern Bering Sea area and winters south to the Aleutians. For nesting it seeks tundra ponds and hides its nest in nearby tussocks of grass. For the rest of the year it favors shallow, muddy coastal waters, and in addition to mollusks, insects and other aquatic animals, consumes enough aquatic vegetation to amount to about one quarter of its diet, a preference unusual in the eiders.

Scoters

These include three large, stoutly-built species of diving ducks, with the males mostly plain black and the females dusky. The drakes of two of them have small white patches in their plumage, their only bright colors being the yellows and pinks of their bills. These birds breed in north temperate or Arctic regions, two of them in both hemispheres. They make their nests on the ground next to fresh-water ponds but spend the rest of the year on salt water. In the United States they winter off both coasts and occasionally get inland to the Great Lakes and other bodies of fresh water where large numbers of non-breeding birds may also spend the summer away from their breeding grounds. The spring courtship displays of the drakes include such movements as lowering the head and rushing across the water, and bowing the head or stretching it upward, the bird meanwhile uttering groaning, grunting or whistling notes. Chasing and short flights may also be a part of the display, as well as whirligig and

circular "dances" in which the birds swim around and around. At least one scoter, the white-winged, has a dashing courtship flight in which several males pursue one female.

These birds migrate in big flocks and large numbers gather to rest and sleep on the water. However, they usually spread out in smaller groups to feed. This they do by diving, often in water thirty or more feet deep, with dives of sixty-five feet having been recorded. Mussels and other shellfish gathered from the bottom comprise most of their salt-water diet. In summer, when the birds are living on fresh water, it is probable that aquatic insect larvae and vegetation become important in their food.

These birds take flight with an effort, needing a running start to get into the air but, once awing, their flight is direct and swift even though it may appear heavy and labored. They fly freely from one mussel bed to another, or to a favorite resting place on the water. They sleep on the water, too, rarely coming ashore, and when they do they walk awkwardly. Locally scoters are called coots (although not related to the coot described on page 166), and coot-shooting was once a popular sport off the New England coast. The rigorous conditions of shooting from a dory on the open ocean in fall weather added zest for those who liked the sea. Gunners take advantage of two peculiar traits of scoters: when the birds fly between a boat and the shore, a gunshot or even a shout may cause them to swing away from the shore and toward the boat; when they fly along a broken coast they usually follow the shoreline but may cross certain headlands at special places. There gunners have learned to lie in wait for them. When they are too high to shoot, a shout from the gunner may quickly bring them down to a lower altitude.

White-winged Scoter

As a nesting bird the white-winged scoter is comparatively well known. It shares the great nurseries of the pond ducks and pochards in the northwestern part of the continent, from our northern states across the prairies of Canada and the vast Mackenzie area to the Arctic Ocean. It is also widespread in the northern part of the Old World, where it is known as the velvet scoter. In the spring the white-winged scoter is the last of the ducks to arrive on the breeding grounds, but its courtship flights, with a number of males chasing a female, are as spirited as those of the pond ducks. It is also the last of the ducks to nest, and the female is laying her eggs when young mallards and pintails in the same marsh have already hatched. As regards most of the prairie ducks, the time of hatching and the time when the immature birds attain the ability to fly varies greatly from brood to brood, indicating individual variation in the time of nesting. In the case of the white-winged scoter, however, there is a remarkable synchronization in hatching dates and in the time, some two to two and a half months later, when the young start to fly. Evidently, with the late start in nesting, any fledgling delayed in getting on the wing would be caught in the early freeze-up in the north.

Soon after hatching, the female white-winged scoter takes her brood to open water and at this time either the broods merge or motherless young join any accessible brood, increasing its size greatly. This behavior, not uncommon in some of the other sea ducks, seems very pronounced in the white-winged scoter and as many as eighty-five fledglings, all under two weeks of age, have been reported with one female. As with most ducks, the males leave the females by incubation time. Some of the drakes may then gather in parties on nearby lakes to moult. Others apparently go to the sea, for in the north great numbers of adult drakes are found in flocks on coastal waters in July. When the birds come to our coasts, the large flocks travel in long lines or in wedge-shaped or massed formations. When feeding, these ducks tend to stay offshore, but sometimes they appear about estuaries and inshore where muddy mussel banks abound.

Surf Scoter

The surf scoter is entirely a North American species, breeding in the far northwest. It is a surprising fact that comparatively few of its nests have been found, for in the winter the bird is common enough on both of our coasts and often turns up on the Great Lakes. As its name implies, this bird likes rough water, feeding about reefs and islets and near the shore where the surf is breaking. This habit contrasts with the common scoter's preference for quiet water.

Common Scoter

The common scoter or, as it is called in America, the American scoter, is a bird of the northern part of the Old World and in North America breeds chiefly in the far northwest—the Alaska–Mackenzie area. In winter it favors quiet stretches of open ocean off both coasts, avoiding the rough waters of tide rips and the breakers around islands and reefs.

Mergansers

The mergansers are the only ducks physically adapted to chasing and catching active prey. The most obvious of these adaptations are the elongated body, with big feet far to the rear, and the long, narrow bill with toothlike serrations along the sides for holding such slippery morsels as fish. This last has given the merganser such local names as "sawbill" and "fish duck."

We have three breeding species of mergansers, two of which we share with the Old World. In all, seven species are distributed in the North Temperate Zone, in southern South America and the Aukland Islands. The habitat of our three species is not the marshes and weedy sloughs favored by the pond ducks, nor yet the Arctic tundra ponds, but clear open water in which fish live. One species, the red-breasted merganser, may even nest on the edge of salt water as well as by lakes and rivers.

In the spring the displays staged by drake mergansers include such activities as stretching out the head and neck, with mouth open; rising up in the water; touching the breast with the bill and suddenly kicking up spurts of water astern; splashing and chasing; and in crested species much raising of the crest. Sometimes as the male displays, the female mirrors some of his actions in a less highly developed way. The formation of pairs follows, and then the female makes her nest in a hole in a tree, among rocks, or on the ground, the site varying individually and with the species. The usual number of eggs in a clutch is from nine to seventeen, though, as in most ducks, this is variable; in color the eggs are whitish, yellowish or greenish. The female alone sits on the eggs, doing so for about twenty-eight to thirty-two days, a longer incubation period than that of most ducks. When the downy young hatch in their hole in a tree they may stay in the nest for a day or so, then jump out and fall to the ground, after which it seems that the female alone looks after them, though the old literature contains references to the drake's being in attendance at this time. A brood of young mergansers, surprised in open water, may go scuttling away over the surface of the water; hence the name "flappers" applied to them at this stage. Often they go ashore and hide among the vegetation. The drake meanwhile has left his family for good, undergone the moult into eclipse plumage, lost his flight feathers and become flightless for a time.

Our three mergansers are all hardy birds and in winter migrate southward little farther than is necessary to find open water, though here too there is a species variation, one kind going chiefly to salt water, another preferring fresh water. In autumn the big flocks of the larger mergansers are seen flying low over the water, their long bodies, small heads and thin bills giving them a characteristic rakish outline. Not until well along in the winter do the males regain their full breeding plumage.

Summer and winter their food is the same—mostly fish. As these birds are agile enough to catch fish, on some salmon and trout streams they are in disrepute with fishermen and special regulations have allowed their destruction. However, it must be remembered that the web of life on any waterway is too complex to enable one to say that simply destroying a predator will automatically benefit some other species. On certain waterways merganser control may be necessary, but action should be taken only after investigation has demonstrated its advisability.

Though the mergansers in general are not highly regarded as sporting birds, on our northeastern coast they are shot and eaten regularly. The chief characteristics of the species in the United States are as follows: the male of the hooded merganser, about nineteen inches long, has a large fanlike crest with a big white patch in it, the rest of its head being greenish black. The American merganser male, about twenty-seven inches long, has a salmon-pink breast and belly and a greenish-black head without a crest. The red-breasted merganser male, about twenty-six inches long, has a reddish band across the breast and a greenish-black head with a long, ragged crest. The females of all three species of mergansers are grayish birds with reddish heads and ragged crests.

Hooded Merganser

The hooded merganser is not at all closely related to the wood duck, but it shares with it a number of characteristics: its favorite haunts are watery woodlands and woodland-enclosed waterways; the drakes of both birds are among the most beautifully colored and patterned of any waterfowl; and both species choose a hole in a tree as their favorite nesting place. Both are birds of the Temperate Zone, and the hooded merganser nests widely in the easternmost states as well as across the continent in the north. Sometimes the two species quarrel over nest holes, and mixed sets of eggs have been found containing both the white, round eggs of the hooded merganser and the greenish and more elongated eggs of the wood duck.

In autumn the northern hooded mergansers move south to spend the winter on the inland waters of our southernmost states. Unlike the other

mergansers, they seem to have little difficulty in rising from the surface of water, but like them they are expert swimmers and divers.

Red-breasted Merganser

The red-breasted merganser is the most northern of our mergansers, nesting across the continent on the edge of the Arctic south to the northeastern states, as well as in Greenland and the northern part of the Old World. As its far northern habitat suggests, the bird does not nest in holes in trees but on the ground, hiding its nest among bushes. A hardy bird, it differs from the other two mergansers in preferring to spend the winters on salt water off our coasts as far north as Alaska and Maine. A few of these birds winter on fresh water from the Great Lakes southward, but it is the American merganser that is seen more commonly on fresh water at this season.

The flocks like to locate schools of fish and then in rough formation drive their panic-stricken prey into the shallows, or into some small pool where they may be caught more easily.

The dive of the red-breasted merganser may start with a neat, acrobatic leap that takes it clear of the water before it plunges headfirst into the depths, or it may disappear underwater without apparent effort. Evidently it does not dive deep—about eighteen feet being the maximum recorded depth—and its dives usually last for slightly less than half a minute. Like the goosander, the red-breasted merganser sometimes feeds not by diving but by swimming along in the shallows with only its head submerged. This species is the most aquatic of our mergansers, but like the others it likes to rest on the shore or on the ice, especially in the spring.

Common Merganser or Goosander

The common merganser, goosander, or American merganser, as it has been called in this country to distinguish it from the slightly different forms of the same species in the Old World, is our largest merganser. It nests across the continent and southward from about the timber line to well into the United States. Thus its nesting range overlaps that of both of the other mergansers. For its nesting site it chooses a hole in a tree or a cliff, or a site among rocks or on the ground. When nesting is over and summer ends, most of these hardy birds move southward, but some winter as far north as the Great Lakes, preferring fresh to salt water. In the spring they move north early, and the pairs of birds, the drake looking huge with his salmon-pink and black plumage, are striking sights on the dark waters of ice-fringed rivers.

Ruddy Duck Group

The most unusual of our ducks is the little ruddy duck. Along with many other wildfowl it uses our interior sloughs and marshes as nesting grounds, though it also nests in central America and the West Indies. In winter ruddy ducks from more northern states migrate southward, along both coasts, to the southern states and to Mexico. A fresh-water duck on its nesting grounds, it also likes shallow brackish bays and estuaries on our coasts, in such places gathering in large flocks in the winter. There it continues to feed by diving, taking mainly aquatic vegetation and seeds as it did in the inland marshes, though it also consumes a fair amount of insects and other invertebrate animal material.

The male ruddy duck, about seventeen inches long, is mostly rufous, with a grayish belly, white cheeks and a black crown; the female is grayish brown, with a blackish cap and whitish cheeks. The ruddy duck's pose is distinctive enough to identify it, as it swims along low in the water with bill drawn back against its chest and often with its rather long, stiff tail cocked up. At nesting time the drake's courting antics include inflating the air sacs in his neck, slapping his bill against his puffed-out chest, kicking up spurts of water behind him, puffing out his back feathers and rising up and scooting across the surface of the water, all the while giving a variety of clucks and calls, none of which sounds like a quack. The female is almost completely silent, a characteristic unusual among the ducks. No nuptial flights are engaged in. This may be because of the difficulty the ruddy duck has in getting off the water; it needs a very long, pattering run before it can launch into its buzzing flight.

After pairs are formed, each builds a large, substantial nest, placing it among reeds standing in water since these birds move very awkwardly on land. In contrast with the nests of most ducks, little or no down is added as a lining. The female lays about eight whitish eggs; these are larger than those of a bird such as the canvasback, which is three times the size of the ruddy. The incubation period, however, is only twenty-one days, the same as that of the blue-winged teal. The hen alone sits on the eggs, but when she leads the downy ducklings off the nest, the male joins the party and helps care for the offspring, a habit not shared by any of our other ducks save perhaps the red-breasted merganser. The parents lead their young out into open water. When danger threatens, the parents neither feign injury nor fly off, but dive and swim away, leaving the young behind. When the ducklings are sufficiently grown the parents abandon their broods and undergo their late summer moult, losing the flight feathers for a time. The brilliant male assumes a lustreless, female-like plumage, which, unlike that of most ducks, is not quickly changed for bright breeding plumage but is worn through the winter until the nuptial plumage is regained in the spring.

Though the ruddy is one of the most distinctive of our ducks, it does have close relatives, other stiff-tailed ducks, scattered in tropical and temperate parts of the world. One of these, the masked duck of tropical America and the West Indies, occasionally strays into the United States.

CHAPTER 17

Chachalacas

THE chachalacas, guans and curassows comprise a family for which we have no English name. They are relatives of the pheasants, which they resemble in shape. Some are brownish and as large as a domestic fowl; others are black or black-and-white, have striking crests, and are nearly as large as turkeys. Their homes are in South and Central America and only one species, the chachalaca, lives as far north as the United States. The chachalaca is a brownish bird, about twenty-four inches long, which occurs in the lower Rio Grande Valley in the extreme south of Texas. It lives in forest and brushlands, moving about in flocks among the branches, feeding on fruit and berries and occasionally coming down to the ground. The male mounts, especially in the early morning, to the top of a tree or bush and utters loud, ringing calls of three or four syllables. It is this call which has given the bird its name (often shortened to "chacha"). Frequently when one bird calls, another will seem to answer, and soon the whole forest rings with the chorus. Presumably this calling is preliminary to the choosing of mates and breeding. Later the nest is built in the fork of a tree—often as much as thirty feet above the ground. Here the female lays three whitish eggs and sits on them for an incubation period of about twenty-two days. The chicks are down-covered at hatching and soon able to follow their parents. The chachalacas are not shy birds and their young are sometimes caught and raised by villagers.

CHAPTER 18

Ptarmigan and Grouse

GROUSE and ptarmigan belong to a family of northern climates. Of the eighteen known species ten occur in North America; two of these (both ptarmigan) are also found in Eurasia. Some of our grouse live exclusively on the ground in open country, while others spend a great deal of time in trees, especially in winter. When alarmed they often crouch motionless to escape observation, trusting that their coloration, which matches their background, will prevent discovery, and only when closely approached do they fly up with a loud whirring sound. The food of grouse and ptarmigan is mostly vegetable; in winter leaves, buds, twigs and, in some species, the needles of conifers, bulk large in their diet. Thus getting winter food is no problem; nevertheless several species make local migrations,

in some cases banding together in large flocks and traveling considerable distances. Another adaptation to winter is their common habit of burrowing into the snow to sleep, sheltered from cold and wind.

The courtship habits of the American grouse and ptarmigan vary greatly with the species. In some, pairs are formed and the males share certain of the family duties. In species that are polygamous the females come to mate on display grounds established by the males, then leave the males on the display grounds and perform all the family duties alone. The nests of the birds in this family are placed on the ground and usually contain from four to fourteen eggs, plain buff or buff richly marked with brown or blackish. The down-covered chicks are active from the time of hatching. Their wing feathers grow quickly and within two weeks they can make short flights. If enemies approach the brood or eggs, the parent often attempts to decoy them away by pretending to be crippled. The brood stays together as a covey into the autumn, and in some species these coveys may merge into large winter packs or bands.

Among the grouse are some of the most challenging game birds, birds that lie close, flush rapidly, offer difficult shots, lead the sportsman into pleasant surroundings and are good for eating. A puzzling phenomenon, especially to those who are trying to apply the principles of game management to these birds, is the fact that grouse populations fluctuate greatly. The birds will be common for two or three years and then scarce for several more, irrespective of the amount of hunting. Such factors as parasites, disease and weather all seem to have a part in these widespread fluctuations.

An aid to identifying grouse is the fact that when two or more species live in the same area, each usually prefers a different type of terrain.

Ptarmigan

There are four species of ptarmigan: two that are widespread in the Arctic; one, the red grouse, that lives only in the British Isles; and one, the white-tailed ptarmigan, that occurs only in the western mountains of America from Alaska to New Mexico. The three species of ptarmigan in America wear a brown or gray plumage, with white wings, in summer, and moult into a white plumage in winter to match the snow. The smallest of the group, the white-tailed ptarmigan, is about thirteen inches long and is distinguished from the other ptarmigans by its white tail. The willow ptarmigan, about sixteen inches long, is in summer a red-brown bird with a black tail. The rock ptarmigan, which is slightly smaller, is a gray-brown bird and in winter has a black mark from its bill to its eye, as well as a black tail.

In the Mackenzie Mountains of the Yukon in July I found the white-tailed ptarmigan females, with their broods of five or six young, common in the grassy meadows at the edge of timber and in the green glades among the dwarf spruces and firs. At this season the old males were solitary and were usually found higher up the treeless slopes, where the terrain was broken and rocky. Not only the adults but also the fledglings were feeding largely on a variety of leaves and fruits. Perhaps at a very early age the young eat insects, as do the young of many other vegetable-eating birds, but if so, they quickly change to the adult diet.

Evidently these birds have a vertical migration, moving up and down the mountains with the seasons, as does the rock ptarmigan, for local trappers told me that when the snow came and the birds had moulted from brown to white, they gathered in the valleys and fed on willow twigs and buds.

The home of the willow ptarmigan (Plate 74) is in the Arctic, north of the timber line, in both America and Eurasia. In spring these birds form pairs and nest on the barrens. They are rather unusual among grouse in that the male does not desert the female during incubation, but stays with her and joins in caring for the young. Young willow ptarmigan eat insects. The summer food of the adult consists of leaves and stems of plants, buds, and berries; when winter comes they eat twigs and buds of willow and aspen. They then gather into large flocks that often number hundreds and occasionally even thousands of birds. At this time some of the birds move south, the flocks looking like snowdrifts in motion. Some of these ptarmigan come as far as southern Canada, but only a few individuals straggle down into the United States.

The rock ptarmigan (Plate 72) lives throughout the Arctic barrens, often, as its name implies, favoring exposed and rocky situations. In the spring the winter flocks break up. Monogamous pairs are the rule, but before the eggs hatch, the cock bird leaves the hen and the territory and wanders away for a time. Later, when the nestlings are partly grown, he rejoins the covey and at about that point the coveys start to move to higher ground, where the vegetation appears and ripens later. Leaves and berries are the rock ptarmigan's main food at this period. With the coming of the snow the coveys, merging into larger bands, descend to the lower altitudes. During the winter they eat the buds and twigs of such plants as Arctic willows. Sometimes the birds even dig through the snow for their food. They sleep among boulders and crevices in the rocks and also dig snug sleeping places in the snow.

Sooty and Dusky Grouse

In our western mountains live two closely related, large-sized grouse, the sooty grouse of the coast ranges and the dusky grouse (Plate 69) of the Rocky Mountains. The dusky grouse, almost twenty inches long, is a dark gray bird with a slate-colored breast; the sooty grouse is much like it but has a gray band on the end of its black tail. Sometimes the two are grouped together under the name of blue grouse. These are tree grouse and their lives center around the conifers in which they spend the winter and on whose needles and buds they feed. They are not always found in the coniferous forests, however, for their seasonal vertical movements up and down the mountains take them into two other types of country. In the spring they move from the pines into the valleys at the lower edge of the timber and there nest in meadows and on brushy ground. As summer advances and the young grow, the old males leave the low country and move up to the open ridges above the timber. Here they gather in small bands and feed on berries. Later the females and fledglings join them there. In autumn they all leave the high, exposed ridges and move into the conifers in which they will perch and feed during the winter.

Such is the annual cycle of these two species of grouse, but they differ from each other in courtship and nesting habits. The sooty grouse perches high in a tree, on a branch perhaps fifty or sixty feet above the ground. Here he utters a series of low-pitched hoots, so powerful that it is said that it can be heard for as much as several miles. This hooting also has a curious ventriloquistic quality, sounding close when the bird is really far away, and far off when it is close. The sooty grouse also gives his courtship display on this lofty perch. The male dusky grouse, on the other hand, calls and displays on the ground, but his series of hoots, while otherwise similar, is feeble and is barely audible a hundred yards away. This hooting is presumably the male grouse's notification to the forest at large, and particularly to the females, that he is on his display ground and is ready to mate. When a female approaches he gives his full display. His tail is erected and spread, the air sacs on the sides of the neck—yellow in the sooty grouse and red in the dusky—are inflated fully, and the surrounding feathers are spread so that their white bases form a snowy circle around the brilliantly colored sacs. The red combs over each eye are inflated with blood until they nearly meet over the crown. Then the cock grouse nods his head a few times, lowers it and as a climax makes a short run with trailing wings and gives a deep call. Despite this elaborate exhibition, the female often appears quite unimpressed as she wanders about nearby.

After mating, the female scratches out a hollow on the ground and lines it scantily with leaves to form a nest. Here she lays her six to ten pale buff, brown-spotted eggs and sits on them until the young hatch. When the chicks are large enough to fly the mother grouse leads them to the high ridges. I have seen these birds in the summer at timber line in the Mackenzie Mountains, with the young eating insects in addition to berries. At this season they were foolishly tame, but later in the season they make fine game birds. In open country they usually lie well and when flushed fly straight and steadily, although quite slowly. When found among high timber on rugged slopes, the birds may flush out of the tops of tall firs or go flying away among protective tree trunks.

Spruce and Franklin's Grouse

The spruce grouse (Plate 70) is the "fool hen" of the north woods, that vast belt of spruce and pine that extends across North America from New England to central Alaska. In the western mountains from southern Alaska to Oregon and Montana lives its counterpart, the Franklin's grouse. The spruce grouse is about sixteen inches long, and the male has mottled gray and black upperparts, black-and-white underparts and a black, rufous-tipped tail. The Franklin's grouse is similar but the upper tail coverts are conspicuously tipped with white and the tail is black to the tip. Only in remote, little settled areas are these species common, for they are truly wilderness birds and retreat before civilization. From personal observation I can corroborate the many stories of travelers who reported that these grouse can be snared with a noose on the end of a stick or can be knocked down with a club. In the summer they walk about in clearings, glades and forest edges throughout the spruce country, and feed on berries, but in winter they retreat deep into the spruce forests, where they perch, feed on the needles and buds of the trees, and sleep on the branches.

In courtship, the male spruce grouse announces himself with a noisy fluttering of wings as he flies from branch to branch or as he walks up an inclined tree trunk. He also gives a display like that of a turkey-cock, strutting about with raised tail and drooping wings.

After mating, the female seeks a dry, open slope, where she hollows out a little depression in the ground at the base of a small spruce tree, lines it thinly, and deposits in it her four to seven eggs. With their bold markings of rich brown on a ground color of brownish buff, these are among the most beautiful of grouse eggs. The female sits on them for about seventeen days, at which time the chicks hatch and she leads them out into the world.

Some of these grouse are killed for food, but on

the whole they are relatively little sought by sportsmen. They live in remote areas, their flesh is not highly prized for the table, and the birds are slow to take alarm, rarely flushing so as to give the hunter a sporting shot as they fly away.

Ruffed Grouse

The ruffed grouse (Plate 76) favors hardwood ridges, mixed forest and deciduous brushlands. Even when it lives in country predominantly coniferous it favors places where aspen and willow grow. Its range extends across North America in the wooded areas of the central and northern United States, as well as in Canada from Novia Scotia to Yukon and in Alaska. This species, sixteen to nineteen inches long, is a rich, red-brown or gray-brown bird with a fan-shaped, black-barred tail and tufts of broad, black feathers on each side of its neck.

The male ruffed grouse greets the spring with his celebrated drumming. This remarkable sound starts slowly, with individual thumps, then quickens and finally merges into a continuous roll that carries a considerable distance. The grouse drums from some fallen log that he has chosen as his favorite station and uses day after day. He produces the sound by standing erect and rapidly striking the air with his wings. This is his self-advertising act and takes the place of the song of the robin or wren. When he is displaying to the female his performance changes. He struts about with his tail widely spread and erect, raises his neck tufts and lowers and shakes his head while making little hissing noises. This performance he climaxes with a little run forward accompanied by a prolonged hiss, and then strikes and holds a pose for a few moments, his tail tilted toward the female and his head turned toward her.

After mating the female makes her nest at the base of a tree and lays in it from nine to twelve eggs. On these she sits for about twenty-four days, at which time the chicks hatch out and are ready to accompany her as soon as they are dry. By the time they are twelve days old they can fly from twenty to thirty feet. The mother is a devoted and courageous parent. Many a boy has been startled, if not frightened, by a mother grouse rushing at him, all her feathers on end, and clucking furiously, and has then been deluded into following her as she fluttered over the ground or ran with her wings dragging, squealing as if in pain, but always just out of reach. While the bird is first intimidating the enemy and then decoying him away, her chicks have scattered and are lying motionless, the dead-leaf pattern of their down making them practically invisible.

By September the young ruffed grouse are as big as their mother and scarcely distinguishable from her. When small they eat many insects, but by August their diet preferences shift to leaves and berries such as the adult birds have been eating in the summer. In the autumn seeds and haws, acorns and beechnuts are important, and the birds also invade the buckwheat fields for grain. Another diet change occurs in the winter, when they live on twigs and buds of trees, often perching high to feed.

Among all the upland game birds the sportsman rates the ruffed grouse as "king." In remote, seldom visited forests, to be sure, this bird is foolishly trusting; when alarmed, it flies up to a branch and sits looking at the intruder. Where much hunted, however, it often becomes very wily, hides and flushes with a whir, and then bores straight through the brush and away. Often the birds seem actually to dart behind trees in order to outwit the gunner.

Contrasted with this astuteness is the peculiar behavior of the "crazy" grouse that appear in the autumn of a year when the birds are particularly plentiful. These birds leave their coverts and turn up in the strangest places. Some have even been known to fly into office windows. It has been suggested that there is some correlation between these oddly behaving birds and the great fluctuation in numbers of the species that seems to take place every eight to ten years. The latest monographs on the ruffed grouse have no explanations of this beyond observing that the fluctuation seems to be the result of the interaction of weather and disease.

Prairie Chickens

A good example of a bird with different names in different parts of the country is this grouse. In the area from New England to Maryland it used to be called the heath hen, and in the Midwest it is known as the prairie chicken. The prairie chicken (Plate 71), about eighteen inches long, is a buff or gray-brown bird with a short, rounded tail, black-and-buff tufts of elongated feathers on each side of its neck, and distinct barring on its underparts. The eastern subspecies, the heath hen, is now extinct, the last few birds, living on Martha's Vineyard, having disappeared by 1932. The prairie chicken, a slightly less brownish bird, still exists from Indiana to Alberta and Texas. It was formerly a bird of the rich, natural grasslands and was considered by some sportsmen of the Midwest to be without an equal as a game bird. The prairie chicken has suffered not only from overhunting but also from the plow, which destroys its natural haunts. Now, however, the picture has brightened for it. Waste land abandoned by farmers is giving it new places to nest and roost and it has learned to eat grain crops on nearby cultivated land. State conservation departments are also successfully planning and working for its welfare as a game bird.

In the winter the prairie chickens live in flocks. With the melting of the snows the males come to an area of stubble or short grass which is to be their communal display ground. They resort to the same places year after year; one such location is known to have been in use for over thirty years. Here, before dawn, the males take up their stances, each bird several yards from its neighbor. Their formal display consists of a short run and a pattering of feet on the ground, then, with the orange air sacs on each side of the neck inflated, the neck tufts straight up, the tail raised and spread, the wings drooping and the head lowered, the birds give their loud, booming call. When many birds are performing, this booming sounds like distant thunder. The females come to these booming grounds and mate, afterward going their way alone to lay their eggs and raise their young, and not rejoining the males until the autumn flocks assemble. Even then, some of the flocks are composed chiefly of females. It seems to be these flocks that are most likely to undertake local migrations in search of better feeding grounds. In summer the food of the prairie chicken includes many such insects as grasshoppers; in fall and winter seeds, including grain, become important in its diet.

A smaller, paler counterpart of the prairie chicken is the lesser prairie chicken of the southern Great Plains. The habits of the two are similar and both have suffered from the cutting up of the country into farms and the subsequent grazing, plowing and mowing. Both birds take advantage, nevertheless, of the food furnished by the farmers' grain crops.

Sharp-tailed Grouse

The plains and adjacent coniferous forest are the headquarters of the sharp-tailed grouse. Its range is wide—from Alaska eastward to Ontario and Quebec and southward to New Mexico. This species is about eighteen inches long, a gray-brown grouse with a pointed tail edged with white and with "V"-shaped markings on its breast and flanks. It lives in shrubbery and brushland wherever these extend into the prairies and wherever they break up the continuity of the spruce forests. In summer the sharp-tail spends much time walking about feeding on grasshoppers, leaves, flowers and fruits. Wheat is one of its favorite foods, as are rose hips and acorns, whereas in winter it often feeds in trees, eating buds and aspen and birch twigs.

The courtship is a community affair for the sharp-tailed grouse as it is for the prairie chicken, and after mating the hen birds perform all the family duties alone. In summer and autumn the broods form small coveys but with the advent of winter they band together into big packs. As with many northern birds they often wander in quest of food. Birds of the far northern parts of the range may move some distance southward in considerable numbers during the winter.

Sage Grouse

Our largest grouse is the sage grouse (Plate 75), the male being about twenty-eight inches long and sometimes weighing up to about eight pounds, and the female about twenty-two inches long. It is a gray-brown bird with long, pointed tail feathers and a black belly. The arid sagebrush plains of the western states and the prairies of Canada are its home. I remember my astonishment at seeing my first sage grouse, a covey of full-grown birds, walking across the road by a ranch house in the Milk River country of Alberta, for they appeared so much larger than I had expected them to be. Later I found them in the sagebrush flats, where they hid until I was close upon them and then flushed with a whir and clatter of wings from the shelter of the bushes. In winter they gather in larger bands in favorite areas, feeding on sage leaves, though earlier, during the growing season, they eat a wider variety of vegetation and even some insects.

The courtship display of the sage grouse is perhaps the most spectacular of any of our grouse. The dancing birds erect their tails, spread their long, pointed tail feathers widely, and inflate their throat sacs until these reach nearly to the ground and almost hide their breast feathers. Their dancing is a community affair, with many males gathering to take part.

CHAPTER 19

Quail, Partridges, and Pheasants

THOUGH these birds are considered first-class game birds, some of the species occurring in America are so familiar, have such attractive plumage, and pleasant voices that they could almost be called favorite song birds.

This family is nearly world-wide in distribution and includes such birds as a tiny quail scarcely as large as a sparrow, the domestic fowl of India, the peacock, partridge, and many pheasants. Related families include the grouse, turkeys, and chachalacas of the United States, the exotic guinea fowl of Africa, and the megapodes of Australia.

In the United States we have only six native species belonging to this family, all of them medium-sized quail, although two species of partridge and one variety of pheasant have been introduced from Europe or Asia and have become acclimatized in this country. American quail are birds of the grassland and brushland; they go about in coveys until it is time to breed, whereupon pairs leave the flocks to scratch out hollows for their sparsely lined nests. The males may help with the incubation and with the care of the chicks; the latter are down-covered (Plate 81) and from the time of their hatching begin to accompany their parents. These family parties may form the coveys of the following autumn, and several coveys sometimes join to form larger bands. Their food is largely vegetable and includes leaves and roots in addition to seeds and some insect food.

In the drier regions of the Southwest the presence of water is an important factor in determining whether or not quail will occur in a locality. Though there are local shifts in quail populations, such as movements up and down the mountains of the West, none of these birds makes long-range migrations.

Our six species of quail, measuring from eight to twelve inches long, may be distinguished as follows: the bobwhite is a brownish bird with a white throat and a white line over the eye; the scaled quail is a slaty-gray and brownish bird wearing a short crest with a whitish tip. The California quail is a grayish bird with a short plume rising from the forehead and curling forward over the bill, and with a black chin patch outlined in white. The Gambel's quail is similar but paler and has a black patch on its whitish belly. The mountain quail, a grayish and chestnut bird, has a long, straight plume rising from its crown; and the Mearns's quail, a variegated bird, has a complicated pattern of black marks on the white sides of the head and its flanks are covered with round white spots. The females of all these quail are duller and less conspicuously marked than the males.

The gray partridge, about thirteen inches long, is slightly larger than the quail and is a grayish bird with a short, rufous tail and a chestnut patch on its belly; the chukar partridge is larger, being about fourteen inches long, and has a pattern of gray and pale pinkish brown, with a whitish throat patch edged with a black necklace running up the side of the head to the eyes, and black and chestnut bars on its flanks.

The ring-necked pheasant male is about thirty-six inches long, including its very long, pointed tail, and has a greenish-black head and a white ring around its neck, while much of its breast and foreback is a rich coppery brown marked with black. The female is only about twenty inches long, has a much shorter tail, and is buff-brown.

Bobwhite

In the springtime the bobwhite quail (Plate 80) sits on some such vantage point as a fence post or a low bough and clearly whistles his name, "Bob-white! Bob-white!" This is his song, his notice that the breeding season is at hand but that he has not yet secured a mate. Sometimes as the winter coveys break up there are fights between the males before mates are secured. Once the pairs are formed, the two birds are inseparable and often the male bird will feed an insect to the female. After mating,

some weeks may elapse before nest-building starts. Then a nest site is chosen among concealing vegetation and the male does at least part of the building. The nest may be in a hollow in a tussock of dead grass or among standing grass or weeds, and the grass is often woven into an arch over the nest, completely concealing it. Here the female lays from fourteen to sixteen creamy-white eggs, and one or the other parent sits on them for the twenty-three days needed to hatch the chicks. The young quail leave the nest shortly after coming out of the eggs and when little more than a week old can make short flights. They are cared for by both parents; and when a predator approaches, the male may be the first to pretend to be crippled, flapping about on the ground to lure the intruder from the chicks which have hidden themselves.

The bobwhite quail is found from New England to Florida, and as far west as Wyoming and New Mexico; sportsmen have also released shipments of bobwhite in the northwestern states, and it has established itself there. It lives in brushland and in open forest and ventures into nearby fields and gardens. Coveys of quail may cruise about over a considerable area, traveling on foot. Concealed by color, they rely on crouching motionless to escape observation, but when danger is too close the whole covey goes up on roaring wings in an action that is explosive in its suddenness. Though I have flushed many a covey of quail I have never become used to it. Usually the birds fly only a short distance before dropping back into cover—often a tangle of shrubbery or a thicket of saplings. Some of them may even perch in trees. When followed up they often scatter. Later, especially toward evening, the birds utter their gentle gathering calls, which guide the members of the covey to each other. As darkness falls the covey goes to roost on the ground, the birds arranging themselves in a circle with heads out, so that one of the flock may warn the others of danger no matter from which direction it comes.

In the South the owners of many big plantations manage their open pine lands and old farms so as to provide shelter and food for quail and improve winter quail-shooting. The northern limit of the quail's range varies with fluctuations in climate. Severe winters cause widespread mortality, whereas good years allow the birds to increase and spread. Some people consider the bobwhite one of the finest game birds, the peer of the ruffed grouse in the Northeast or the prairie chicken of the prairies; others love it as a songbird whose cheery whistle is one of the pleasantest of the familiar sounds of springtime. The masked bobwhite of Arizona and Mexico is best considered a subspecies.

Scaled Quail

The home of the scaled quail is among scattered cactus and mesquite clumps, on greasewood flats, and in the piñon and juniper foothills of the desert country from Arizona and Colorado to Texas and southward into Mexico. Although when startled at close range they flush and fly a short way before they light and run again, the birds depend on their fleetness of foot, rather than on flight, to escape danger.

To some people their blue-gray plumage makes the name "blue quail" seem appropriate; as I watched coveys of these birds in the Pecos Valley of New Mexico the whitish tips of their crests were often very conspicuous and made a local name, "cotton top," seem more suitable.

These desert birds eat many green leaves, tender shoots, berries and such succulent parts of desert plants as the fruit of the prickly pear, all of these supplying at least part of their water requirement. However, where water is available, the scaled quail make regular trips, coming perhaps hundreds of yards, to drink. In addition, they eat tiny seeds and at times there is a larger percentage of insects in their diet than in that of any other American quail.

The scaled quail's nesting time often follows the coming of the spring rains on the desert. Then there is drinking water and tender new vegetation to make life easier. The coveys of quail split up into pairs and each pair makes its nest in the shelter of a bush. From twelve to fourteen eggs, whitish with fine brown spots, are incubated by the female for about three weeks. The male, who has been on guard nearby, then joins the group and both parents help care for the brood. Late in the season the smaller parties sometimes merge into larger bands that contain more than a hundred birds.

California Quail

The state bird of California is the California or valley quail (Plate 79), whose range extends from Washington and western Idaho southward into Lower California. It is a well-known and popular bird of farmland and range country, and one that is also tolerant enough of man to live in city parks. This quail adapts itself to a wide variety of conditions; it is found from the humid coastal belt to the edge of the Mojave Desert, where its range

overlaps that of the desert-loving Gambel's quail, and also in the hills, where it meets the mountain quail which also frequents still higher altitudes. The California quail must have open ground in which to seek its food of leaves and seeds, shrubbery in which to take shelter, and thick trees or bushes in which to roost for the night. The question of the water needs of these quail has long been a matter of discussion and, recently, of experimentation. It now appears that the California quail can hatch, mature, and live through the year without drinking any water, provided enough succulent vegetation is available. If such water-rich vegetation is not available during the hot, dry summer they die, despite the presence of nutritious food.

The start of the California quail's breeding season is marked by the fighting of males in the coveys and the sound of loud, three-syllable gathering calls. The pairs are then formed and the flock dissolves, while the unmated males continue to call. At first both members of the pair feed together but gradually the male takes up sentry duty, perching in a bush ready to warn his mate of danger. She lays her fourteen or so golden-brown, spotted eggs in a nest under the shelter of a bush or a tussock of weeds, and ordinarily does all the incubation, while the male stands guard. If she disappears the male may take over and sit on the eggs and hatch the young. Both parents usually care for the brood, but the male continues to act as sentry and is bolder than his mate in the defense of the nestlings. He has even been seen to attack and rout a prowling dog. Strangely, this species rarely uses the crippled-bird ruse to lure away intruders.

As the chicks grow up and the family groups merge into larger coveys, the male's guarding activities gradually taper off, and by winter they have come to an end. When the covey is alarmed the birds run, reluctant to fly, but when they do take wing they flush with a sudden whirring flight and scatter widely.

The coveys usually contain from fifteen to forty birds, a pathetically small number compared with the flocks of up to a thousand birds that are said to have thronged to the favorite drinking places in earlier days. At present, attention needs to be focused on adequate management and protection of the California quail if we are to continue to have them as game and song birds.

Gambel's Quail

Gambel's quail (Plate 81) is the common quail

of the desert region extending from southern California and Idaho to the extreme western part of Texas. Although a desert quail, it is more dependent upon water than the scaled quail and is most common along draws and watercourses, where even in the dry season it can find enough to drink.

In southern Arizona we learned to look for these quail and their broods in springtime near the windmills used for pumping water into the cattle troughs. Such artificial water-supply systems and irrigation projects have increased not only the water supply, but also the food for these birds in some areas; this is particularly true in the Imperial Valley in California. Only where succulent vegetation is available can the Gambel's quail go without water to drink.

In the early spring the winter coveys break up as the birds pair. They make their nests in a thinly lined hollow hidden in weeds or at the base of a bush. Very exceptionally they may use a thrasher's old nest in a cactus. In the nest ten to seventeen whitish eggs with purplish-brown spots are laid and incubated by the female. Both parents look after the brood of fluffy, active chicks. As soon as the young have grown, the family broods join together to form coveys, which have been recorded as containing as many as five hundred birds. The coveys frequent the thickets of mesquite and quail bush and feed over the nearby open ground, eating seeds, plant leaves, shoots and buds.

When feeding, the covey is said to have a sentinel, usually some old male, perched in a bush to warn of danger. When alarmed, the birds prefer to escape by running, retreating into thick brush. They will not lie to a dog but tend to keep on running. When hard pressed they flush with a whir and fly strongly, sometimes going a considerable distance, and scatter widely. If not further disturbed they soon begin to call and, guided by these notes, form into a covey.

Mountain Quail

The mountain quail is mainly a California and Lower California bird, though it does also range northward as far as Washington and eastward into Nevada and western Idaho. As its name implies, it is a bird of the mountainsides, and each year some of the birds undertake a miniature migration on foot for the sake of a better wintering area. Before the snows come, and while food is still abundant, the coveys start to walk down the mountain slopes from the higher altitudes to their winter range below the snow line.

The quail very much prefer to live in brushland, mixed or deciduous woodlands, and on the edge of coniferous forests. In the desert mountain ranges of the Southwest they can live only where they can reach drinking water on foot daily. Their diet includes a wide variety of seeds, berries, flowers, leaves and buds. The mountain quail feed early in the morning, rest, preen and dust in the middle of the day, feed and visit water in the late afternoon, and roost on the ground at night.

From the top of a rock, bush or stump the male, in breeding season, gives clear loud whistles of several notes. Soon the birds form pairs, a nest is made under a concealing bush, a tuft of grass, or a log, and about ten to twelve creamy-white eggs are laid in it. When the young hatch both parents help care for them, and both may use the broken-wing ruse to try to distract an intruder from their chicks.

Though these birds are common locally, they were never present in as great numbers as the California quail. But living as they do in dense cover in difficult terrain, they have not suffered so much from hunting as have some species. When hunted, they often run off under cover of shrubbery, and when flushed a covey may scatter widely, so that a day's shooting can mean a great deal of strenuous exercise for the gunner.

Mearns's Quail

Mearns's quail (Plate 77) is a Mexican species that reaches the northern edge of its range in Arizona, New Mexico and Texas. There it lives on the mountainous slopes, on rough, rocky ground among patches of rank grass and oak scrub, and sometimes it ranges into open rocky pine woods. The natives of this mountain area call it the "fool quail" for like some other wilderness birds, such as the spruce grouse, Mearns's quail often allows an observer to approach close to it. When alarmed, it crouches motionless and trusts to being overlooked; it can almost be stepped on before it flushes with its whirring flight. In the spring the male perches on a low, exposed rock and gives a short trill or a low, tremulous whistle. Pairs are formed and the nest is made in a hollow under the edge of a tussock of grass. Both the male and female help incubate the eight to fourteen whitish eggs and both birds are active in caring for the young. The fall and winter coveys are usually small, the size of the family broods, and there is often a downhill migration in the autumn and a return trek in the spring. Besides feeding on seeds, grass blades, leaves and some insects, these birds use their long, strong nails to scratch out and eat the bulbs of some of the wild lily-like plants of the mountains.

Gray Partridge

The gray or European partridge—the Hungarian partridge or "Hun" of our sportsmen—runs the ring-necked pheasant a close second as a successfully introduced game bird, and in some places it is even more plentiful and popular than the pheasant. Its native home is in Europe and Asia where it is one of the important game species; it was first introduced into America in the eighteenth century. By 1934 over 260,000 of these birds had been imported into the United States. The attempt to establish it in North America has been successful in twenty-three states and provinces, chiefly in the Midwest and the northwestern states and on the prairies. In the Midwest and on the prairies it favors agricultural land; in the Northwest it prefers land in the vicinity of irrigation, though in Oregon it thrives in the drier parts of the state and even on some rangeland. Though it has failed to flourish in the desert areas or in the humid eastern states, the species has taken hold well in the better farming country of the Maritime Provinces of Canada, where I have hunted it over the rolling oatfields of the Annapolis Valley in Nova Scotia.

In the autumn the "Hun" goes about in coveys of up to two dozen birds. They run when disturbed and usually all in a covey flush, with noisy wing beats and cackling calls, well ahead of the hunter. After gaining a little altitude they flap and sail to another cover—which always seems to be over a hill or beyond some brush well out of sight. After the winter the coveys break up into pairs and the female makes her nest in a hedgerow or amid last year's dead grass. Here she lays her clutch of eggs, averaging about sixteen, and incubates them, while the male stays on guard nearby. He also helps with the care of the young. The young birds eat many insects but vegetable food, including grain and seeds in season and greenstuff in the spring, is the mainstay of the adults' diet. As one would expect of a bird that eats vegetable food and thrives in well-settled areas, they damage tomatoes and strawberries, pick holes in melons and pull up sprouting corn.

Chukar Partridge

The chukar partridge (Plates 82, 83) is the most recently established of the three species of introduced game birds in America, the pheasant and the gray partridge having preceded it. So far the chukar has been only locally successful, and only in the West. There its favorite habitat, more than that of any other game bird, is rocky, barren, open country, so that it seems unlikely to conflict with any of our native species. The original home of the chukar was in the region from southern Europe to Asia and most of the birds imported here have come from India. Attempts at introducing them began as early as 1893, in Illinois, but have been intensified since 1930. In the past fifteen years over forty states have introduced the birds but only in California, Nevada, Idaho and Washington have these efforts been very successful. The birds have done best in Nevada, where in 1934 between five and ten thousand birds were liberated. By 1948 shooting seasons were opened and the next year on one area of about two square miles of rocky canyon an estimated one thousand birds were shot by hunters.

Starting the annual cycle of the chukar with the winter, we find the bird in coveys, feeding in the open grass country and roosting among rocks. It frequents both the higher slopes where the wind blows away the snow and the valleys where food is abundant. With the coming of spring, pairs are formed for a brief period; then the males leave the females and gather in bands while the females carry on alone. The female uses dead grass to line her nest, which is a slight hollow among sheltering vegetation, and lays about nine eggs and sits on them until the young hatch after an estimated twenty-three days. The female alone cares for the chicks until they are about half grown, after which the male rejoins the covey. Since water is scarce in this region during the summer, the coveys concentrate wherever there are springs, creeks, or stock-watering troughs. With the return of winter the coveys wander away and spread out again, since the snow can supply their need for water. The birds feed on the ground. In winter, they live mainly on grass blades; in summer they eat some insects but depend heavily on grass seeds, the basal shoots of grass, which they dig out with their bills, pine seeds, and, whenever locally available, grain, field crops, and berries.

The chukar is a sociable bird and is usually found in coveys containing a dozen or so individuals. They provide good shooting, flushing fairly easily and flying strongly and well. The coveys often scatter after flushing, giving the hunter many singles to be followed up.

136]

[continued on page 157

87. *Sandhill Crane at nest*

[ELIOT PORTER]

88. *Limpkin*

[ELIOT PORTER]

89. *Virginia Rail*

[HAL H. HARRISON : NATIONAL AUDUBON]

90. *Florida Gallinule*

[ALLAN D. CRUICKSHANK : NATIONAL AUDUBON]

91. *Purple Gallinule*

[ELIOT PORTER]

92. *Purple Gallinule*

[ELIOT PORTER]

93. *Ruddy Turnstone*

[ALLAN D. CRUICKSHANK: NATIONAL AUDUBON]

94. *Whooping Crane*

[LORUS J. MILNE: BLACK STAR]

95. *Surf-birds*

[ALLAN D. CRUICKSHANK: NATIONAL AUDUBON]

96. *American Coot*
[ALLAN D. CRUICKSHANK:
NATIONAL AUDUBON]

97. *American Coot*
[ALLAN D. CRUICKSHANK:
NATIONAL AUDUBON]

98. *Upland Plover*

[MASLOWSKI AND GOODPASTER]

99. *Long-billed Curlew*

[RAY C. ERICKSON: FISH AND WILDLIFE SERVICE]

100. *Ringed or Semi-palmated Plover*

101. *Wilson's Plover*

102. *Piping Plover*

[HELEN CRUICKSHANK:
NATIONAL AUDUBON]

103. *American
Oyster-catcher*

[ALLAN D. CRUICKSHANK:
NATIONAL AUDUBON]

104. *Killdeer*

[ELIOT PORTER]

105. *Upland Plover*

[DAVID G. ALLEN]

106. *Bristle-thighed Curlew*

[DAVID G. ALLEN]

107. *Woodcock*

108. *Marbled Godwits*

[ALLAN D. CRUICKSHANK: NATIONAL AUDUBON]

109. *Wandering Tattler*

[KARL W. KENYON]

110. *Red-backed Sandpipers*

[ERIC HOSKING]

111. *Lesser Yellow-legs*

112. *Northern Phalarope*
    (*young*)

113. *Northern Phalarope*

114. *Hudsonian Godwit*

[DAVID G. ALLEN]

115. *Stilt Sandpiper*

[DAVID G. ALLEN]

116. *Red-backed Sandpiper*

[DAVID G. ALLEN]

117. *Semipalmated Sandpiper*

[EDWARD PRINS]

118. *Western Sandpiper*

[DAVID G. ALLEN]

119. *Knot in early fall*

[EDWARD PRINS]

120. *Willet*

121. *American Avocet on nest*

122. *Black-necked Stilt*

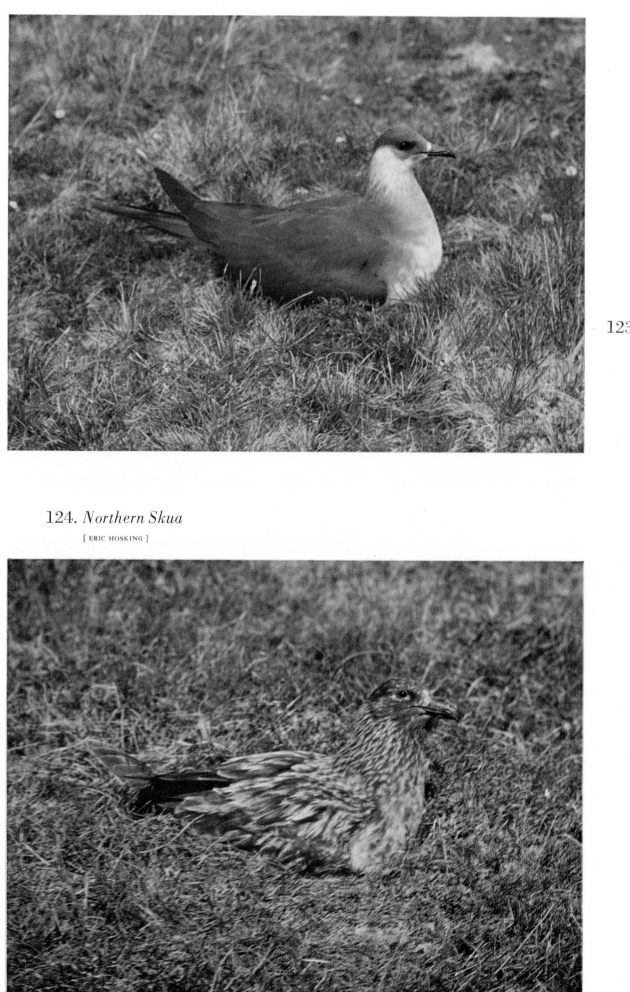

123. *Parasitic Jaeger*

[ERIC HOSKING]

124. *Northern Skua*

[ERIC HOSKING]

125. *Great Black-backed Gull*

[ALLAN D. CRUICKSHANK: NATIONAL AUDUBON]

126. *Glaucous-winged Gull (immature)*

[ALLAN D. CRUICKSHANK: NATIONAL AUDUBON]

127. *Western Gull*

[ALLAN D. CRUICKSHANK: NATIONAL AUDUBON]

[*continued from page 136*

Ring-necked Pheasant

The ring-necked pheasant (Plates 84, 85), like the chukar, is an immigrant introduced to provide us with another grassland game bird, and this introduction has proved very successful. The original home of this bird and its near relatives was the region from the Caucasus across central Asia to China and Japan. Its original range may have included Europe, too, for there is some evidence of this from ancient kitchen middens, but most historians think that the Greeks brought the bird to Europe from Asia Minor, and that the Romans under Julius Caesar aided its spread throughout the expanding Roman Empire.

The first successful introduction of pheasants into America was in 1882, in the Willamette Valley of Oregon. In 1892 a phenomenally successful shooting season was opened there and this spurred other areas to stock grass and brushlands with these sporting birds. Now pheasants are widely distributed across our continent in the northern and central states and in parts of extreme southern Canada. In Asia there have long been many closely related varieties of this bird. Several of these were introduced into the United States, especially a black-necked and two ring-necked subspecies, one with a greenish and the other with a more grayish back and rump. All these, including the black-necked, Mongolian and Chinese pheasants, have hybridized, so that our birds are now a mixed race, the characteristics of ringed neck and grayish-green rump predominating. The iridescent green head and the coppery-brown body plumage make these birds among our most colorful species.

Pheasants usually thrive best in grain-growing farm country where there is abundant waste grain for food, and where they can find shelter in dense, coarse herbs or shrubbery. There is one outstanding exception to the pheasant's reliance on agriculture in this country and that is in the sandhill country of Nebraska, where the birds flourish without being dependent on crops for nourishment.

The abundance and hardiness of the pheasant make it a very popular game bird. When alarmed it likes to run to cover, rather than fly, and when a hunter beats through a piece of cover he may find the birds have skulked in the last corner, delaying their flying as long as possible. Then they flush fairly easily and with a whirring of wings. Once in flight they resort to gliding, now and then giving a few flaps of their wings, and usually go no great distance before dropping back to the ground and running again. In winter they do not go about in true flocks but may gather in favorite feeding places that offer them good shelter.

In spring the pheasants spread out over the fields. While the grass was still short I have watched two cock pheasants patrolling the boundary between their territories, each intent on keeping the other from intruding. Now and then one of the cocks would stop, utter a short crow and flap his wings. In his courtship display the cock partly spreads one wing, spreads and tilts his tail, lowers his head and walks around the female with short steps. Polygamy is probably more common among the pheasants than monogamy. The female alone takes over family duties. She scratches out a hollow in the ground in sheltering vegetation, carelessly lines it with a little dry vegetation and lays in it her eight to fifteen eggs. On these she sits from three to four weeks until the young hatch, whereupon she leads them through meadow and swale. Though seeds are the chief diet of pheasants, they also eat many insects as well as a wide variety of fruits, vegetables, tubers and plant stalks. When they have finished feeding, the young pheasants roost in cover on the ground, or, if full grown, may also roost and sleep in trees.

The chief predators preying on the ring-necked pheasant are the goshawk, the great horned owl, the skunk and the fox. These natural enemies are sometimes declared to be the factors that keep down the pheasant population. It is improbable, however, that they are really important limiting factors. Studies have shown that in some places the pheasants killed on highways by automobiles may be greater in number than those killed by predators. Despite the great success of the pheasants in some areas, in others such climatic factors as humidity, heavy snow or aridity have prevented them from establishing themselves.

There have been complaints that the pheasant destroys the eggs and young of such other game birds as quail, and that it competes with such species as the sharp-tailed grouse, but these complaints seem to be of local occurrence. The gardener, too, complains of its depredations on a wide variety of truck crops and growing corn, but in view of this splendid game bird's widespread popularity some disadvantages must be tolerated and local remedies sought.

CHAPTER 20

Turkeys

Associated with Thanksgiving dinners since the time of the Pilgrim Fathers and one of the most familiar of barnyard fowl, the turkey (Plates 73, 86) is rarely thought of as the native American game bird that it actually is. There are only two species of turkeys: the ocellated turkey of Central America and the common turkey, which ranges from Mexico into the woodlands of the southern and eastern United States. It was a variety of the common turkey, with white-tipped upper tail coverts, that the early Spanish explorers found domesticated by the Indians in southern Mexico and introduced into Europe shortly after the discovery of the New World. This was the ancestor of our do-

mestic turkey, and the bird that the early colonists brought back across the ocean to America. It interbreeds readily with our wild bird.

The name turkey is sometimes said to have been given the bird because of confusion concerning the country of its origin. More probably it was suggested by the voice of the bird, as some of its calls sound like the syllables "turk-turk-turk—."

The turkey gobbler with the fanlike spread to its tail, with drooping wings, bright red wattle and bronzy plumage, struts and gobbles in the spring sunshine. It is polygamous and gathers a harem of hen turkeys. For a time they stay together, walking about feeding on leaves, grass, nuts, berries and grasshoppers. The gobbler keeps a watchful eye on his consorts, warning them of approaching danger and driving off other males. Soon the time comes for nesting and the hens steal away to scratch out hollows under logs or bushes or at the bases of trees, line them with dead leaves, and lay in each nest from eight to fourteen brown-spotted eggs. On these the hen sits until, in about four weeks, the young hatch. These downy creatures are active from the day they come out of the shell and by the time they are two weeks old can fly into trees and roost there for the night. The young birds and the females stay in flocks during the fall and winter while the old gobblers choose strictly masculine society. At an earlier period, when turkeys were abundant, family parties joined to form bands of one hundred or more birds. When food became scarce in one place they wandered widely on foot until they found open woodland rich in nuts or berries. Today turkeys are gone from the former northern part of their range, which once extended to Maine, Ontario and South Dakota. The men who shot great numbers of them are responsible, but one wonders if such remarkably large game birds could have survived in any but large, little-visited wilderness areas. Now they can be found only in remote sections of our more southerly states.

It is perhaps significant that in the early days the turkey was often reported as being overtrusting and stupid in its contacts with man, recalling the behavior of the spruce grouse. The present-day wild turkey is a shy, suspicious bird, running fast and far from threatening danger: it too has retreated before civilization.

CHAPTER 21

Cranes

C RANES live in open country, marsh, grassland or steppe, where they walk about eating both plant and animal food. The birds are wary and their height gives them an advantage in watching for enemies. When they fly their necks are fully ex-

tended and their long legs trail far beyond their short tails. Often they go in large flocks and at times these soar on motionless wings high in the air. Many species have trumpet-like calls whose loudness is the result, it is said, of the length and convolutions of the windpipe within the breastbone, recalling a similar characteristic in some swans. The well-known dancing of the cranes is evidently connected with their courtship habits, although it is also performed in other seasons. Once mated, the birds are monogamous. Each pair, leaving the flock, constructs its bulky nest on the ground. Here two eggs are laid. The young birds that hatch from them, covered with down, are very soon able to follow their parents in searching for food.

The cranes belong to an old and declining group. This is shown by the fossil record, which goes back to the Eocene period, and also by the existence in the present day of a number of scattered families related to the crane, each including only a few species, notably those of the kagu of New Caledonia, the limpkin and the sun bittern of the Americas, and the roatelos of Madagascar. The cranes themselves are a small family, with only fourteen species, some of which are found in every continent except South America. Of the exotic species in the group, the crowned crane of Africa, which appears on an East African postage stamp, and the demoiselle crane, with its pearly gray plumage and svelte shape, are worthy of special note.

In the United States there are two species of cranes: the sandhill crane, which may be up to forty-five inches long, and is gray with a naked, red forehead; and the whooping crane, about fifty inches long, which is white with black wing tips and a naked, red face.

Sandhill Crane

One of my most unforgettable experiences was watching sandhill cranes (Plate 87) migrating southward in autumn along the line of the Mackenzie Mountains of the Yukon and the northern Rockies of British Columbia. Flocks numbering anywhere from a dozen to a hundred birds passed high overhead, some of them in "V" formation, others flying in diagonal lines, now straight, now wavy. Constantly the birds were calling; their thrilling, bugle-like voices heralded the approach of each new flock as it drove southward, and after dark continued to sound through the night to indicate that the birds were still passing. Other observers in recent years have recorded congregations of from 30,000 to 100,000 sandhill cranes in their favored stopping-places in the Dakotas and Nebraska. These were undoubtedly birds on their way from the Arctic tundra to their wintering grounds, which stretch from the interior valleys of California to Texas and southward to Mexico. There they roost nightly in big

flocks on sandbars in the rivers or in shallow lakes. During the day they feed in the grainfields, gleaning the harvested areas or grazing and grubbing out newly planted crops.

Besides the birds that nest on the Arctic tundra, other sandhill cranes used to nest in marshes and bogs southward as far as Ohio and northern California. Today, when so much of this plains area has been settled, the cranes no longer come there in numbers to nest. Only remnants of the former nesting populations have survived in this region, the most easterly one being in Michigan. On their way north in March or early April these Michigan birds stop on the Jasper-Pulaski Game Preserve in Indiana and crowds of people drive there from as far away as Chicago to see them. Another isolated population has its home in Florida and westward along the northern coast of the Gulf of Mexico, and yet another in Cuba. It used to be the fashion to give each population a separate name: little brown crane for the northern birds; sandhill for the plains birds, which are larger; Florida crane for the southeastern birds, and Cuban cranes for the Cuba birds. They are all one species, however, and are best called sandhill cranes.

The dancing of the sandhill crane, as we have seen, is related to its courtship procedure, but nevertheless takes place the year around. In fact, one young crane raised in captivity started to dance when it was only a few days old, acting, according to its owner, "much like a small boy releasing pent-up energy." In the winter, when the flocks come in to roost, some of the birds may dance, jumping up six or eight feet with their wings half open. Some of them also bow repeatedly in a characteristic fashion, but in most cases they simply bounce up and down. On their nesting grounds they also perform a more graceful dance, including much whirling and bowing as well as bouncing.

Since the sandhill crane has a nesting range that extends from Alaska to Cuba, it can be expected to nest in many sorts of places, and so it does—by fresh-water ponds on the Arctic tundra, in shrub-studded bogs, in thinly wooded marshes, and amid the luxuriant vegetation of southern swamps. The birds form pairs and these select and defend a watery territory, taking turns at sitting on the two olive-buff eggs for the thirty-day incubation period. Swamp ground and a nest surrounded by water may satisfy the long-legged parents and may be an aid in discouraging predators, but when the young hatch they are led to nearby drier land, even if they have to swim part of the way to get there. There they grow up under the care of both parents, the family walking about and living on a diet that includes the roots and stems of herbaceous plants, berries and seeds, as well as insects and such animals as frogs, and crayfish. By the time the young are from two to two and a half months old they are making short flights. In a few months the family groups join with others to form the winter flocks.

Whooping Crane

The whooping crane (Plate 94) is making a last-ditch stand against extinction, and its situation is critical. In 1940 there were 32 wild birds in existence; in 1949 there were 35; in 1954 there were 24; in the spring of 1955 there were only 21. In addition there were two crippled, captive birds in the Audubon Park in New Orleans. The latest news is that in the 1955 autumn migration 28 birds, including 8 young, arrived on the Texas refuge. One adult appeared to be missing.

The last survivors of the whooping cranes winter on the Aransas National Wildlife Refuge, established in 1937 on the Texas coast, where the bird has been intensively studied under a co-operative project of the U. S. Fish and Wildlife Service and the National Audubon Society. An extension of this project was an attempt to discover where these white cranes nested, for the last known nest had been reported from Saskatchewan in 1922. Though the birds brought an average of four young back to the refuge each year, no one knew where they were raised. In 1954 no young were brought back. Aircraft were chartered to search through the Canadian wilderness north of the prairies to find the cranes in their summer home. Success in the ten-year search was finally reported in 1955 when Willam A. Fuller of the Canadian Wildlife Service and Edward Wellein and Wesley Newcomb of the U.S. Fish and Wildlife Service, flying across Wood Buffalo National Park, spotted three nests. These were in the great area of muskeg, swamp and forest, lying on the border of Alberta and Mackenzie, which had been set aside to save the last of the wood buffalo. It is a wilderness area, far beyond ordinary travel routes, and the wood buffalo have prospered there. Let us hope it will also help save the cranes. An Audubon Society official, R. P. Allen, has spent most of his time since 1946 studying the species intensively. Allen went at once to the nesting grounds, and is investigating possible ways of increasing the number of young raised and cutting down the annual losses.

One would think the great size of the whooping crane, and its white plumage and black wing tips, would make the bird unmistakable, yet in the early records it was confused with the sandhill crane. After a survey of these records, Allen feels that the whooping crane population was never large; in 1869, for example, it probably numbered only about 1,300 birds.

The whooping crane, a shy bird for all its size, is a victim of civilization. Its chief breeding range formerly stretched from Illinois and Ohio to southern Manitoba and central Alberta, and most of this area has now been taken over by man. The whooping crane's nest is a large mass of dead vegetation placed well out in a big marsh surrounded by water. The young birds are cared for attentively by both parents, who in the early days of chickhood find food and break it up for the youngsters. The family group normally stays together through the autumn and migrates south without splitting up. In former days the winter home of the whooping crane was in the lowlands along the Gulf of Mexico and in Central Mexico. Food was apparently never a problem for the whooping crane. Though it seems to eat more animal food than the sandhill crane, it is omnivorous, consuming green vegetation, roots, insects and other animals as they become available. In the Aransas Refuge the birds feed mostly in shallow water, and crabs, crayfish, shrimp and razor clams form an important part of their diet.

CHAPTER 22

Limpkin

THE limpkin (Plate 88) is a unique species, so different from any of its relatives in the heterogeneous group of cranelike birds that it has been given a family classification to itself and placed between the cranes and the rails. This bird is the last of an ancient line that, according to fossil evidence, flourished in North America just after the Eocene period. The present-day limpkin is a brown, white-spotted and white-streaked bird about twenty-eight inches long. A tropical American species, it reaches its northern limits in the marshes of Florida and southeastern Texas.

The wails and shrieks of the limpkin are such dominant sounds in marshes in which it lives that it has been given the local name of "crying bird." Partly like a rail and partly like a crane in appearance, the limpkin walks or wades about in the open marsh on the edge of dense vegetation and along timbered streams; it also sometimes perches in trees. The only ones that I have seen were flushed close to

our boat in the saw-grass marsh country near Lake Okeechobee in Florida; with necks stretched out to the full and legs extending behind them, they flew with slow, firm strokes far out over the marsh. Earlier accounts speak of the trusting and unsuspicious nature of these birds and also of the gradual decrease in their numbers. Although the bird is found in only a few areas in Florida, it is still common in some of the great marshes. In 1951 one investigator was able to find 250 occupied nests in the St. John's River marshes in five days of intensive search. The nests are basin-shaped structures of dead grass placed among the stems of growing grass; in other habitats they may be in bushes or in the low branches of trees at the water's edge. In these nests are laid the four to eight eggs of olive-buff spotted with brown; the young are covered with brownish down at hatching and become active shortly afterward.

Though early writers referred to the great variety

of food eaten by the limpkin, including frogs, lizards, and worms, more recent writers mention the large fresh-water snail as its favorite food. Dr. Alexander Wetmore of the Smithsonian Institution writes that it gets the snail out of its shell by picking up the creature in its bill, planting it firmly in the mud with the opening upward, working its mandibles down on either side of the operculum and twitching off this covering. The exposed snail is then pulled out and swallowed.

CHAPTER 23

Rails, Gallinules and Coots

MOST rails are shy, secretive birds of the marshlands, where they spend their lives in the dense grass or reed-beds. Their extremely thin bodies allow them to slip between grass stems, and their long toes support them when they walk on soft mud or across floating vegetation. They usually stay concealed in the vegetation, but at dawn and dusk some of them walk out onto mud flats or appear at the edges of ponds. There they forage for their food of insects or worms, varied with seeds, walking with a bobbing motion of their heads; if at all nervous they flick the absurdly short tails that they keep cocked up over their backs. If alarmed, they are likely to scuttle back into cover and it may be almost impossible to make them take wing. If forced to fly they do so with their short wings flapping and their big feet dangling, and soon drop back into the marsh to hide. This apparently feeble flight is deceptive, however, for some of these birds make long migration flights over hundreds of miles of open water.

There are several non-typical rails. Some, like the yellow rail, frequent dry grassland, these being among the most elusive of birds; some in the tropics of Africa live in brushland or on the floor of the forests. Most rails can and do swim on occasion, and such rails as the gallinules and coots spend much of their time swimming.

Our marshes in the springtime are noisy places and the loud cries of the rails add to the marshland chorus of red-winged blackbirds, marsh wrens, grebes and frogs. To know which rails are living in an area one must learn their voices, for most of them are more often heard than seen.

American rails are usually monogamous, both birds co-operating in building the nest. This is usually well hidden in the grass or other vegetation, and in wet locations is set from a few inches to a foot or more above the water. It is a substantial, basin-shaped structure made from dead vegetation; sometimes the grass overhead is woven into a concealing, dome-shaped "roof." Not infrequently rails make several other nests in addition to the one in which the eggs are laid, a habit shared by another marsh-dweller, the long-billed marsh wren. The number of eggs laid by the American species varies, but is usually large, clutches of eight to twelve eggs being common. The eggs are a whitish or buff color, with brown spots. In some species both parents take turns sitting on the eggs for a period varying from sixteen to twenty-five days; the downy young are mostly black in color and are able to follow the parents soon after hatching. With the coming of winter the birds of more northern latitudes move southward, some only to our southern states and others as far as South America.

We have in the United States only a small proportion of the 130 known species of rails. The family has a world-wide distribution, except for the Arctic and Antarctic, and is notable for the success with which it has colonized isolated islands in the Pacific and South Atlantic. On such tiny islands rails tend to lose their powers of flight through a reduction in the size of their wings.

Rails, coots and gallinules are customarily listed as game birds, but only a few of them, notably the clapper and the sora rails, actually provide much shooting.

King Rail

The home of the king rail is in the fresh-water marshes of the eastern part of the United States. On the approach of autumn the birds of the more northern marshes move to the southern states for the winter. The king rail, about seventeen inches long, has reddish-brown striping on its back, black-barred flanks, a buff-brown throat and breast, and a rather long bill. Its clucking or calling—a "creek" or "cark"—is commonly heard, coming from the depths of the marshes, but the bird itself is seen much less often. However, the king rail does at times walk about in the open, whether on mud bank or grassy meadow. My favorite place for watching king rails is on a little-used road crossing a cattail swamp; there the birds walk about with deliberate steps. They evidently favor such places elsewhere, too, and on roads through the ricefields of Arkansas, where the birds are common, the number of king rails killed by automobiles is significantly large.

Clapper Rails

There are two species of clapper rails, one living in the grassy salt marshes of the Atlantic coast from Connecticut to South America, and one in the salt marshes of California and the lower Colorado River. The birds, about fifteen inches long, are very similar in appearance and habits and look like pale, more grayish, salt-water editions of the king rail of our fresh-water marshes. The large, chicken-like tracks they leave in the soft mud along the edges of the tidal streams are clear evidence of their presence, as are their loud chucking, clacking, or cackling calls. Though good skulkers, they can sometimes be flushed and will then spring straight up in the air above the marsh grass before flapping off in slow, direct flight. When high tides flood the marshes many of these rails are forced into small areas of marsh and others gather on floating timbers and railway bridges. Tides driven by storms to exceptional heights can be devastating to these birds at nesting time. Many nests are washed away and the young, attempting to swim with their parents toward higher ground, are carried out to sea.

Too often the nesting behavior of birds has been attributed entirely to blind instinct and it is a pleasure to record an observation of another kind. During a study of the clapper rail on Cobb's Island, Virginia, an observer found that this bird could recognize one of its own eggs outside its nest and would pick it up and put it back in the nest.

Because of the abundance of these birds in certain marshes, and their fairly large size, sportsmen in some localities consider them good game birds. Formerly their eggs were collected for food; their abundance in the New Jersey marshes in those days is indicated by Audubon's statement that in one day an egg-collector could gather a hundred dozen clapper rail's eggs.

Virginia Rail

The Virginia rail (Plate 89), about ten inches long, is a smaller and more reddish edition of the king rail. Chiefly a bird of the fresh-water marshes, it is distributed across the continent from southern Canada into Mexico, and is also found in South America. The birds that nest farthest northward winter in our southern states, or in Central or South America. Like its near relatives, this rail lives among vegetation and is known best by its voice, a guttural "cut-cut-cutta-cutta-cutta," repeated at brief intervals and interrupted by grunts. However, the Virginia rail can sometimes be observed if one watches quietly at the edge of a marsh or along a marsh roadway; if fortunate, one may see parents with their young or a solitary adult foraging in the open for insects or worms.

This bird is occasionally shot when flushed by a gunner who is after snipe or other rails, but it has never received much attention from sportsmen.

Sora Rail

Of all the marsh rails the sora is the one I have found most easy to observe, especially during the spring migration. Concealing cover being scanty in the marshes, the birds can at such a time be seen walking about over floating vegetation. Then, too, they flush rather readily, heading for the nearest dense cover. From such places comes their characteristic call, a rolling whinny consisting of from ten to fifteen short, whistled notes. The sora, about nine inches long and with a short, stout bill, has a slate-colored throat and black chin in its breeding dress, whereas the immature sora has a buff throat and chin.

Although the sora usually flushes reluctantly and travels only a short distance with a weak-looking flight, it is, surprisingly enough, a long-range migrant. In summer it nests all across the continent in southern Canada and as far south as California and Maryland, and in winter it is found from our southern states to South America. In the summer pre-sumably its food is largely animal matter, insects, worms and other small invertebrates, but in the autumn it seems to take more plant food, often fattening, for example, on wild rice.

The sora, along with the clapper rail, has been one of the rails chiefly sought by gunners. Though it nests mostly in fresh-water marshes, on migration it also frequents salt marshes and tidal estuaries. In the latter areas the rising tide makes it possible for the gunner to pole a shallow-draught, flat-bottomed boat through the marshes and thus flush the birds; as they then fly slowly away, they offer easy shots.

Black Rail

The tiny black rail is extremely difficult to observe. It lives in fresh-water marshes and grassy fields, where it runs about on the ground. It prefers to escape on foot rather than by flying, though sometimes, when one has almost stepped on it, it will flush and fly a short distance. Like the other rails, it advertises its presence with characteristic notes, the female calling a "croo-croo-croo-o," much like the beginning of the yellow-billed cuckoo's song, and the male answering with a series of "kiks" or "kuks."

The black rail, about six inches long, is a slate-colored bird with some chestnut and small white spots on its back. It has a wide summer range, from New England to Florida and Iowa, with another isolated population living in the marshes of the Pacific coast states. The wintering grounds are probably in Central America for the most part. Though they are shy, secretive birds, on migration they sometimes become stranded in big cities, one recently having been brought to me at the Museum after it had turned up in a fourth-floor office in downtown Chicago.

Yellow Rail

The yellow rail is an elusive, little-known bird, about seven inches long, with buff-yellow plumage, a black-streaked back, and a large white patch on its wing. It lives in the larger, drier, grassy marshes where it spends its time under dense vegetation and makes its presence known by a series of ticking or clicking notes which have been likened to the sound of pebbles tapped together. To see a yellow rail is an event, for when alarmed it not only runs rather than flies but also resorts to crouching and hiding. A bird dog is indispensable for finding this rail and, once a bird has been located, it is often possible to walk over to it and pick it up. In their winter quarters yellow rails are sometimes found in dry hayfields, and the birds are so reluctant to fly when the hay is being cut that they are occasionally caught and killed by the blade of the mowing machine.

The summer range of the yellow rail is a wide one, extending from New England and eastern Canada to the southern Mackenzie River Valley and California; in winter the birds move to our southern states.

Purple Gallinule

Its green back and purple head and neck, set off by its red bill and pale blue frontal shield, give the purple gallinule (Plates 91, 92) a rich tropical appearance. This is appropriate, for it is a tropical species of South and Central America, ranging regularly north into the United States only as far as Texas and South Carolina. The deep, open, herbaceous swamps, especially those where pickerel weed abounds, are its home. To anyone with an eye for color the presence of the blue pickerel-weed blossoms and the blue of the gallinule in the same marshes may seem more than chance. This gallinule walks about over the lily pads and other floating vegetation—it is admirably fitted for this by its long toes—bobbing its head and flitting its tail in typical rail-fashion. When it comes to clear water it swims from one clump of vegetation to another, or may fly across with dangling legs. Gallinules are less secretive than marsh rails and are comparatively easy to see, but the purple gallinule is shyer than its more dully colored relative, the Florida gallinule. At nesting time, however, it places its shallow platform nest in a tussock of grass or cattails out in the water, rather than in the pickerel weed. At this time it is often quite bold in defending its home against snakes or human intruders. It will dash at the enemy, cackling and calling loudly. Like most of the rails it is often noisy. Ordinarily one does not think of rails as preying on other birds, but in Louisiana the purple gallinule has been found to eat the eggs and young of other small marsh birds in addition to its regular diet of frogs, aquatic insects, snails and other invertebrates, and vegetable food such as wild rice. The birds are a nuisance in the rice fields, for they not only eat the grain but bend down the stems in getting at the seeds.

Like most rails, the purple gallinule seems to be feeble when on the wing, but striking proof of its ability to make long-sustained flights is furnished by stray individuals which occasionally wander to Tristan da Cunha, one of a tiny group of islands in the central South Atlantic half way between Cape Horn and the Cape of Good Hope. In making this flight the birds take advantage of the prevailing westerly winds of those latitudes, but to reach the islands from South America they must pass over at least two thousand miles of open ocean.

Common or Florida Gallinule

The common or Florida gallinule (Plate 90), about fourteen inches long, has a red bill and shield on its forehead, and slate-gray plumage with a white streak in its flanks. In the marshy ponds and watery marshes where it lives, its loud and varied clucking, squealing, and squawking are heard from dawn to dark. Florida gallinules are not nearly so shy as most rails; they are often seen swimming in open water on the edge of a marsh, their heads bobbing in time with their feet. Often they come out onto the floating vegetation or walk about boldly on mud flats or even in grassy meadows. There they continue to search for their food, which is largely vegetable, consisting of seeds, roots and greenstuff, with a sampling of whatever small invertebrates they come across in their foraging.

This is the only member of the rail family that has a nearly world-wide distribution. It summers from New England, Ontario, and California southward throughout South America in this hemisphere and in the Old World is widely distributed in Europe, Asia, the East Indies and Africa. In England it is known as the moor hen, and I have seen it in London on the ornamental waters of the parks and on the adjacent lawns. A number of our rails occasionally build their nests in low bushes in the marshes, and the common gallinules seem to do this more often than most, although their nests, shallow basins of dead vegetation, are ordinarily placed among aquatic vegetation, a little above the water. As with most rails, the chicks on hatching are covered with black down, but about the head and neck this is tipped with shining white and on the head the scant down allows some reddish skin coloring to show through.

Sometimes sportsmen out for other game may shoot a few gallinules, but in general they are not highly regarded as game birds.

American Coot

The coots, of which we have one species in the United States, the American coot (Plates 96, 97), have broken with rail tradition. Scorning the retiring habits of the marsh rails, they have adopted a swimming life. The gallinules have already foreshadowed this change both in their habits and in the color and ornamentation of their young, but the coot has modified its habits still further; it has even acquired lobes on its toes to help it swim, in contrast with the slender toes of gallinules and rails.

The American coot, about sixteen inches long, has a white bill and frontal shield and slate-colored and black plumage. Open water is the coots' favorite habitat. Except in the breeding season they gather in great rafts made up of flocks which may contain hundreds of birds. They may also walk about on shore or perch on floating logs, but when alarmed they flee to open water rather than to the shelter of the reeds as do their relatives the marsh rails and gallinules. There is little chance of confusing coots with ducks, for their outline is distinctive; they have rounded backs, thick necks and downward-tipped bills and their heads move back and forth, keeping time with their swimming feet.

Coots are interesting birds to watch, for they are usually busy. They feed by picking aquatic vegetation from the surface or catching insects and other small aquatic animals, and they also dive to bring up waterweed, which they eat at the surface. They consort with ducks like the canvasback when the latter are diving for waterweed; the coots often pilfer this food from the ducks rather than dive for it themselves. Though the coots seem to be on good terms with the ducks which frequent the same waters, they sometimes fight among themselves, striking with both wings and feet, seemingly sitting on their tails in the water to do so. When coots change their positions on a lake, they frequently skitter across the surface, making a pattering noise with their feet and flapping their wings. When driven to flight they need a running start to take off, and then, their heads and necks outstretched and their legs extending behind, they fly at a fair speed with rapidly beating wings.

The coots' nests are quite rail-like: shallow basins of reeds or other dead vegetation built over the water among the marsh vegetation or in the open, or sometimes floating structures like those of grebes. The eight to ten eggs are buff speckled with brown, and both the male and the female take turns at covering them during the twenty-three to twenty-five days until they hatch. The downy chicks are mostly black, like other young rails, but with much orange and red in their heads and with the black down of the underparts tipped with white.

The "mud hen" or "blue peter," as the coot is also called, is little esteemed as a game bird. Although it is of fair size, has edible flesh, is almost stupidly slow to take alarm, and is not apt at escaping or hiding, it has thrived instead of decreasing in numbers. Sportsmen know it as the despised "mud hen," and there is little sport in shooting it as it swims or skitters across the water. Indeed, on some duck waters where coots gather in great numbers, gunners begrudge them the food they eat that might otherwise be left for ducks.

A number of other species of rails, including the water rail of Europe, a relative of our Virginia rail; the spotted crake of the Old World, a relative of our sora rail; the corn crake, an Old World grassland rail; and the European coot, have been recorded as straying to our hemisphere, but too rarely to be considered a part of our bird life.

CHAPTER 24

Jacanas

JACANAS are medium-sized marsh birds noted for their long toes and especially their very long toe-nails, which give them an expanse of foot that enables them to walk about over the floating vegetation of marsh and pond. This habit has given them the name lily-trotters. Unlike rails, they seldom seek concealment; indeed our American jacanas sometimes raise and extend their wings, exposing a conspicuous yellow patch on their quills, which calls attention to them when they would otherwise have passed unnoticed. When alarmed they fly to another part of the marsh.

The jacana family is a small one, comprising only seven species, all of which live in or near the tropics. Our single American species comes northward only as far as the lower Rio Grande Valley in Texas. There it feeds on insects and seeds and makes its scant nest in the open on floating water-plants. The four eggs laid are remarkable for the dark scrawls and lines that ornament the buff-brown shell, and from them hatch chicks which are handsomely patterned in white, chestnut and brown and are active from the time of hatching.

In this species the female is larger and more brightly colored than the male, and, as one might therefore expect, it is the male that takes most, if not sole care of the eggs and the young. Both sexes are armed with sharp spines on the bend of the wing. It is believed that these weapons are used in some sort of intra-species fighting.

CHAPTER 25

Sandpiper Family

THE shore birds include the oyster-catchers, the plovers; the snipes and sandpipers and their relatives; the avocets and stilts, and the phalaropes. As our southern swamps are the headquarters of the breeding herons, and the prairie sloughs and swamps are the nurseries of the pond ducks, the Arctic tundras are the nesting strongholds of our shore birds. Since most of these shore birds nest in the north we see them only as birds of passage in the United States.

Some, like the red-backed sandpiper, winter on our coast, while others, like the golden plover and the buff-breasted sandpiper, winter in southern South America. The fall passage is the more leisurely one, the birds lingering several months on their southward journey. This is the time when our ocean beaches, mud flats and salt marshes are crowded with these birds, their flocks numbering hundreds and even thousands. When the rising tide forces them to fly up from the flats, the flocks swirl into the air in dense clouds that twist and turn and in the distance look like smoke. The remarkable precision with which all the birds in a flock wheel and bank together is a tribute to their visual alertness and instantaneous co-ordination.

While many species of shore birds go south only

along our coasts, others travel both coastwise and through the interior of the continent. Still others, such as Baird's sandpiper, migrate southward chiefly through the interior. The southward migration of shore birds from our northern states begins very early and is well under way by mid-July. The northward migration, especially of the long-range migrants from the pampas of the Argentine, is much more hurried than the southward, and a different route is often followed. Many of the birds go north via the valley of the Mississippi, so that our more northern beaches are often comparatively deserted in the spring. Frequently the spring migration in the northern states is not entirely over until late May or early June, and since birds are moving southward by early July, it is clear that their stay on the breeding grounds is very short. It is probable, however, that the latest arrivals in the north are not among the earliest southbound travelers.

The fact that many individuals of species that nest in the Arctic regions do not join the northward migration but remain behind on their wintering grounds has caused much confusion. It has, in fact, given rise to reports of these birds breeding in the south. None of these reports, however, has been substantiated, and it appears that the birds which stay behind are individuals that fail to breed because they are sick, crippled, or otherwise incapacitated.

The courtship of many of our shore birds includes a song delivered while the male bird flies about in the air and a display given while the bird is on the ground. Pairs are formed in the springtime and the males of many species help with incubation and care of the young. The nest, a scant affair with little lining, is typically on the ground in the open and many species place their nests inland, on Arctic tundra or on grass fields or plains. There are usually four eggs, though a few species lay fewer eggs, and these are heavily marked so as to harmonize with their surroundings. The down of the newly hatched young, too, is colored in patterns which serve to conceal them. Soon after hatching the chicks become active enough to follow the old birds. The parents are often very solicitous of the nest and the young and in some species will fly about, noisily scolding a human intruder.

Typically, shore birds trot along the edge of the salt water or on the shores of a pond, or wade in the shallow water, picking up or probing for small animals such as insects and their larvae, crustaceans, and mollusks. Some of the birds however, feed in grassy meadows and swamps, and others on the prairie grassland; other exceptions are the wood-

cock, which likes wooded country, and the phalarope, which prefers to swim in the water.

Fifty years ago shore birds were much hunted for sport and for the market. Shooting from pits dug at the water's edge and blinds built in the marshes, hunters wreaked havoc on the flocks, a single shot often bringing down scores of birds and leaving many others crippled. Even the tiny, sparrow-sized least sandpiper and the semipalmated sandpiper, which shore gunners used to call "oxeyes," were not immune. The Eskimo curlews and golden plovers were reduced to the verge of extinction; the Eskimo curlew is still at that verge even though most other species have made a great recovery since they have had legal protection.

Most shore birds are now completely protected by law, and properly so, for the birds are too easily decimated on their narrow migration routes, and their reproduction potential, four young to a pair at the most, is too low for them to be able to offset heavy losses. Many people, moreover, get pleasure from seeing flocks of these birds unmolested on the beaches. The woodcock and the snipe, aberrant shore birds that live in thickets and swamps, are in a slightly different class as game birds. They are retiring, solitary species—difficult birds to find and shoot. But their reproductive potential is also low, and it is necessary to watch their numbers and adjust the hunting accordingly if they are to be preserved.

Besides the sandpipers, the sandpiper family includes the woodcock, snipe, curlew, dowitcher, willet and tattler, among other birds. It is a large and diversified family of birds, most of which nest in northern regions and are seen in the United States only during their spring and fall migrations. At these times many of these species swarm in great numbers on the beaches.

The American species are as follows: the woodcock, snipe, curlews, upland plover, spotted sandpiper and solitary sandpiper; the yellowlegs, tattler, and willet; the knot, purple and pectoral sandpipers; their close relatives, the smaller sandpipers; the dowitchers; the stilt sandpiper and buff-breasted sandpiper; the godwits and sanderling. These species are described below.

Woodcock and Wilson's Snipe

Woodcock and snipe are not easy to see, for they are retiring birds that take advantage of their protective coloration to escape observation. They do this so effectively that it is very difficult indeed to spot them on the ground. The woodcock, about eleven inches long, including its long bill, is a reddish-brown bird and the Wilson's snipe, about the same length, but more slender, is a buff-brown bird.

The woodcock (Plate 107) is a very specialized member of the sandpiper family, with short legs, a long bill, and large eyes set far up and back in its head. It is a solitary bird of the thickets and wooded swales of eastern North America, with colors to match the dead leaves of the forest floor—soft, rusty browns and grays. Only when you are close upon it does the bird spring up on whistling wings and clear the tops of the alders or birches among which it lives. It is active in the twilight, flying to open glades to probe into the soft earth for the earthworms on which it likes to feed. Often the first signs of a woodcock's presence are the pencil-size borings it has made in the ground and its whitewash-like droppings splashed nearby.

The courtship of the woodcock includes a flight song. Starting just before dark the male flies up from some open place, perhaps an old field on the edge of brushland. The bird circles upward and as it begins to climb more steeply whistling is heard—presumably produced by the stiffened outer primaries of the wings. At the apex of its flight it moves forward in short bursts of flight, producing an intermittent whistling with the wing quills. It then begins to descend in a series of steep glides, and twittering calls, presumably vocal, are heard as it comes to earth near its take-off point. Between flights it utters a series of harsh, nasal cries that sound like "peent." These flight songs are generally given in the evening and before dawn but may go on all night.

In the northern part of its range the woodcock is only a spring and summer resident. It returns there and nests very early in the spring. Thus, many photographs of woodcock show a bird on its nest with the surrounding ground covered by a late snowfall.

To many sportsmen the woodcock is a favorite game bird. It lies well to a dog and flushes quickly and cleanly. Though its flight in the open is not difficult to stop, the bird often flushes from cover where briars and saplings favor its escape.

The European woodcock is a larger and rather differently patterned red-brown bird that has occasionally been found as a straggler in eastern North America.

What the woodcock is to thicket and copse, the Wilson's snipe is to swamp and bog: a long-billed bird that probes into the earth for its food and trusts to its color to help it escape notice. Naturally its protective colors are different from those of the wood-cock and are the lighter browns and tans of dead grass. When flushed the snipe goes quickly up and away with a peculiar, twisting, zigzagging flight which has given it a special place in the sportsman's book as a difficult target to hit. It often utters a harsh "scape" as it flies. In the autumn snipe are rarely seen on the ground, but in the spring when they are migrating north, small flocks can be seen sitting in the short grass of meadows by a pond, sunning themselves, preening and sleeping and apparently resting from their traveling.

Wilson's snipe breeds across the continent and while some of the birds spend the winter as far south as South America, others winter as far north as they can find an unfrozen bog. I have flushed them in midwinter from tiny, quaking bogs in Nova Scotia when the rest of the ground was snow-covered and the temperature was near zero.

Like the woodcock, the Wilson's snipe has a flight song. The bird circles high above the marsh, now and then making a peculiar winnowing or bleating sound. This is undoubtedly not vocal music, but is produced by air rushing past the outspread tail feathers of the bird as it changes its flight in the air. The snipe's habit of hiding in the marshes is so well known that it comes as a surprise to find it occasionally at nesting time perched conspicuously on a dead branch.

Besides our Wilson's snipe, there are two snipe from the Old World that have been found as strays in North America: the great snipe and the Jack snipe.

Curlew

Curlew are medium-sized to very large shore birds with long—sometimes very long—and strongly downcurved bills, and with backs patterned in browns and blacks. In North America we have four breeding species, each with its special attributes. The long-billed curlew, about twenty-three inches in length, with a bill that may be as much as seven inches long, is a buff-brown bird with no pattern of stripes on its head. The Hudsonian curlew, about fifteen to eighteen inches long and with a bill of only three or four inches, is a gray-brown bird with a white line over the eye, another in the center of the crown, and black lines between them. The Eskimo curlew, only about twelve to fifteen inches long, is similar to a small, short-billed Hudsonian curlew. Because of this similarity the two birds are easily confused, and most of the recent reports of the Eskimo curlew, a species that is on the verge of extinction, are probably in error. The bristle-thighed curlew is a more buff-colored edition of the Hudsonian curlew, and has flank feathers ending in elongated bristles.

The largest and the most southern species is the long-billed curlew (Plate 99). Formerly it nested widely in the central part of the continent, especially on the prairies. One corollary to this breeding distribution was that the turning of the prairies into farmland made much of the curlew's nesting area unsuitable for it. A great diminution of the bird's numbers was inevitable, and this was hastened by shooting. Its breeding range is now much restricted. At one time large numbers of these birds wintered on our southeastern coast, but they are now rare east of the Mississippi. The long-billed curlew is better off, however, than the whooping crane and the trumpeter swan, which have also suffered from the destruction of their nesting habitats on the prairies, for it is still fairly common in the West and winters from our southwestern states to Central America. In the summer it feeds on insects on the prairies, but in the winter the flocks may also be found along the ocean, eating small crustaceans and mollusks and other animals of the shore.

A similar species, the European curlew, has been recorded in America as a stray.

The Hudsonian curlew breeds on the Arctic tundra from Hudson Bay to Alaska. There is a rather different Old World subspecies of this curlew, called the whimbrel, which has also strayed to the United States. The Hudsonian curlew migrates southward mostly along the coasts to reach wintering grounds that extend from Mexico to South America. On its summering grounds the bird feeds on insects of the tundra and later on such fruit as crowberries. In migration it favors mud flats and sand beaches, where it eats crabs and other marine organisms, and also sometimes goes into the marshes, meadows and fields. The Hudsonian curlew is a shy, wary bird, usually traveling in small flocks, and perhaps it is this shyness, along with the inaccessibility of its breeding grounds, which has enabled it to maintain its numbers.

The bristle-thighed curlew (Plate 106) has a very restricted breeding range in the hill country of Alaska, a breeding range that was discovered only in 1948, when the first nests and eggs were found. From its nesting grounds it moves in the fall to the Alaska coast and thence flies to the islands of the South Pacific. There it sometimes feeds on the eggs of nesting sea birds—a habit rare among shore birds, but one this curlew shares with the turnstone.

The Eskimo curlew was once a common bird that nested on the Arctic tundra, migrated in great numbers in the autumn to Labrador, where it fed on crowberries, and came in immense flocks—often in company with the golden plover—to fields, pastures and marshes in New England. From our northeast coast it flew over the ocean to South America, where it wintered on the pampas of Argentina. On its return migration in the spring this curlew, like the golden plover, moved north through the interior of the continent on its way to the tundra. All this is a thing of the past. The big flocks of unsuspicious Eskimo curlew and golden plover were especially vulnerable to gunners, and the birds virtually disappeared before adequate protection was given them. While the golden plover, as we have seen, has survived and increased, the Eskimo curlew is practically extinct although occasionally bird watchers report sighting what seems to be this bird. It is difficult to keep track of the Eskimo curlew's numbers because there is no infallible field characteristic by which it can be distinguished from the Hudsonian curlew. The only one which distinguishes it with certainty is the fact that its flight feathers have plain inner webs, as compared with the barred ones of the Hudsonian curlew. To see this it is necessary to have the bird in hand.

Upland Plover or Bartramian Sandpiper

The upland plover (Plates 98, 105) has somewhat the appearance of a small curlew, but has a shorter, straight bill. It is a bird of the pastures and meadows of the northeastern states, the prairies of the Midwest and the grasslands and tundras of Alaska. On its nesting grounds one hears the sweet, mellow, rolling trill that it utters sometimes when awing high in the air and sometimes when perched on a fence post. Its nest is typical of those of shore birds in construction but not in location, for it is well concealed in the grass. In the autumn the upland plover migrates through the interior of the continent and beyond to the pampas of South America, where it winters.

Spotted Sandpiper

The best known of our shore birds is the spotted sandpiper. This results partly from its wide nesting range, which extends across the continent from Alaska and California to Labrador and the Carolinas; and partly from its wide choice of nesting sites, the only special requirement being the nearness of water, whether at sea level or high in the mountains, in arid or humid country. That the spotted sandpiper is so widely known is also partly the result of certain unusual habits of the bird and the ease with which it can be identified. This is the sandpiper that flies along the shore ahead of you, alternating short strokes of its stiffly held wings with glides as it makes little half-circles out over the water, calling its distinctive "peet weet," and then lighting ahead of you again. There it wags its tail up and down in the exaggerated fashion which accounts for its local name of "teeter tail." It is about eight inches long, brown above, and in summer has conspicuous rounded spots on the breast.

Probably almost all shore birds swim upon occasion but the spotted sandpiper seems to do so most often. When closely pursued, the downy young of this species will take to the water and swim and dive, though their usual method of escape is to crouch motionless and depend on their protective coloration. Adult spotted sandpipers have been seen to dive to escape the attack of a hawk and the adult can dive into water and continue its flight under water, swimming with partly spread wings.

Along sandy beaches or muddy flats near the ocean, a stream, or a pond, or in nearby fields or meadows, the spotted sandpiper seeks its food—a wide variety of insects and other invertebrate animals from both land and water. The bird also catches small fish, even young trout from hatcheries, and sometimes snatches insects on the wing as they fly by.

When in its summer home the spotted sandpiper does not gather into flocks. Even on migration to its winter home, extending from the State of Washington and the Carolinas to South America, the birds travel only in small, loose flocks.

Solitary Sandpiper, Yellow-legs, Wandering Tattler and Willet

These shore birds are rather tall and slender, with a gray or slate, rather than a brown, tinge to their plumage. Though you may find some of them on mud flats or even on beaches, all except the tattler, which prefers rocky shores, are more likely to be seen in marshes or feeding in shallow pools. The solitary sandpiper is only about eight inches long; it is a rather dark grayish bird with a dark rump like its back, and dark legs. The lesser yellow-legs, about ten inches long, is similar but has a white rump and yellow legs; the greater yellow-legs, about fourteen inches long, is similar but larger. The wandering tattler, about eleven inches long, is very distinctive, its breeding plumage being heavily barred with black on the underparts. The willet, about sixteen inches long, has conspicuous black and white wings.

Solitary Sandpiper

The muskeg, that mixture of bog and spruce of the north country that extends across the continent, is the summer home of the solitary sandpiper. There it lays its eggs in the deserted nests of tree-nesting birds such as robins and rusty blackbirds —a rare habit among shore birds. Its winter home is in South America, but like many shore birds its migrations are not clear-cut, a few birds wintering in our southern states and a few spending the summer in northern and mountain states south of where they are known to breed.

The solitary sandpiper is a slender, graceful bird, like a smaller, darker edition of the lesser yellow-legs. In migration, which extends across the continent, it usually travels alone, as its name implies, or in small parties. A trusting, unsuspicious bird, it wades in shallow ponds in the forest or amid grassland, sometimes in little ponds in marshes where one would expect snipe, and sometimes in big, flooded marshes where yellow-legs feed. It tilts and nods its head and body like the yellow-legs, rather than teetering its tail like a spotted sandpiper, and it has one distinctive habit: when alighting it poises for a moment with its wings spread above its back and then folds them. Sometimes, too, it raises and spreads its wings when it is standing. Whether it is awing or afoot, its movements are remarkably light and agile, and it even pursues and catches insects on the wing.

The green sandpiper of the Old World is a close relative of the solitary sandpiper and it also lays its eggs in the old nests of tree-nesting birds. The wood sandpiper of Europe is another bird that sometimes does this. Both of these birds have been recorded as strays on this continent.

Yellow-legs

There are two species of yellow-legs, the greater and the lesser (Plate 111), but they are so much alike that it is not easy to tell them apart. Even their calls are similar, though the lesser yellow-legs tends to repeat its sharply whistled alarm, "wheu," twice, whereas the greater repeats a similar call three times. They are noisy birds, always ready to spring up and send out an alarm to the whole marsh —whence their alternative names, "telltale" and "tattler."

Both species make their summer homes across the continent in Canada north of settled areas, and their main winter home in southern South America, although a few birds spend the winter as far north as our southern states. Their migration routes are not quite the same. The greater yellow-legs commonly migrates along both our coasts, the lesser yellow-legs traveling more commonly east of the Rockies and on its southward journey passing in numbers down our Atlantic coast. In the spring most of these birds return north through the interior.

Mud flats with shallow pools, and marshes and fields with short grass and standing water are their favorite haunts on migration. Here these tall, graceful birds, with their habit of tilting their bodies and bobbing their heads, wade about, picking up a wide variety of insects and other invertebrates from the water and mud, the greater yellow-legs in particular catching many small fish. The lesser yellow-legs is the commoner and goes in larger flocks. Both these birds were among the favorites of the old-time shore gunners.

Another closely related species, the redshank of the Old World, has been recorded in the New World in Greenland.

Wandering Tattler

Judging from the scant information we have, the wandering tattler (Plate 109) nests on gravelly bars in rivers above timber line in Alaska and in nearby Siberia. It migrates southward along our Pacific coast and to the islands of the South Pacific for the winter. When on our shores it favors rocky coasts and reefs, where it feeds at the edge of the waves along with the black turnstone. In Asia lives the closely related Polynesian tattler, which is perhaps only a subspecies of the wandering tattler and which has been recorded on the Pribilof Islands of the Bering Sea.

Willet

The willet (Plate 120) is a noisy, conspicuous bird on its nesting grounds, and where these birds are common I have had half a dozen of them flying about me on their showy black-and-white wings, scolding or whistling the "willet" or "pil-wil-willet" that has given them their name. Where trees are present willets may perch in them and continue their scolding there.

The breeding distribution of the willet is fragmented and unusual: some of them nest in the western interior of the continent, on the prairies and plains; others nest in Nova Scotia; and others in the coastal area from New Jersey to Florida and around the Gulf of Mexico.

The eastern birds live in coastal marshes, on mud flats and beaches, and nest on the sand, among marsh grass, or in nearby meadows or pastures where the nests can be well concealed. The western birds live around the prairie sloughs and lakes. With such a wide range of habitat their food must vary widely. Insects are probably important to them in some areas, but along the coast small crabs are sometimes their chief food.

In migration the birds travel in flocks and are found on both coasts as well as in the interior. The species winters from our southern coastal states southward to South America.

The Knot, Purple and Pectoral Sandpipers

These sandpipers are a size larger than the small, brownish-backed kind so common on our beaches and mud flats. The knot, ten inches long, has a red breast in its breeding plumage, a whitish breast and a silver-gray back in the winter, and a whitish rump at all seasons. The purple sandpiper, about nine inches long, is slate-colored above, has yellow legs in winter, and, depending on its age, a slate-colored or spotted breast. The pectoral sandpiper is about nine inches long, brownish and much like many other smaller, brown sandpipers except that its breast is streaked and contrasts sharply with its white belly.

Common Knot

The knot (Plate 119) is a typical sandpiper, usually seen on the beaches and broad mud flats. There it is one of several species that go in flocks often containing hundreds of birds. In flight the flocks may swirl and circle, appearing in the distance like smoke. When feeding, walking along, and probing the sand for the tiny animals hidden there, the birds may be so close together that they give the impression of a moving carpet. Though knots are near relatives of the small brown-backed sandpipers of the flats and are much like them in habits, they are easily distinguished by their somewhat larger size and the generally gray color in their winter plumage, or by the reddish underparts of their breeding dress. They often associate with the black-bellied plover and the turnstone.

In the early days the knot, though only about ten inches long, was one of the group of larger sandpipers sought by the shore gunner. The bird is with us in the spring and autumn, in passage from its Arctic nesting grounds to its winter home, which extends from our southeastern states to South America. Another species, the eastern Asiatic knot, has been found as an accidental visitor in Alaska.

Purple Sandpiper

The only shore bird that makes its winter headquarters on the New England coast is the purple sandpiper, a dark, stocky, yellow-legged bird. Its favorite haunts at this time are the rocky promontories, offshore rocks and islands. There it feeds at the edge of the tide and turns over stones and rummages through seaweed for tiny shrimps, crabs and other animals of the shore. It must continually dodge the dashing waves of the winter storms, but it seems to mind a wetting less than most shore birds and in calm weather it sometimes alights on the water.

Unlike the many shore birds that swarm southward in July, the purple sandpiper is a late migrant and the main flights arrive in New England in November or even December. The flocks, small for sandpipers and consisting of a few score birds at most, show little fear of human beings. Of course they have small contact with humans, since few persons visit their rocky, surfbound winter habitat or the high, rocky tundra of the eastern American Arctic where they breed. The same species also lives in Europe and Asia. In the Bering Sea area there is a near relative, the Aleutian sandpiper, which is sometimes considered the same species. In winter plumage the two are much alike, but in summer the Aleutian bird is quite different, with red-brown in its plumage. In habits it is, like the purple sandpiper, a dweller on rocky coasts and reefs. It winters on the Pacific coast only as far south as Oregon.

Pectoral Sandpiper

The pectoral sandpiper is a little larger than most of the small sandpipers of beach and mud flat. It is about nine inches long, has a strongly marked breast, and prefers wet, short-grass meadows, shallow marshes with standing water, and the muddy margins of creeks and ponds, of either fresh or salt water. The flocks in which it travels scatter when feeding. Their reaction to an intruder is sometimes to stand motionless, watching him, and sometimes to crouch and hide. Often the birds of a flock will flush singly from almost directly underfoot, darting away in erratic, zigzag flight like snipe, and giving hoarse calls. Once well under way, however, their flight is as swift and direct as that of their relatives.

On its Arctic nesting grounds the male pectoral sandpiper stages an unusual courtship display, greatly distending his throat and breast and giving deep, musical calls. These sandpipers' winter quarters are in South America, which they reach by routes leading mostly east of the Rocky Mountains, traveling both inland and coastwise in the autumn and chiefly inland in the spring. A very similar species, the sharp-tailed sandpiper of Siberia, is occasionally recorded on our Pacific coast.

Other Smaller Sandpipers

Among the hosts of shore birds that swarm on our beeches and mud flats as birds of passage there are a half-dozen species of tiny sandpipers, each only six to eight inches long, which are puzzlingly alike in appearance and habits. They are the least, semipalmated, Western, red-backed (known in its European form as the dunlin), Baird's and white-rumped sandpipers. Only the serious student equipped with binoculars and a good guidebook and alert to fine detail will learn to identify them all. Though small in size, they bulk large numerically and are important because they include some of our commonest species, their flocks often containing hundreds and sometimes even thousands of birds.

The least sandpiper, with brownish back and greenish legs, is the smallest of these species; the semipalmated sandpiper (Plate 117), with grayer upperparts and black legs, is only slightly larger. The impression of the tiny webs at the base of its toes can sometimes be seen in the tracks the bird makes in wet sand or in mud. The Western sandpiper (Plate 118) is very much like the semipalmated in the autumn, but it has a longer and heavier bill, and in the spring is a more rusty brown. These three are the smallest of the group and are only six to six and a half inches long. Baird's sandpiper is larger, about seven and a half inches long; it looks like the least sandpiper but is a more yellowish brown and has a finer pattern on its back and more buff color in its breast. The white-rumped sandpiper, the size of the Baird's, has one diagnostic characteristic in all of its plumages: as it flies away a patch of white rump feathers is visible. The largest of these six sandpipers is the red-backed (Plates 110, 116), which is about eight inches long, and has, in the spring, a very distinctive red back and black belly. But in the autumn, when it has grayish upperparts and white underparts, its relatively long, slightly downcurved bill becomes important in its identification.

All six of these sandpipers nest in the north, the Western having the most restricted breeding range, nesting only in Alaska, while the Baird's and white-rumped nest from Alaska to Baffin Island, the semipalmated from Alaska to Labrador; the least from Alaska and British Columbia to Labrador and Nova Scotia, and the red-backed in the Arctic of both the New and the Old World.

In their winter quarters these birds show differing patterns of distribution. The Baird's and the white-rumped sandpipers are long-range migrants, wintering in southern South America; the red-backed winters on both our coasts; the Western sandpiper winters mostly on our Pacific coast; the semipalmated winters from our southeastern coast as far south as Patagonia; and the least sandpiper winters from our southern states on both coasts southward to South America.

The migration patterns of these sandpipers also differ: the white-rumped and the Baird's are the most common in migration through the Mississippi Valley, while the bulk of the red-backed migration is along the coasts. The Western sandpiper travels mostly west of the Rockies, and the semipalmated, east of the Rockies. The least sandpiper is widespread across the continent.

As one might expect of numerous and strong-flying birds that make long migrations, these sandpipers do not strictly adhere to narrow migration routes, a few of them spreading out widely, especially in the autumn. For example, some of the Western sandpipers get as far as our southeastern Atlantic states and are sometimes even common there in the winter.

We speak of spring and autumn migrations, but with some of these shore birds the time that elapses between their leaving our northern states on their way to their breeding grounds and their return is so short that the two migrations almost overlap. The last of the least and semipalmated sandpipers leave New England during the first week in June, going north, and by the first week in July the southern migrants are again on the New England beaches, with most of them there in July, August and September. The red-backed sandpiper, on the other hand, goes north by the end of May and does not return to New England until September. The northward migration must be delayed until the melting of the snow, but even then the birds may be ahead of the season, and writers tell of seeing them feeding on the frozen northern lakes in May.

The spring migration is a hurried one, and in that season many of the beaches or mud flats that held many birds for several months in the autumn may be vacant or may be visited by the birds for only a few weeks. More of the birds are likely to return in the spring through the interior of the continent than along the coasts. Though it is more leisurely than the one in the spring, the fall migration can be hurried, too, for the Baird's sandpiper that arrives in New England by early August reaches its winter home in southern South America in September.

The red-backed, least, and semipalmated sandpipers (east of the Rockies) and the Western sandpiper (west of the Rockies) are the birds that form many of the flocks of small sandpipers, often numbering many hundreds, that swirl off our beaches. The Baird's and white-rumped, though abundant locally, are usually seen in smaller flocks. The habits of these four species are generally similar. The flocks feed in dense formations, trotting along the sand or mud, their bills pointed downward, dabbing here and there for tiny bits of animal life—crustaceans, mollusks, insects—always intent on their business of finding food. On ocean flats the flooding tide may drive them off and immense flocks will gather on exposed bars and high beaches to await the falling tide that will expose the flats again. They are not shy and even while feeding often allow a close approach by an observer. In flight they stay together and the flocks wheel in unison, flashing now white, now dark against the sky as they turn.

Each species tends to flock by itself, but there is a wide variation in this. Not only do the flocks sometimes mix with each other, but also with many other shore birds, from the ring-necked plovers and the knots to such larger shore birds as the curlews and black-bellied plovers.

There are four other small sandpipers that must be mentioned here because of their occasional occurrence on this continent. They are the long-toed stint of Siberia, the rufous-necked sandpiper of Siberia, the curlew sandpiper of Asia and the spoonbilled sandpiper of Siberia. Except for the expanded, spoon-shaped tip of its bill, this last is very much like a least sandpiper. This is another example of how a similar structure can develop independently in a number of different birds—in this case in a sandpiper, an ibis (the spoonbill) and a duck (the shoveller).

Dowitchers

The dowitchers, with their long bills, look like connecting links between the snipe and the sandpipers, but in their habits they are more like the sandpipers. They are about eleven inches long, with a reddish breast in their spring plumage and a grayish one in their more or less spotted winter dress. In both plumages they have a large white patch, conspicuous in flight, on the lower back and rump. Whether the long-billed and the short-billed dowitchers represent two species or are local representatives of one was for long a matter of debate. The answer, based on recent studies, seems to be that they are two species: the northern, long-billed bird that nests on the damp tundra from northern Alaska to the northern Mackenzie River region, and the more southern, short-billed bird that nests from the tundra-like muskeg of southern Alaska to Alberta and Hudson Bay. The possibility that they also nest in Ungava is still being investigated. In migration the birds move southward along both coasts as well as in the interior. They fly in flocks, often in association with other shore birds, and feed on the mud flats and sometimes the sand flats of the coasts and of the marshes and ponds. In this they are like sandpipers, but in actual feeding they often drive their long beaks full length into the mud in snipe and woodcock fashion. A favorite name for them among the old-time bay gunners was "robin-breasted snipe." Both species winter from our southern states to South America.

Stilt and Buff-breasted Sandpipers

These two sandpipers are somewhat different in appearance from the many other small sandpipers in the family. The stilt sandpiper (Plate 115), about eight and a half inches long, has a chestnut patch on its face and has heavily barred underparts in its breeding dress; the buff-breasted sandpiper, about eight inches long, has underparts of a uniformly yellow buff.

The stilt sandpiper is notable for its long legs, which give it a superficial resemblance to the lesser yellow-legs, a species with which it often associates, for both of them like to feed in shallow water. But the stilt sandpiper is a less nervous, more phlegmatic species. It usually travels in small flocks and the birds stay close together as they feed, slowly and methodically exploring their immediate surroundings. They lack the dash and the bobbing movement of the lesser yellow-legs. The stilt sandpiper is nowhere a very common bird. It breeds on the tundra from Hudson Bay to Alaska and much of its migration seems to be through the interior of the continent rather than on the coasts. This sandpiper is a long-range migrant and its winter home is in southern South America.

Among the sandpipers the buff-breasted is unique not only in having buff underparts but also in its pose and habits. Only about the size of a spotted sandpiper, but with longer legs and neck and a short, thin bill, this yellow-brown bird recalls in some ways the larger upland plover. Like the latter, it prefers grassy places to mud flats or beaches, and stands with its head up watching anyone approaching. Its color matches its background so well that it is difficult to see until it flies up. It travels in flocks, sometimes of hundreds of birds, but the birds are not shy and when disturbed seldom rise together, only a few of the nearer ones moving off at a time.

This bird is another long-range migrant, going from its summer home on the edge of the Arctic Ocean to the pampas of Argentina and Uruguay. Once it was enormously abundant in the Mississippi Valley during migration but it is one of the species that suffered from overshooting. Moreover, its migration route is relatively narrow and its passage rapid, so that it is now one of our rarer sandpipers.

Godwits

In flight some of these magnificent shore birds look as large as ducks, but their long bills, straight or upcurved, make them easy to identify. The marbled godwit (Plate 108), from sixteen to twenty inches long, is a buff and brown bird. The Hudsonian godwit (Plate 114), from fourteen to sixteen inches long, has a dark brown breast in spring, a whitish color below and gray above in its winter plumage, and a tail that appears white on the basal half and largely black at the tip. The bar-tailed or Pacific godwit, about fifteen inches long, has underparts that are reddish brown in the spring and whitish in the autumn, and its tail like its back is barred with black and white.

The large marbled godwit nests on the prairies from Alberta to South Dakota; the smaller Hudsonian godwit, one of our rarest shore birds, nests on the tundra from Hudson Bay to Alaska, while the Pacific godwit, a subspecies of the Old World bar-tailed godwit, has an outpost breeding colony in Alaska. Their migrations and their winter homes differ as sharply as their summer breeding grounds. The marbled godwit winters from our southern states on both coasts south to northern South America, and its migration fans out east, west and south from its nesting range. The Hudsonian godwit winters in southern South America, with few known stops along its migration route. After breeding, the birds of this species from as far west as Alaska fly east to the eastern Canadian seaboard.

Then, unless driven by storms onto the New England or New York coast, they apparently fly over the ocean to South America, for there are very few records of them from our southeastern states or from the West Indies. In the spring they appear on the Texas coast and apparently go up the Mississippi Valley to the prairies and to the tundra farther north. The Pacific godwit goes from Alaska to the islands of the South Pacific for the winter.

All three species are bold and noisy on their nesting grounds, flying about and scolding an intruder, but they become shy after deserting their inland breeding places and coming to the edge of salt water to winter. The marbled godwit, second to the long-billed curlew in size among our shore birds, joins flocks with those of the curlew and the willet when wintering on the sand flats, beaches and mud flats of our southern coasts. There they probe the sand and mud for edible sea animals.

A fourth species, the black-tailed godwit of the Old World, has been recorded in Greenland.

Sanderling

This is the whitest of the small beach birds in autumn, and is a little larger than some of the small sandpipers, being about eight inches long; in spring its upperparts and breast have a rusty tinge. Sometimes as the little flocks trot along sandy beaches, dodging the breaking waves, their bills slanted downward and now and then dabbing at the sand or probing for active insects, they look like ludicrously hurried workmen or so many clockwork toys. I have found this species the most widespread of the shore birds on the sandy shores of Lake Michigan; they will forage near picnickers and one evening I saw a flock fly into a parking lot, unmindful of the cars, and run up a nearby sand dune, apparently to spend the night there.

As is true of many shore birds, their migration is not clear-cut. They nest in the Arctic and winter as far south as South America, but occasionally some birds stay as far north as British Columbia and Massachusetts in the winter, while others spend all summer as non-breeders on their wintering ground.

The ruff of Europe, a sandpiper about eleven inches long, is of casual occurrence in the eastern United States.

CHAPTER 26

Plovers, Turnstones and Surf-birds

THE plovers and their near relatives, the turn-stones and the surf-birds, form a family in the great group of shore birds of which the sandpiper is perhaps the best-known type. These three groups of birds are especially characteristic of our ocean beaches. In America we have eleven species of these birds that are of regular occurrence and several more that have occasionally strayed to this continent from the Old World. The American species are best grouped as follows: the ring-necked plovers; the killdeer; the mountain plover; the black-bellied and golden plovers; the surf-bird and the turnstones. It should be noted that a few of these, although "shore birds" in name and appearance, live far from the shore.

Ring-necked Plovers

Among the hosts of small, puzzlingly similar shore birds our four species of ring-necked plovers come as rather a relief from the point of view of easy iden-

tification. Their plover status is evident from their outline, which shows a rather large head and a short neck. When feeding they stand upright, occasionally bobbing their heads, and now and then bending over to peck at the ground, rather than walking or standing with their bills down like feeding sandpipers. They are about six to eight inches long and their adult plumage is characterized by a more or less complete, black neck-ring and a white forehead with a black bar behind it. The four species of regular occurrence in America can be recognized by the following characteristics: the ringed or semipalmated plover (Plate 100) has a dark brown back and yellowish legs; the piping plover (Plate 102) has a pale gray back and yellow legs; the snowy plover has a still paler back, its black neck-ring has a break in the front, and it has blackish legs; and the Wilson's plover (Plate 101) has a rather dark brown back, pinkish-gray legs, and a longer, heavier bill than the other three species.

[179

These ring-necked plovers are all much alike in habits, nesting by making a hollow in the open in sand, gravel or earth, with little or no lining. The number of eggs laid by some of the more southern species tends to be less than the standard four eggs per clutch of northern-nesting shore birds. In the winter, when all four species occur in some of our southern states, they may gather in loose flocks of their own kind or in association with other shore birds. When on the water's edge, looking for the small animal life on which they live, they tend to scatter rather than stay in the close flocks usual among sandpipers.

Open beaches or tidal flats are these birds' typical habitat, although they also occur by inland waters, and the coloring of their upperparts bears a relation to their favorite haunts. They are all rather trusting in temperament, and their whistled calls are sweet and melodious.

The ringed plover (Plate 100) is the most northern of these species and nests in the Arctic of both the Old and the New World. Until recently the common American ringed plover, which has more webbing at the base of its toes than the Old World form, was called the semipalmated plover and was considered a species distinct from its Old World relative. In this hemisphere it nests from Alaska to Nova Scotia and northward through the Arctic Islands, and winters from our southern states southward. Commonly seen in migration, especially along our coasts, it frequents both sand beaches and mud flats for feeding and sleeps in flocks on the sand above the reach of the waves.

The Wilson's plover frequents both mud flats and sand beaches. It is a much more southern bird than the ringed plover and breeds from South America to our southern States as far north as Virginia. Sometimes the birds nest in loose colonies, but the nests are usually well separated. Like some of the other ring-necks, a pair of these birds will sometimes make several dummy nests in the neighborhood of the nest that is actually used for the eggs.

The piping plovers, which live on light-colored beaches, have a shadow-like quality as they trot about on the glaring sand, and when they stop moving they seem to disappear into their background. These birds nest locally from southern Alberta and the Gulf of St. Lawrence southward to Nebraska and North Carolina and winter from South Carolina to Mexico.

The snowy plover is the palest of the four and matches the white sand of the beaches of the Gulf of Mexico area, which is the farthest north that it

comes from its main range in Central and South America and the West Indies.

There are two other species of this group of plovers that have strayed to our area. One is the Mongolian plover of Asia, which has been recorded in Alaska. The other is the little ringed plover of wide distribution in the Old World; it has been recorded in Alaska and California.

Killdeer

In our northern states the killdeer (Plate 104) is a favorite spring bird, returning even before the meadowlark and the red-winged blackbird, when the melting snow has exposed only patches of bare field. The killdeer's summer range is from southern Canada to South America; in winter, it retreats from the northern edge of its breeding range only far enough to escape the snow.

The killdeer is only about ten inches long and is our only plover with two black bands across the breast and with a rufous rump. In summer it lives on moist, grassy flats by lakes or streams, and nests in pastures and fields, and even in city parks, where its many loud musical calls, including the "kill dee" which has given it its name, have helped to make it well known. Although it is less a bird of beach and mud flat than many plovers, it still shows a marked liking for the water. In the western United States it frequents sloughs and impounded waters rather than open prairie, and in winter in our southern states flocks of killdeer may join other shore birds on beaches and in marshes.

The killdeer's injury-feigning ruse or distraction display, as it is sometimes called, is so highly developed and so easily observed that it is a classic of its kind. The parent birds generally leave the nest while the intruder is still some distance away, and circle about, calling. When the danger comes closer one bird drops to the ground and flutters there, tail spread, one wing held up, the other beating the ground as though in distress. If the intruder continues to approach, the birds will try to lead him away from the young, perhaps by trailing one wing; if he turns away the display is repeated until he is far from the nest.

Mountain Plover

The mountain plover, about eight inches long, has plain gray upperparts and white underparts, summer and winter. This dull-colored bird has forsaken the usual plover habitat of beach, mud flat and other damp places and made its home in the dry grasslands of the prairies, plains and mesas of our western states. Here its chief food is grasshoppers and it nests in the open far from any water. After the nesting season is over the birds gather in flocks and at this time some visit water holes and flooded fields. Their summer range extends from southern Alberta to North Dakota, northwestern Texas and northern New Mexico. Their migration is a short one, the birds wintering to the southwest of their breeding range, from Arizona and California to Mexico.

A relative of the mountain plover, the dotterel of Europe and Siberia, has been recorded in Alaska.

Golden and Black-bellied Plovers

These two large plovers have black underparts when they are in breeding dress, and whitish ones in winter. The golden plover is slightly smaller than the black-bellied and its upperparts are more brownish or golden. The black-bellied plover, which is about twelve inches long, has a white rump and a patch of black feathers under the wing where it meets the body; the golden plover, about eleven inches long, has no black patch under the wing and its rump is colored like its back.

The American golden plover is an Arctic-nesting bird noted for its patterns of migration and the length of its non-stop, overwater flights. These birds build their nests on the tundra from Alaska to Hudson Bay. In the autumn a few of them migrate down the Pacific coast, and others through the interior of the continent, but most of them fly eastward to the Maritime Provinces of Canada and the New England states, and then overseas to South America, where they winter on the pampas of the southern part of that continent. In the spring the bulk of them return by a different route, coming up the Mississippi Valley and across the prairies to their Arctic nesting grounds. Another subspecies, the Pacific golden plover, nests in parts of western Alaska and in Siberia. Few of these Alaskan birds find their way south into the Americas; rather they migrate to the Hawaiian Islands–Australia–China area of the Pacific.

The golden plover suffered greatly from overshooting and reached a low in numbers about the turn of the century. Immense numbers were shot on coastal flats and in grassy fields when stormy weather drove them ashore in New England in the autumn and again when they appeared on the prairies in the spring. For a time it seemed that the golden plover and the Eskimo curlew, with which it traveled, were both headed for extinction. Protection arrived in time for the golden plover, however,

and once again flocks of the birds travel their migration routes.

The European golden plover, which occasionally occurs and breeds in Greenland, is very similar to our bird but represents another species.

The black-bellied plovers also nest in the Arctic, but the summer period when they are absent from the United States on their breeding ground on the northern tundra is a short one. They appear in the northern states in May and early June, moving northward, and by the second week in July the adults are coming south again, to be followed in a month or slightly longer by the white-bellied young birds. They are a circumpolar species; in this hemisphere they migrate both along our coasts and through the interior on their way to and from their wintering grounds, which extend from the southern states to South America. They travel in flocks usually containing from twenty to fifty birds, but immense numbers may at times congregate on beaches. Here they feed over the extensive sand beaches and mud flats at low tide. With the flood tide they move to nearby marshes or meadows.

This species is the largest of our plovers, and is a striking bird in its black-and-white breeding plumage. It has a melancholy, whistled call that is one of the most distinctive bird voices on our beaches. The black-bellied plover was a favorite quarry of the old-time shore-bird gunner, but it was a much warier bird than the golden plover and managed to maintain its numbers in spite of the hunting.

Lapwing

The lapwing is to Europe what the killdeer is to America, a large, noisy, well-known plover that lives in cultivated fields and pastures. It is about thirteen inches long, has iridescent, bronze-green upperparts, a blackish throat, and a slender up-curved crest. There were only a few records of this bird's occurrence on this continent until 1927. Then, in the fall of that year, large numbers of lapwings suddenly appeared in Newfoundland, and smaller contingents arrived as far north as Baffin Land and as far south as the province of New Brunswick. Thousands of these birds are said to have made the transatlantic crossing that year, and we know that at least one of them came from England, for it carried a band placed on its leg there the year before. Apparently all of these immigrating lapwings perished.

Surf-bird and Turnstones

The structure of these species links them to the

plovers, though in general appearance they are more like stout sandpipers. The surf-bird, about ten inches long, has a white rump and a white tail with a broad black band across the end; the ruddy turnstone, about nine inches long, has a red back, a black breast and black streaks on its face when in breeding dress, and an elaborate pattern of black-and-white on its wings, tail and rump, exposing this pattern as it flies. The black turnstone shows a similar black-and-white pattern in flight but has a blackish head and breast as well as blackish upperparts when it is in breeding plumage.

The surf-bird (Plate 95) winters along the rocky shores and reefs of our Pacific coast, feeding on barnacles, small mussels and other small sea animals. Usually these birds gather in small flocks and they often associate with Aleutian sandpipers and black turnstones.

The nest and eggs of the surf-bird were unknown until 1926, when two ornithologists found them high above timber line in the Mt. McKinley area in Alaska. The nest is a typical, scanty plover affair, placed in the open. The type of country in which the surf-bird nests—rugged rock slides far from the sea —bears considerable resemblance to the reefs that the birds frequent in winter. Another interesting point, though its significance is not clear, is that in the Mt. McKinley area the summer range of the surf-bird is almost identical with that of the white or Dall's mountain sheep.

When a bird has such a name as ruddy turnstone (Plate 93), you know it must have a reddish plumage at least part of the year, and that it turns over stones, among other objects, in its search for small animal life. But this bird also feeds in several other and quite different ways. On its breeding grounds on the Arctic tundra its food consists largely of insects. On migration, when it feeds on gravel and sand beaches, on mud flats or in dry fields, it may turn over stones or rummage through seaweed for its food, pick up food in the open, chase small crabs, or excavate for crab eggs in the sand. On its winter grounds, which extend from our southern states southward, it has been found eating the berries of bushes on which it perches, and on Laysan Island in the Pacific it has been found to break open terns' eggs and eat their contents.

The black turnstone chooses the edges of tundra ponds along the Arctic coast for its breeding places. There, before the eggs are laid, the birds go through their courtship, including a flight high in the air, from which there drifts down a winnowing sound not unlike the aerial flight song of the Wilson's snipe. This is probably mechanical music produced by the air rushing past the wing or tail feathers. While it is on its nesting grounds the black turnstone is an alert, noisy bird, always ready to give an alarm and to fly about an intruder, scolding him. In the old days, when sea otters were still being hunted, the hunters are said to have detested this bird because it alarmed the prey.

In winter the black turnstone shares rocky coasts and reefs along the Pacific coast with the surf-bird and the Aleutian sandpiper. Dodging between the waves that dash against the rocks, it feeds here on such sea animals as crustaceans and mollusks. Like the other turnstone it sometimes turns over seaweed and pebbles on the beach in its search for food.

CHAPTER 27

Oyster-catchers

OYSTER-CATCHERS are large shore birds with strong bills. There are only six species in the family and except that some of them have showy black-and-white plumage, and others are all black, they are much alike in all parts of the globe. The American oyster-catcher (Plate 103), a large black-and-white bird about nineteen inches long, with a large, red bill, ranges from South America northward along the Atlantic coast as far as Virginia. Formerly it ranged north to New Jersey, and also commonly to California. A second species, the black oyster-catcher, is restricted to the Pacific coast from California to Alaska. It is an all-black bird, about eighteen inches long, with a large red bill. These

are the only two species occurring in the United States, although the European oyster-catcher, a distinct species, has been reported in Greenland.

The oyster-catcher might more appropriately be called oyster-opener, for it actually opens oysters and other bivalves. When the shellfish are first uncovered by the falling tide and have not yet closed their shells, or when the rising tide is covering them and they are just opening, the oyster-catcher will thrust its stout, wedgelike bill into a shell, sever the muscles that hold it together and devour the hapless bivalve. The birds also pry from the rocks such animals as barnacles, and probe the sand for other invertebrates.

[183

The type of shore these birds frequent varies with the locality. In the United States the American oyster-catcher lives along the sand beaches and oyster reefs; the black oyster-catcher favors rocky shores of islands. The nests vary accordingly; they are either depressions in the sand, sometimes lined with pebbles or shells, or hollows lined with bits of stone in the bare rocks or in the scant turf on islands. The eggs occur only two or three to a nest. After the breeding season the oyster-catchers sometimes gather into flocks but most of them do not migrate, preferring to spend the winter on our coasts.

CHAPTER 28

Stilts and Avocets

SEVERAL long-necked, very long-legged, slender shore birds of fairly large size form a separate family; this family includes the stilts with their straight bills, the avocets with their upturned bills, and the Himalayan ibis-bill with its downturned bill. The distribution of the group is widespread in the warmer parts of the world, with two species occurring in the United States.

The American avocet (Plate 121), about eighteen inches long, has a black-and-white back and a white head, neck and underparts. The head and neck are tinged pink in the breeding season. The black-necked stilt, about fourteen inches long, is black above and white below.

As the American avocet wades along it swings its head from side to side so that the upturned bill sweeps sideways through the water. Apparently small animals are thus encountered and swallowed, which is precisely like the feeding technique of the spoonbill. Sometimes the avocet's head is completely underwater as it feeds; and when it gets into water too deep for wading, it swims, assisted by the partial webs between its toes. The bird at times feeds while swimming, even tipping up like a duck to sweep its bill along the bottom. Feeding avocets often gather in flocks containing hundreds of birds and sometimes arrange themselves in extended ranks as though driving their prey ahead of them.

The nesting grounds of the avocet are mostly in the western interior of the United States, extending as far eastward as Texas and Iowa, and northward into the prairies of Canada. The birds nest in colonies, and prefer muddy edges of lakes and ponds and extensive marshes with shallow pools in open country for their summer homes.

The nest is sometimes placed on an open mud flat and consists of little more than a scant depression in the dry mud, or it may be a more carefully lined hollow among the grass. When flooding threatens the eggs, avocets have been known to build up their nests until they are twelve to fifteen inches high. With the end of the nesting season the birds move southward and winter from California and Texas to Central America.

The black-necked stilt (Plate 122) is a tall, slender bird remarkable for the length of its legs. It usually wades in shallow water to feed, snatching its food of small insects and other small animals from the surface of the water. Its legs are so long that it must bend them to reach the ground with its bill. Wet, muddy or grassy meadows and flooded fields where water fills the hollows, and scattered tussocks and hummocks that afford dry sites for the nests are its favorite breeding areas. The birds often nest in loose colonies comprising from a few pairs to a dozen or so. They are very noisy and demonstrative about their nests and young, circling about and scolding at any intruder. Two natural hazards may affect the success of the nesting: floods may destroy the nests, or the drying up of the ponds may make the area undesirable. The stilt's main home is in the tropics, and the bird nests from Peru and Brazil in South America northward to Florida in the East and to Utah and Oregon in the West. After the nesting season the birds which nest in the northern part of the range withdraw southward somewhat and winter on extensive marshes or shallow lagoons in our southern states.

CHAPTER 29

Phalaropes

THE three species of phalaropes, the red, the northern and the Wilson's, form a family closely related to the sandpipers. They have partly webbed toes and thick, waterproof plumage, and spend much of their time swimming in the water, instead of running along the beaches. In breeding habits they are unique among their relatives in that the female is larger and more brightly colored than the male, takes the initiative in courtship, and leaves the care of the eggs and young to the male.

The phalaropes are from seven to ten inches long and their sandpiper-like forms, along with their swimming habits, identify them at once. In summer they are brightly colored: the red phalarope has reddish underparts and a white face; the

female Wilson's phalarope has white underparts, a black and a reddish stripe on the side of the neck, and a pale gray crown; the female northern phalarope (Plates 112, 113) has white underparts, except for a reddish band on the sides and front of the neck below its white throat, and a dark gray head. In winter plumage, all three of these species are gray-and-white and are rather similar to each other, so that only such details as the following will identify them: the red phalarope has a gray back without streaks and a thick bill; the northern phalarope has a streaked back and a very thin bill; and the Wilson's phalarope differs from the other two in lacking a white stripe on the wing and in having a white rump.

The red phalarope is the most northern of these birds, breeding on the high Arctic islands and coasts around the globe, where it feeds in the little ponds, floating buoyantly, swimming with bobbing head, and snatching insects from the surface of the water. Sometimes it immerses its head to reach food on the bottom and even "up-ends" like a dabbling duck if the water is deep. A characteristic phalarope trait is to whirl rapidly about on the water, apparently to stir up quiescent water insects and make them easier to find. The birds take wing easily and chase flying insects in the air. With the approach of autumn they migrate southward along both coasts, usually well offshore. The flocks are quite sandpiper-like, swirling up off the water, swinging, wheeling, and lighting on floating seaweed or coming back to the water again. It is said that these birds sometimes light on whales as they come to the surface and pick bits of food off them. The birds in migration appear in numbers on the shore itself only when driven in by heavy storms. Most of them pass our coast well offshore on their way to the waters off South America, though some of them, migrating over the Atlantic, may join the flocks of phalaropes wintering off the coast of West Africa. During the winter they live on the open ocean and are truly pelagic, resting on the water and feeding on tiny invertebrate marine animals.

The northern phalarope is also a circumpolar breeding species but despite its name is less northern than the red phalarope, which it closely resembles in habits. In our hemisphere it travels chiefly well off the coasts but also migrates in the interior of the continent where it is seen on the Great Lakes and more commonly on the lakes of the prairies. Numbers of these birds winter at sea off the west coast of South America.

Wilson's phalarope is a bird of the temperate zone whose breeding range is the western interior part of America from British Columbia to central California and east to Illinois. It shares the marshes and sloughs of our prairies with the host of marsh birds that summer there. In its summer home this phalarope is not so much of a swimmer as its two relatives. Much of the time it walks about the muddy margins of the ponds like a sandpiper, though when it wades beyond its depth, it swims readily and like the other phalaropes up-ends to reach its food on the bottom. While feeding, this bird sometimes uses its bill, like the avocet and spoonbill, with a sidewise motion, sweeping the water for small insect food. In migration the Wilson's phalarope passes through the central and western part of the United States from Texas to California as it journeys to and from its South American wintering waters; it is rare on the Atlantic coast.

CHAPTER 30

Gulls

THE gulls form a remarkably uniform group of birds and are closely related to the jaegers and terns. They are long-winged and web-footed and have somewhat elongated bills, more or less hooked at the tip. The smaller species have a light, bounding flight resembling that of the tern; the larger species have a slower, steadier and more powerful-looking flight, whether beating along, sailing and gliding (Plate 135), or circling on upsweeping air currents. Sometimes gulls following a steamer hang with motionless wings, riding on updrafts of air created by the ship's passage. They often light on the water and float buoyantly, with wing tips and rear end of the body high. They swim well but to dive underwater for food they, like the terns, need the impetus of a dive from the air. They often light on piers, beaches or mud flats and walk about easily. Some of the gulls that nest in the scat-

tered spruce forests of the far north habitually light in the trees, though they seem quite out of place there.

Gregariousness, whether feeding, resting or nesting, is a striking trait in these birds. Scores or even hundreds of them, sometimes of several species, forage together in flocks or gather about favorite feeding places. At times breakwaters are white with resting gulls. Never is this liking for company more apparent than at nesting time, when some colonies contain thousands of breeding birds.

In feeding, gulls have very broad tastes. They are often considered to be scavengers and predators, and some are known to be markedly insectivorous. In fact, they are omnivorous, eating any animal food that comes their way, whether it be alive or dead. They wait about sewage outlets and congregate around garbage dumps or fishing wharves.

[*continued on page 209*

128. *Laughing Gull*

[ALLAN D. CRUICKSHANK: NATIONAL AUDUBON]

129. *Herring Gull*

[ALLAN D. CRUICKSHANK: NATIONAL AUDUBON]

130. *California Gull*

[ALLAN D. CRUICKSHANK: NATIONAL AUDUBON]

131. *Heermann's Gull colony*

[LEWIS WAYNE WALKER]

132. *Ring-billed Gull in winter*

[ALLAN D. CRUICKSHANK:
NATIONAL AUDUBON]

133. *Franklin's Gull*

[HELEN CRUICKSHANK:
NATIONAL AUDUBON]

134. *Red-legged Kittiwake*

[KARL W. KENYON]

135. *Gull in flight*

[M. H. BERRY: SHOSTAL]

136. *Sabine's Gull*

[DAVID G. ALLEN]

137. *Common Kittiwake*

[JOHN MARKHAM]

139. *Glaucous-winged Gull*

[ROGER T. PETERSON : NATIONAL AUDUBON]

140. *Bonaparte's Gull in winter*

[ALLAN D. CRUICKSHANK : NATIONAL AUDUBON]

141. *Caspian Terns*

[EDWARD F. DANA : NATIONAL AUDUBON]

142. *Forster's Tern at nest*

[ALLAN D. CRUICKSHANK: NATIONAL AUDUBON]

143. *Common Tern and young*

[ALLAN D. CRUICKSHANK:
NATIONAL AUDUBON]

144. *Arctic Tern*

[TORREY JACKSON]

145. *Roseate Tern*

[ALLAN D. CRUICKSHANK: NATIONAL AUDUBON]

146. *Royal Tern colony*

147. *Least Tern*

148. *Royal Tern*

149. *Sooty Tern*

[ROGER T. PETERSON : NATIONAL AUDUBON]

150. *Black Tern*

[ERIC HOSKING]

151. *Common Murres and Glaucous-winged Gull*

[KARL W. KENYON]

152. *Black Tern*

[EDWARD PRINS]

153. *Cabot's Tern*

[ALLAN D. CRUICKSHANK:
NATIONAL AUDUBON]

154. *Brunnich's Murre*

[KARL W. KENYON]

155. *Crested Auklets*

[KARL W. KENYON]

156. *Chinese Spotted Dove*

[CHARLES W. SCHWARTZ]

157. *Common Murres*

[ERIC HOSKING]

158. *Black Skimmer*

159. *Razor-billed Auk*

[ERIC HOSKING]

160. *Black Guillemot*

[DAVID G. ALLEN]

161. *Paroquet Auklet*
[KARL W. KENYON]

162. *Crested Auklets*
[KARL W. KENYON]

163. *Tufted Puffin*

[KARL W. KENYON]

164. *Atlantic Puffin*

[TORREY JACKSON]

165. *Horned Puffins*

[PETER STETTENHEIM]

166. *Horned Puffin* (*close-up*)

[PETER STETTENHEIM]

167. *Rock Dove*

168. *Band-tailed Pigeon*

[*continued from page 188*

To be eaten by gulls, living animals do not have to be small enough to be swallowed whole, the great black-backed gull having been described as killing other birds and even ailing lambs and then hacking them to pieces in order to swallow them. Carcases as big as those of caribou and whales also attract them. Animals bearing hard outer shells are not completely protected from them, for like crows some gulls carry shellfish up in the air and break them open by dropping them on the beach. Gulls can snatch food from the surface of the water without wetting their feathers, they can dive from the air, or they can light in the water and feed there. After flying along a beach to locate food they often land and walk to it. They visit inland meadows for grasshoppers and other insects, this being the normal habit of those species which nest on the prairies in summer. Where flying insects are abundant, the gulls hawk for them, catching them on the wing; where the farmer is plowing, gulls follow him for whatever animal food the newly turned furrow may expose; and in the autumn on the barrens of the Arctic the birds eat crowberries. Besides eating a wide variety of fish and invertebrates they take small mammals, and in sea-bird colonies destroy enough eggs and young of other species to be a disturbing factor; this is especially true when visiting humans frighten away sitting parents who are shyer than the marauding gulls.

Since gulls are sturdy, adaptable birds, the migrations of most species are not very long, and the birds fly south only just ahead of the severest cold and ice. At the extremes, however, the Sabine's gull nests in the Arctic winters on the coast of Peru, whereas the Ross's and the ivory gulls, which are Arctic residents, are birds of the pack ice in the winter.

As a group the gulls are birds of the North Temperate and Arctic zones, and a large proportion of the estimated forty-three species nest in these regions. Gulls are scarce in the tropics and there are only a few species in far southern latitudes.

The presence of gulls in an area in the summer is not necessarily a sign that they are breeding nearby. Not only do breeding gulls often make long trips from their nests for food but, like shore birds, non-breeding individuals spend the summer far south of the breeding colonies.

The breeding of our various species of gulls is similar in all cases. The birds pair and resort to colonies, and there both parents share in building a fairly substantial nest of moss, twigs, grass or other vegetation. The colonies are often on islands where the nests can be built on the ground. Sometimes the birds protect the nests by placing them on the ledges of cliff faces. On the prairie lakes, the Franklin's gulls frequently build their nests of reed stems among the standing reeds of the deep marshes. Some species occasionally nest in trees and others, like the Bonaparte's gull, do so habitually. Commonly there are three eggs to a clutch, dark olive in color, with a mottled pattern of dark brown. Both parents take turns at sitting on the eggs until, after three to four weeks, the young hatch. The nestlings are thickly covered with down and are soon able to walk about and swim, but those hatched in tree nests or on cliff faces must stay in the nests until they can fly. In either case, the parents bring them food until they learn to fly.

The usefulness of gulls as scavengers in the harbor and on the beach should be noted, and their importance as destroyers of insect pests is attested by the monument to them in Salt Lake City, placed there by grateful Mormons when gulls came and ate the locusts that threatened their crops. On the other hand, the propensity of some of the larger gulls for eating the eggs and young in sea-bird colonies sometimes rouses the guardians of sea-bird sanctuaries to action against them, and their eating of fish at fish weirs often annoys the fishermen. Perhaps the true value of gulls, everything considered, lies in the rugged beauty and the grace they bring to harbor and seashore.

Most gulls when adult are predominantly gray and white, with some black; their winter plumage is duller than that of summer. The plumage of the young birds of some species passes through several brownish stages before they become adult. The eighteen American species vary in size from about thirteen to thirty-two inches in length.

Gulls with White-tipped Wings

Two of our gulls have the back and the upper surfaces of the wings—the so-called mantle—pale gray and the whole wing tips white. One of these species, the glaucous gull, is one of our largest gulls, measuring up to thirty-two inches in length; the other, the Iceland gull, is smaller, reaching about twenty-six inches in length, and has a more slender bill.

The glaucous gull is one of the winter gulls of the United States, coming as far south as California, the Great Lakes and New York City at this season. It mixes with other common gulls but can be distinguished by its greater size—for it is even larger than the great black-backed gull—and by its white wing tips. Its home in other seasons is in the far north and it breeds in our hemisphere as far south as Newfoundland in the east and Alaska in the west, making its nest on sea cliffs or on islands, often near other sea-bird colonies. Like the great black-backed gull it has the reputation of destroying the eggs, young and even adults of other species, and the list of what it is known to eat ranges from the flesh of dead whales to worms and crowberries.

The Iceland gull nests only in Greenland. In winter, however, it comes south along the Atlantic coast as far as New Jersey, and also journeys inland to the Great Lakes. With their white wing tips these gulls are easily distinguished from the herring gulls, with which they are associated in our waters, and look more like small copies of the glaucous gull, another of our winter gulls. However, the close relationship between the Iceland gull and the herring gull seems to be demonstrated by the populations on Baffin Island, which are intermediate between the two. The status of several of these northern gulls, including Thayer's and Kumlien's gulls, is not clear, all of them looking like subspecies of the herring gull. This is a problem the solution of which will require field work in the Arctic.

Various Gray-mantled Gulls

There are five of these gulls which are very similar in appearance. The glaucous-winged gull of the Pacific coast is the largest; it is about twenty-six inches long, and is the only one with a pattern of gray on its white wing tips. The herring gull, about twenty-four inches long, has flesh-colored legs and a yellow bill with a red spot in the lower mandible. The California gull, about twenty-two inches long, has greenish legs and a yellow bill with a red or a black-and-red spot in the lower mandible. The ring-billed gull, about twenty inches long, has a yellow bill with a black band near the tip; and the short-billed gull, only about seventeen inches long, has an unmarked yellow-green bill. The last four species all have a black-and-white pattern on their wing tips.

The glaucous-winged gull (Plates 126, 139) nests on the Pacific coast from Alaska to Washington. Here the birds gather in huge colonies on coastal islands. Their neighbors at the nesting sites are such birds as puffins, auklets and murres, as well as petrels and cormorants. The glaucous-winged gulls apparently do not eat their neighbors'

eggs, differing in this respect from the Western gull. Once the nesting season is past, this species spreads out and is common along the Pacific coast, traveling as far south as California during the winter. Along with the glaucous, herring, California, Western and short-billed gulls, they feed along the beaches, follow coastwise shipping, frequent the harbors, and gather where garbage, sewage or offal from the cleaning of fish is available.

It is the herring gull (Plate 129), however, which is *the* seagull or harbor gull to many people, for this is the commonest gull in most parts of the northern hemisphere. In America it nests as far south as northern British Columbia, North Dakota, New York and New Jersey, both along the seacoast and by inland waters, and in winter it is common on both the Atlantic and Pacific coasts.

Like many other gulls the herring gulls are sociable, whether they are following in the wake of a coastal ship, clamoring over a garbage scow or a fishing boat, resting on a sand spit or nesting on an island. Their loud, harsh voices are a familiar part of the atmosphere along our waterfronts, ocean beaches and tidal flats. The herring gull makes a common practice of dropping shellfish from a height onto the sand to break them open. When it does so, however, it is sometimes victimized by crows. If a crow is on the beach where a gull drops a shellfish, it will walk over and seize the morsel of cracked-open shellfish while the gull is coming down.

The California gull (Plate 130) nests by the western interior lakes from Great Slave Lake in the Northwest Territories to California and North Dakota. It forms large colonies on its nesting grounds. It spends the winter on the Pacific coast. It is very like the herring gull not only in appearance but also in habits, and it has been suggested that they both belong to the same species.

The ring-billed gull (Plate 132) is another of our common, widely distributed gulls. It is like a slightly smaller herring gull, but the black band or ring on the bill of the adult is a good field mark, and the young birds in some plumages have a black band on the end of the tail that is also distinctive. This is one of the gulls that scavenges along our shores, the flocks fluttering and screaming over the water, or sits resting with other gulls on the breakwaters, piers or sandbars. I have seen ring-billed gulls on Lake Michigan using a peculiar diving technique in feeding on small fish that were evidently just too deep for them to reach. When a gull would see a fish beneath it, it would rise only two or three feet and then dive headfirst into the water, evidently getting impetus enough to reach the fish and sometimes going down until only its wing tips showed above the surface.

In winter the ring-billed gull is common on both our coasts and on some of our larger inland lakes. In the summer it nests in colonies on islands in inland lakes from Alaska to northern California, on prairie lakes, in the Great Lakes and in the Gulf of St. Lawrence. Naturally its summer neighbors differ widely from place to place. On the prairies its near nesting neighbors include California gulls, common terns, yellow-headed blackbirds and many pond ducks; in the Gulf of St. Lawrence they include herring gulls, eider ducks, auks and guillemots. Insects are one of the main foods of the colonies nesting in prairie country. I have also found these birds along the roads, feeding on ground squirrels run over by automobiles—taking the part played by vultures farther south.

The short-billed gull nests in the Alaska–Mackenzie area in the northwest, often placing its nest in a spruce tree. In winter it is found off our Pacific coast, in some places in considerable numbers; this bird seems to be more pelagic than other Pacific Coast gulls. It is said that this is the only gull that catches smelts, diving from the air for them. It is also reported that when the birds rise from the water with their fish, glaucous-winged gulls often rob them of their prey. The short-billed gull consorts with other gulls along the waterfronts of seaport towns, though it is less bold and less given to resting on piers than its larger relatives.

This species is also widespread in the northern part of the Old World, where it is called the mew gull or common gull.

Black-backed Gulls

Two of these gulls are distinguished by having a black mantle with an otherwise white plumage: the great black-backed gull, about thirty-one inches long, of the Atlantic coast; and the Western gull, about twenty-five inches long, of the Pacific coast.

The great black-backed gull (Plate 125) shares with the glaucous gull the distinction of being our largest gull. Its black mantle has earned it such local names as "saddleback" and "coffin-carrier." Though some of these gulls winter on the Great Lakes, they are chiefly a North Atlantic species, nesting on the coast or on islands in nearby lakes. In winter on the American side of the Atlantic they range as far southward as Delaware.

The bird-lover is presented with a problem by the habits of this gull. It is a strikingly colored, magnificent creature and a worthy addition to any sea-bird sanctuary; it is also a strong and predatory bird that not only eats almost anything of animal origin that floats in the sea or is found on its shores, but has been known to kill weakly lambs and eat other sea birds and their young and to take their eggs. In sea-bird sanctuaries some measures may be necessary to control this species.

The lesser black-backed gull, a similar but smaller bird, is a European species that has been recorded as a casual visitor to this hemisphere.

The Western gull (Plate 127) is the common dark-backed gull of our Pacific coast. It nests in great colonies on rocky islands off the coast from Washington to California. Here its near neighbors include pelicans, cormorants and murres. This gull has a record of being an inveterate egg-eater, especially when human visitors scare away sitting birds. When the nesting season is over the Western gulls spread along the entire coast, associating with other gulls, following schools of fish, gleaning whatever there is of animal food on the beaches, dropping shellfish on the shore, sitting on piers and wharves waiting for scraps to be thrown out, and following coastal vessels for the garbage from their galleys.

The slaty-backed gull is a bird of the Siberian side of the Bering Sea that sometimes occurs in Alaskan waters.

Black-headed Gulls

These include three common, small gulls characterized by gray mantles and, in summer, by black heads: the laughing gull, about sixteen inches long with nearly solid black wing tips; the Franklin's gull, which is slightly smaller and darker on the back and has some white marks on its black wing tips; and the Bonaparte's gull, about thirteen inches long, which has a big white streak along the forward edge of the wing.

Each of these species has a different breeding range and nesting habitat. If it is nesting on or near the beaches or salt-water marshes on our Atlantic coast, from Maine to Florida and Texas, it is a laughing gull. If it is nesting on a floating or anchored nest in open water or in a reed bed in a slough or lake in our northern prairie region, it is a Franklin's gull. If it has a stick nest in a spruce tree in the northern forests, where lakes and ponds are common, from British Columbia and Alaska to Hudson Bay, it is a Bonaparte's gull. The Franklin's and the laughing gulls winter on our southeastern coast, the laughing gulls southward from South Carolina, the Franklin's southward from Louisiana. The Bonaparte's gulls winter on the southern parts of both coasts, and in migration they pass in great numbers through the Great Lakes and along the larger river valleys.

These gulls, ranging in size from medium to small, all have a light, buoyant flight and are expert enough to catch insects in mid-air. Indeed, some of them may course like swallows over a meadow, filling up on surprisingly small morsels of prey. They are less given to scavenging than some of the other, bigger gulls, but probably upon occasion they will eat floating garbage.

The laughing gull (Plate 128) has a call that can be written, "ha, ha, ha, ha"—whence its name. This is a bird of the tidal estuaries and coasts, both summer and winter, and its compact breeding colonies often contain thousands of nests.

Besides feeding by snatching food, small fish and other marine animals from the water, the laughing gull sometimes alights on the head of a pelican as it emerges from a dive and picks food from the pelican's bill before it can be swallowed. This gull has also been observed chasing terns and robbing them of their fish, and is in turn pursued and robbed of its prey by jaegers and man-o'-war birds.

During the summer the Franklin's gull (Plate 133) is far from being a sea gull. In that season, this species is a prairie gull, nesting in sloughs and lakes in great colonies that contain tens of thousands of birds. During the day the birds spread out over the prairies to feed, eating many insects there. These gulls nest in colonies of their own kind but they have many close neighbors on their lakes, including coots, black terns, canvasback ducks, and yellow-headed blackbirds. With the approach of winter the Franklin's gulls leave the prairie for their migration overland to the Gulf of Mexico and beyond; they are of rare occurrence on either coast.

The Bonaparte's gull (Plate 140) seems very much out of place in its summer home—perched in the spruce trees of the northern forests and feeding on insects over the lakes and ponds near which it nests. The big flocks of these gulls that winter off our coasts change their diet to fish and a wide variety of other marine animals. Sometimes as the flocks carry out their search over the waters, the birds dive like terns, and I have seen them waiting near flocks of feeding red-breasted mergansers for the sake of the small fish that the mergansers' underwater activities frightened to the surface.

There are two other dark-headed gulls that occur here as visitors from the Old World. One is the black-headed gull, which has been recorded a few times in this country, and the other is the little gull, about eleven inches long—even smaller than the Bonaparte's gull—which is being recorded with increasing frequency in winter on our northeastern coast and even as far west as the Great Lakes. Perhaps it is becoming a regular winter visitor. Needless to say, the winter birds do not have the dark head characteristic of their breeding plumage, and so must be identified with great care.

Heermann's Gull

This Pacific Coast gull (Plate 131) is about twenty inches long and is the only American gull that is gray on the undersurface as well as above: it has a white head, a red bill and a black tail. It nests entirely on the Pacific coast of Mexico, and after the breeding season migrates northward like some of the herons and is then found as far north as British Columbia. In addition to catching fish for itself and picking up whatever animal matter it can find, this gull is a hanger-on of the pelican. The bird waits for the pelican to make a catch and then when the pelican has drained the water out of his pouch, the Heermann's gull tries to snatch the fish before the pelican can swallow it. There is an element of risk in this; one observer writes of a gull that got its head caught when the pelican snapped shut its bill and escaped only after a great deal of flapping about.

Kittiwakes

Kittiwakes are gray-mantled gulls with wing tips of solid black. The common kittiwake (Plates 137, 138) is about seventeen inches long and has black legs; the red-legged kittiwake (Plate 134) is about fifteen inches long and has red legs.

The common kittiwakes are more truly birds of the open ocean than most of our gulls, great flocks of them spending the fall and winter about the fishing grounds miles off the shore. There are a number that have made transatlantic crossings, as shown by the birds that have been banded in the British Isles and recovered in Newfoundland. These birds gather about fishing boats that are cleaning fish and they habitually follow steamers. They do not completely shun the shore, big flocks sometimes feeding along exposed tidal flats.

At nesting time, in the spring, the birds go to little ledges on steep, ocean-fronting cliffs and there construct their nests, sometimes thousands being built on a single cliff face. As with many other birds, the cries of the kittiwakes seem contagious and the calling of a few birds often starts an uproar in the whole colony—which ends as suddenly as it begins.

The kittiwake is a northern nesting bird, with southern outpost colonies in our hemisphere in the Gulf of St. Lawrence and the Aleutians. Winter drives the northern birds southward to sojourn off our Atlantic and Pacific coasts.

The red-legged kittiwake is almost entirely a Bering Sea species, nesting only on three islands there and wintering in adjacent waters.

Three Arctic Gulls

There are three species of gulls which nest in the Arctic and are rarely seen in the United States. The ivory gull, about sixteen inches long, is the only one of our gulls that has a pure white adult plumage set off by black legs. It could also be called an ice gull, for it is typically a bird of the pack ice of the Arctic. It nests on far northern Arctic islands where late-remaining ice prevents easy access to its nesting places, and in winter it migrates regularly only to the edge of the pack ice in the Bering Strait and off the Labrador coast.

Sabine's gull (Plate 136) is a small, fork-tailed species, about thirteen inches long, with a gray head and a black ring around its neck. It nests on the Arctic tundra in scattered localities around the globe. The only known wintering place of this bird is off the coast of Peru. The known migration route passes so far off our Pacific coast that few bird students ever see this gull. No well-defined migration is known in the Atlantic, though the bird has occasionally been seen on our east coast, and in the interior as well.

The Ross's gull, even more truly an Arctic bird, is known to nest only at the mouths of a few rivers in northwestern Siberia. Most of these birds spend the winter among the pack ice of the Arctic Ocean and feed among the moving ice floes. There are only a few records of their straggling south through the Bering Strait or to western Europe. This species is about thirteen inches long and has a black neck-ring like that of the Sabine's gull, but its head is white, its white body plumage is tinged with rose, and its tail is pointed.

CHAPTER 31

Terns

TERNS are slender, long-winged sea birds, often with deeply forked tails, and this, appropriately, has earned them the name of "sea swallows." Small to medium-sized birds, they are close relatives of the gulls, specialized for flight and not for swimming. Their webbed feet are small, they rarely rest on the water, and they do not swim well. When resting, the birds gather on the strand at the water's edge or perch on floating wreckage. Many species of terns have the same basic color pattern, white with a gray mantle and a black cap, and the sexes are alike.

The smallest species, the least tern, is about nine inches long and has a white forehead and a yellow bill. The Arctic, common, roseate and Forster's terns have red or black-and-red bills and the outer tail feathers are extended, forming a deeply forked

tail and giving the birds a length of fifteen to seventeen inches. The gull-billed tern, about fourteen inches long, has a shallowly forked tail, and a stout, gull-like, all-black bill. The crested terns, the elegant, royal and Cabot's, are from fifteen to twenty inches long and have the feathers of the nape elongated into a short crest, most noticeable when the birds are perched. The Caspian tern, with a heavy red bill, is much larger than any of the crested terns, but its tail is short, having only a shallow fork, so that the bird is only about twenty-one inches long.

A few species of terns have quite different color patterns. The black tern, about ten inches long, has a black head and underparts and a gray back and rump; the sooty tern, about sixteen inches long, has black upperparts and white underparts; and the noddy tern is dark brown above and below except for a pale gray crown and a white forehead.

In winter and in their immature plumage many of these birds have less distinctive markings and are more difficult to identify.

The flight of terns is light and bounding. The birds feed by flying low over the water, snatching fish from the surface without wetting their plumage, or flying higher over the water, hovering, and then plunging headlong in a dive that may take them completely under the surface. Some terns, especially those of the marshes, feed mainly on insects on the wing.

Terns are typically birds of the sea beaches, resting in flocks, feeding in the adjacent waters in loose parties, and continually giving shrill, sharp cries. Some species frequent both the ocean and the larger lakes, and a few are typically marsh birds at nesting time. As a group the terns are tropical, most of the forty species making their headquarters in tropical areas, but ten species nest on the United States mainland, and two more nest in the Dry Tortugas near the Florida keys. As one would expect of a group of tropical origin, long migrations are the rule for these birds, though a few species go no farther than our southern coasts to winter. One species, the Arctic tern, is an exceptionally long-range migrant and goes from the Arctic to the Antarctic, crossing the Atlantic to Europe as part of its long journey.

Terns are sociable birds, whether feeding, resting or nesting. More than one species may nest together and their colonies often contain thousands of nests. The birds are active, excitable, and much more high-strung than the gulls, and there is constant movement in and about a colony. The nests of most species are often little more than hollows scratched in the sand or depressions in gravel or rocky shores, with no attempt at concealment. Whether or not nest material is added depends upon whether or not any is immediately available; this makes for considerable variation in the nests. Certain marsh terns, such as the Forster's, sometimes make substantial, gull-like nests; at other times they place their eggs in simple hollows on floating masses of vegetation. The noddy tern nests in bushes. The eggs range in number from one to three, and are grayish or brownish, with many dark markings. Both parents take turns in sitting on the eggs, the period of incubation varying with the species from about fifteen to twenty-six days. When the broods hatch out they are down-covered, and the parents carry fish in their bills to feed them. Ordinarily the young terns stay near the nest site; if they are dis-turbed they may wander about the colony and gather into large bands, but even then the individual adults and chicks seem to recognize each other, apparently doing so by voice. After about a month the young birds begin to fly, but they continue to associate with the parents and are fed by them probably until they start on their southward migration.

While the plume trade flourished, the terns, many of which nested on easily accessible beaches, suffered heavily from the feather hunters. The least terns especially were greatly reduced in numbers on our Atlantic coast. With protection they have again increased, and their breeding colonies and flocks feeding offshore are again characteristic of our beaches. The greatly increased use of the beaches for human recreation may have a more and more detrimental effect on some terns.

Least Tern

The least tern (Plate 147) is a dainty bird characterized by light, graceful flight and shrill, sharp cries as it passes along our beaches in the summer. At that time its associates are the piping plover on the northern sand beaches, and the Wilson's or snowy plover in the south. It nests not only along our Atlantic, Gulf of Mexico and southern California coasts, but also on the bars and islands of the Mississippi River system. The least tern is less sociable than certain other terns, and its nesting colonies, scattered along the beaches, more often comprise scores than hundreds of birds.

The nests are usually simple hollows in the open sand, less often on mud flats or on shell reefs, and their lining is limited to bits of shell or pebbles. The two or three eggs laid in the nest resemble these shell fragments or pebbles in their color patterns, and thus are well disguised. The adult birds fish in the nearby waters, flying low and snatching fish from near the surface or hovering higher over the water, and then plunging down for their fish. After the nesting season the birds move southward and winter for the most part in South America, although a few of them remain as far north as our Louisiana coast.

Common, Arctic, Roseate, and Forster's Terns

A great many different terns are similar in appearance, having whitish and grayish bodies with black caps, and the common tern (Plate 143), the Arctic tern (Plate 144), the roseate tern (Plate 145), and the Forster's tern (Plate 142) are strikingly alike. To distinguish them attention must be paid to such details as the red, black-tipped bill of the common tern; the all-red bill of the Arctic tern, and the black bill, with perhaps a little red in its base, of the roseate tern. The Forster's tern has a bill like the common tern but its wing tips are paler rather than darker than the back. Though these four species are so similar, each has its own special characteristics.

The most remarkable feature in the life of the Arctic tern is its long-range migration from the Arctic to the Antarctic. Because of this, as has often been pointed out, the Arctic tern probably enjoys more daylight hours each year than any other bird. For a time it was doubted that so long a migration took place, but recent investigation has shown that many Arctic terns do go south of the Atlantic and spend the northern winter season among the pack ice of the Antarctic. The Arctic tern is a circumpolar nester and breeds in our hemisphere as far south as northern British Columbia, northern Manitoba, and New England. Some of the birds migrate along our Pacific coast, staying well out to sea, but in the main migration, the birds apparently cross the Atlantic from the northeastern part of our continent to Europe, and then fly south to the Antarctic. They have been seen migrating in mid-ocean, stopping to rest on floating wreckage, and banded birds have been recovered in Europe and South Africa. The longest Arctic tern flight recorded is that of one banded as a nestling in Greenland and recovered in Natal, southeastern Africa, after a flight of about eleven thousand miles, which the bird had made in the less than three months it had been able to fly.

The common tern nests farther southward than the Arctic tern. In our area it nests in scattered localities from central and eastern Canada to North Dakota and North Carolina, and also in the states bordering the Gulf of Mexico. In migration it passes along both coasts, and some of the birds winter in Florida.

The roseate tern is another species of the warmer parts of the world. In this country it nests along the Atlantic coast from Nova Scotia to Virginia, and migrates along that coast, wintering from Louisiana to Brazil.

Forster's tern is exclusively an American species, nesting by inland waters from California and Washington to Minnesota and Illinois, with other populations on the coasts of Virginia, Louisiana and Texas. In migration it may be found on both coasts, but it winters chiefly from California and South Carolina southward to Central America.

The Arctic, common, and roseate terns usually nest on sand beaches, gravel bars or rocky places, often on islands or on the edge of the sea, and the Arctic and common terns also nest by large inland lakes. The roseate tern, which is more strictly a sea bird, usually nests along with other species, sometimes in enormous colonies. None of these three terns does much nest-building beyond scratching a hollow in the ground and adding a few bits of vegetation. Forster's tern in summer is, however, a bird of fresh as well as salt marshes and it makes a substantial nest among grasses or heaps of washed-up vegetation, or, in lakes, on floating masses of cattails among tall, thick tules over deep water.

Typically these terns forage for their food by flying over the water, often in flocks, and, when they locate fish, diving headlong into the water for them. Since the Forster's terns are more typically marsh birds, they often take insects, picking them from the water or catching them on the wing.

Two related species of rare or limited occurrence in the United States are the Aleutian tern (similar to the common tern but with a white forehead when in its breeding plumage), which has a limited breeding range in the Bering Sea area and migrates along the west side of the Pacific to spend the winter in Japan; and the Trudeau's tern, a white-headed tern of South America, which has only once been recorded here, in New Jersey.

Gull-billed Tern

Though the gull-billed tern nests by the edge of the sea or by lakes, its feeding habits take it most often to land. There it flies about, swooping down on insects, snatching them from resting places or capturing them in flight. It may even walk about looking for its prey or follow the plow and eat a variety of creatures ranging from worms to frogs and mice. Like most birds it is adaptable and sometimes does feed over the water, diving for fish like any of the fish-eating terns.

It is almost cosmopolitan in the warmer parts of the globe; in the United States it ranges northward along the southeastern coast to Virginia, and in the West nests by the Salton Sea in California. Formerly it nested as far north as New Jersey, largely in the salt marshes, but apparently it now favors the sea beaches for its nesting colonies. Though it much resembles in appearance a number of other gray-backed, black-capped terns, its heavy, all-black bill makes it fairly easy to identify.

Crested Terns

We have three fairly large, black-capped terns in which the feathers of the nape are lengthened to form a short crest. All three are southern species and birds of the seashore. One, the elegant tern, has a very restricted range in the Lower California area of Mexico, and like Heermann's gull moves northward after the breeding season and occurs on the California coast in the autumn. The second, the royal tern (Plates 146, 148), nests along the Atlantic coast as far north as Virginia, but on the Pacific coast not farther north than Mexico. (The records of this tern from California are of non-breeding birds.) The third is Cabot's tern (Plate 153), found along our southeastern coast from Virginia southward to the West Indies and Central America. This bird also occurs in West Africa and in Europe, where it is known as the Sandwich tern.

The royal tern, the largest of these, is about twenty inches long and has a red bill; the elegant tern is very similar but is only about seventeen inches long; and the Cabot's tern measures about fifteen inches and has a black, yellow-tipped bill.

The two species that nest in the United States, the Cabot's and royal terns, favor flat, sandy, coastal islands and seem to like each other's company, often nesting in the same colonies. Their nests are simple depressions in the open sand placed close together and with little or no lining. In such flat coastal areas there is the hazard of the nests being flooded by high water, and the authors of *South Carolina Bird Life* write of a colony of eleven thousand nests of royal terns on the South Carolina coast that was largely destroyed by a high tide.

As might be expected, these larger terns often fish farther from shore than do the smaller species, diving into the water in typical tern-fashion. The royal tern also flies along close to the water and picks up fish from near the surface.

Caspian Tern

The largest of our terns, the Caspian tern (Plate 141), is about as large as a medium-sized gull, is built rather heavily for a tern, and has a fairly steady, powerful flight. It is one of the cosmopolitan species. In America it nests in many scattered localities, on islands in lakes of the interior, from Great Slave Lake in northwestern Canada to California and Michigan, and on coastal islands in the Gulf of St. Lawrence and off our southeastern coast. Two or three eggs are laid on the sand or gravel or on floating masses of dead vegetation. Though some colonies contain hundreds of nests, these birds also nest in smaller congregations. Reflecting their less sociable nature, their colonies are often somewhat withdrawn from those of the gulls or other terns nesting

nearby. In feeding, too, the Caspian tern is often seen alone. Despite its size, it is a graceful bird in flight. To get the fish on which it lives, it often dives from the air, as do the smaller sea terns, but it also alights on the water and feeds there in gull-fashion. The Caspian tern has been accused of eating young birds and of robbing other terns and small gulls of their catches. In winter our inland Caspian terns move to the coast, and in this hemisphere they winter in the southern coastal states and Mexico.

Black Tern

Forsaking the sand beaches and gravel bars used by so many of our terns for nesting, the black terns (Plates 150, 152), like a few others, go for the nesting season to the interior marshes. There, protected from four-footed predators by the standing water, they build solid nests among the reeds, or crude ones on masses of floating rubbish, on old muskrat houses, or in grebes' nests. They usually gather in small colonies and are extremely bold and vociferous in defense of their eggs or young, circling overhead, screaming, diving down and even repeatedly striking an intruder.

Sometimes when they are feeding, little parties of these black terns beat back and forth over the water with their bills pointed downward, watching for insects on the surface and dropping down to seize them. They also feed over meadows, swooping down among the grass heads to pick off insects resting there or to snap up those in flight. This occurs in summer, when the black tern is one of the common birds in our inland marshes from east central Alaska to California, and from Ontario to Tennessee.

When autumn comes the black tern flies to South America for the winter. Most of them migrate through the interior of the continent, although some reach the Atlantic coast and there feed over the salt water, fishing with the common terns.

A somewhat similar Old World species, the white-winged tern, has been recorded as a straggler in the United States.

Sooty Tern

The sooty tern (Plate 149) nests by the tens of thousands on the Dry Tortugas, small islets near the Florida keys, but only occasionally wanders to our mainland coast. Its main range is in tropical seas where the birds gather in numbers to breed on isolated islands. The most interesting point in its biology is that while in the Dry Tortugas it nests once a year, in summer, as do most birds, whereas on Ascension Island in the South Atlantic it nests once every nine months. This conclusion is based on records gathered over a long period by Dr. J. P. Chapin, of the American Museum of Natural History, but the cause of this nine-month cycle for one population of this species remains a mystery.

A close relative of the sooty tern, the bridled tern, has occasionally been recorded in our southeastern states.

Noddy Tern

The noddy tern is widespread around tropical and subtropical coasts and islands, its breeding colony nearest to our coastline being in the Dry Tortugas, about sixty-five miles west of Key West. Here the birds appear for the summer season, make their nests in the cactus and other bushes, sometimes as high as twelve feet above the ground, raise their single young, and leave again in the autumn. Strangely little is known about what they do the rest of the year. The noddy tern is a paradox as a sea bird, for it nests on small islands and gets its food from the sea but apparently rarely wets its feathers except when it bathes—which it does by touching the surface of the water in flight.

It gets its food by waiting until underwater enemies drive small fish to the surface, where the bird picks them up. It rarely rests on the water, but perches ashore or on any bit of flotsam or even on the heads of swimming pelicans.

The discovery of the singular homing ability of the noddy terns by Dr. J. B. Watson in 1907 occupies an important place in the annals of our study of bird navigation. Watson found that the breeding birds of the Dry Tortugas seldom fed more than fifteen miles from their nesting island. Nevertheless, a bird that he shipped to Cape Hatteras, outside the normal range of the species and about 1,000 miles away along the shore, and released there, was back at its nest in five days. Other birds released in the Gulf of Mexico returned home in three days, from a point about 460 miles away, over open water without landmarks. Experiments are still being carried on to find out how birds find their way; so far we have no clear-cut answers to the problem.

CHAPTER 32

Skimmers

SKIMMERS (Plate 158) are in general ternlike, with black or dark brown upperparts, white underparts, and small red feet. Their bill, however, is most peculiar, the lower mandible being as thin as a knife blade and much longer than the upper. The seacoast of our southeastern states is their main home in the United States, the flocks resting on sandbars or beaches and feeding over nearby waters. They breed on the Atlantic coast from New Jersey southward to South America, and winter from Florida southward.

The flight of skimmers is swift and graceful and when feeding, whether by day or by night, they fly with the lower mandible cutting the water, passing again and again over the same place. Some fish may be seized in this random "plowing," but it has also been suggested that the movement of the bill in the water, made conspicuous at night by phosphorescence, attracts small fish, which are then caught by the skimmers. They also feed by wading in shallow water and catching small animals with a thrust of the bill, a method one would think quite unsuited to their short legs and the strange shape of their bills.

At nesting time these birds are gregarious, gathering in colonies on offshore sandbars or islands.

There the birds scratch little hollows in the sand and lay clutches which usually contain four eggs. These are pale blue, or whitish, and heavily marked with brown; when the downy young hatch they are gray, mottled with black, both eggs and young being thus colored to match the sand on which they rest. While the nestlings are small the parents bring

them predigested food and regurgitate it for them, but later they bring whole fish.

The family to which the skimmers belong is a small one, containing only three species, but widely distributed over the warmer parts of the globe. Besides the American species, the black skimmer, there is one in southern Asia and one in Africa.

CHAPTER 33

Jaegers and Skuas

J AEGERS and skuas are close relatives of gulls, but their flight is more hawklike, their bills more hooked, and they have adoped predatory habits and piratical methods of getting food. They spend more time at sea than do most gulls, making long migrations over oceans, and spending the winter at sea.

These maritime habits have made it difficult to find out just what parts of the ocean they frequent in winter, and what their habits are at this season, which leaves much still to be learned about them.

There are three species of jaegers and one skua. The jaegers are variable in color, having light color phases in which the upperparts are dull brown and the underparts are white, and dark color phases in which the whole bird is brownish black. The shape and length of the elongated tail feathers of the adult jaegers and skuas serve as identifying characteristics. The immature birds are very difficult to identify. In November, on the southern shores of Lake Michigan, I am almost sure to see a few dark-plumaged jaegers flying low over the water, but rarely can I do more than guess at the species involved.

The parasitic jaeger (Plate 123), from sixteen to twenty-one inches long, has pointed central tail feathers that extend a few inches beyond the rest of the tail. The pomarine jaeger, about twenty-one inches long, has central tail feathers of normal width, extending a few inches beyond the rest of the tail and ending in a twist. The long-tailed jaeger, about twenty-two inches in length, has central tail feathers that are narrow and pointed and extend as much as ten inches beyond the rest of the tail. The skua is a much larger, stouter-bodied bird than the jaegers, though with its short, square tail it is only about twenty-two inches long. It is dark brown and has a white patch in each wing at the base of the flight feathers.

The three species of jaegers nest on the Arctic and subarctic tundra all around the globe. The parasitic jaeger often nests in colonies, whereas the other two are more solitary at nesting time; all three have nesting habits much like those of the gulls. The nests are scantily lined hollows on the open ground and the clutch usually consists of two eggs. These eggs are protectively colored, olive blotched with dark brown, and the parents take turns sitting on them for the three or four weeks that it takes the down-covered young to hatch. The chicks are brown above, paler below. Some reports indicate that the fledglings walk away from the nest very soon; others that they remain in the nest for a long period. In any case they are fed by the parents for about a month, that is, until they are on the wing.

When these birds are on their nesting grounds their diet is varied. Hawking about over the tundra, they swoop down and snatch up lemmings, young birds and insects, or pursue and kill such small birds as longspurs and sandpipers, harry terns and small gulls until they disgorge the fish they have caught, and feed on crowberries or carrion.

Jaegers of all three species migrate along our shores, sometimes well out to sea, and a few visit the Great Lakes. There are only a scattering of other inland records. They usually migrate singly or in small parties. In their winter quarters at sea farther south, about which we have scant data, there are probably few gulls or terns to rob and they may have to fish for themselves in gull-fashion.

The northern skua (Plate 124) is not truly a North American bird, for it nests only in the northwestern Atlantic from Iceland to islands off Scotland. Its wide wanderings over the ocean, however, bring many of this species to the fishing banks off Newfoundland and New England in summer. It winters chiefly in the eastern Atlantic.

Although this skua is only about the size of a herring gull, it harries even the great black-backed gull as well as smaller species to make them drop or regurgitate their prey. In robbing a gannet it may seize the bird by the wing, bring it down on the water and hold it there until the gannet gives up its food. Despite this habitual piracy, the skua can and does fish for itself and also picks up or dives for fish offal.

The other skuas nest in the southern hemisphere. On our west coast, however, the Chilean skua has been found as far north as British Columbia in summer, before its breeding season begins, and it has been suggested that some of the wide-ranging birds seen in the North Atlantic during the summer may be migrant Antarctic skuas from the South Atlantic. Among the unsolved problems concerning these birds is the basic one of how many species there are, and until we know the skuas better it is best to consider them all one species, with several subspecies and an interesting bipolar distribution.

CHAPTER 34

The Auk Family

THE members of this family go by such a variety of names—auk, murre, dovekie, guillemot, murrelet, auklet, and puffin—that one is likely to forget that they are all auks and very similar in form and structure. They are distantly related to the buoyant-winged gulls and to the fleet-footed sandpipers and plovers, but the auk family has specialized in swimming and diving in the coastal and offshore waters of the oceans. The auk group is small, containing only about twenty-two species, and is limited to the temperate and Arctic parts of the North Atlantic and the North Pacific, with about fourteen species nesting in the Bering Sea area.

The birds in this family are rather stout-bodied and short-necked, with small, webbed feet placed far back on their bodies, and with short, narrow wings. The species vary in size from the tiny least auklet, which is about six and one-half inches long, to the murre, which is about as large as a medium-sized duck, though it might be added that the extinct great auk was considerably larger, having been about the size of a small goose.

The typical color pattern for both sexes is blackish above and whitish below, often with a black throat, although some species are generally blackish below or mottled with black. There are white patches in the wings of the guillemots, white patches on the faces of the puffins, and most auklets as well as puffins have elaborate head plumes or bill decorations. Outside of the breeding season all these birds often have a whiter plumage, especially on the underparts, and the elaborate, decorative feathers of the head are moulted.

The birds of this family are adept at diving and

once underwater they swim by means of their wings, as though flying through the water, and use their feet only in maneuvering. The food they capture varies with the species; some feed largely on fish whereas others eat the floating and swimming invertebrates, such as shrimps, that swarm in Arctic waters. Some of the larger auks are clumsy in landing or taking off on water, but not so the smaller species, which practically fly in and out of the water. In the air the auks' small wings beat rapidly and carry them in direct, rapid flight; an exception to this was the great auk, which was flightless. On land some of the auks stand flat on the whole tarsus, resting in an upright position that recalls that of the penguin, and move about with an awkward shuffle, whereas others stand upright on their toes and run nimbly about over the rocks.

The auks come to land only for nesting. Then they gather in immense numbers on certain favorite, rocky islands offshore or on inaccessible cliffs on the mainland facing the sea. A very few species fly inland to nest on mountain slopes a number of miles from the sea. Several species often nest together and in close proximity to such other sea birds as gulls, cormorants and petrels, and the resulting tens of thousands of birds make these among the most notable of bird colonies. In such colonies some species are conspicuous; the murres cover the rocks and line the ledges, and auklets and puffins sit about on the rocks, fly this way or that, or float on the nearby water. Some of the species, however, come to the nesting colonies only at night, and during the day are either hidden in underground nests or are off to distant fishing grounds.

Crevices in cliffs, nooks and crannies among rocks on talus slopes or among boulders covering beaches are the favorite nesting places of auks. If turf-covered slopes are available, some birds will dig burrows. A few, such as the murres, lay their eggs on open rocks or ledges without any protective covering. Only the puffins carry nesting material into their burrows; the other species lay their eggs on bare rock, soil, or gravel. Most of these species lay a single egg; only a few lay two eggs. The eggs are either white, with or without a trace of spotting, or are boldly spotted. Both parents take turns at sitting on the eggs, the incubation period varying from about three to seven weeks according to the species. The young hatch densely covered with down and at first stay in the nest and are dependent on the parents for food.

There is a wide variation in the development of the young of different species of the auk family. In some the nestlings when only partly grown and still flightless may flutter and bounce down to the sea and swim away under parental care. Others stay in the nest until full-grown. Among the puffins, the adults desert the full-grown young bird, which, after a few days of fasting, emerges from the burrow and goes to the sea by itself.

After the nesting season the birds spread out from their breeding colonies. Their migrations are not extensive except when they are forced out of Arctic waters by the ice, and even then some of them feed among the cracks and open leads of water in the sea ice. In general, auks do not remain on the coasts in winter but move out onto the open sea some miles away from shore. There they sleep on the water and feed beneath its surface. There are sporadic influxes of some species onto the coasts outside their normal wintering ranges, and individuals have been found stranded in the country miles from the sea. Incidentally, these movements seem to correspond to the periodic flights of the snowy owls from the Arctic.

Auks are shot as game birds only locally on our northern coasts, but the eggs of some species have long been gathered as food for humans. The Eskimos in the far north also catch some of the smaller species for food by hiding among the rocks where the nesting birds swarm and scooping them out of the air with a net.

The rocky fastnesses in which most of these species nest, their small size and their habit of wintering on the open ocean seem to have protected many of them adequately. The wholesale gathering of eggs for food that once decimated some species is a thing of the past, and many sanctuaries have been established where the birds can breed unmolested. However, in the sanctuaries a danger still threatens from another source—the gulls that eat their eggs, especially those of the murres, which nest in the open. Ordinarily the eggs are continually covered by one or the other of the parents, so that gulls rarely have a chance to take more than an occasional egg, but well-meaning sightseers and even bird students may flush the murres from their eggs and thus give the gulls a chance to do real damage.

There are six extant species of auks on the Atlantic coast, all of them with black-and-white plumage. They are as follows: the dovekie, which is the smallest, being about the size of a robin; the larger puffin, which has a thin, high, triangular-shaped and partly red bill; the black guillemot, which is all black in summer except for a white wing patch; the common and Brunnich's murres, which are about seventeen inches long and have slender bills; and the razor-billed auk, which is similar to the murres but has a thin, high bill with a white line across it.

There are other species in the Pacific area and they can be grouped as follows: the auklets, which are very small to medium-sized birds with thick bills, most of them with head plumes in their breeding dress; the murrelets, which are small birds with slender, pointed bills; the puffins, which are large birds with large, thin bills; and the larger, slender-billed murres.

Great Auk

The great auks are extinct. They had been preyed on by man since the Neanderthals caught and ate them at Gibraltar and left their bones to be found in later ages, but it was the crews of sailing ships, raiding the nesting colonies, that made the most catastrophic inroads. The last bird in Newfoundland was killed about 1800 and the last in Iceland in 1844.

The great auk used to nest on rocky islets in the Gulf of St. Lawrence, off Newfoundland, Iceland and Great Britain; in winter it migrated southward as far as Florida in the United States and the Mediterranean in Europe. Its migrations were made by swimming, for it had such small wings that it was flightless, resembling the penguin in this respect. By an interesting train of events the name penguin was first given to the great auk and only later came to be applied exclusively to the group of flightless, swimming birds of the southern hemisphere known as penguins today.

The great auk stood about two feet high, its name deriving from the fact that it was the largest of the auks. Its color scheme was a common one in the group: mostly black above and white below.

As nesting sites the birds chose rocky ledges to which they could walk from the sea, and there they laid and brooded their single, spotted egg. Presumably the nestling followed the adults to the sea before it was half grown and thereafter spent much of its life at sea, feeding on fish and traveling by swimming and diving.

Razor-billed Auk

The razor-billed auk (Plate 159) is the closest living relative of the extinct great auk, but is only about seventeen inches long, or about half as large as the other bird. The razor-bill is one of the sea fowl that frequent the ledges of sea cliffs and rocky coasts of the North Atlantic from the Bay of Fundy to Great Britain. Black above and white below, with a black throat in summer, it is most easily distinguished from the throngs of murres by its deep bill with a white line across it. Unlike the murres, the razor-bill prefers to lay its single egg in some sheltered place, such as a crevice or under a boulder, resting it on the bare rock. For about the first two weeks after hatching, the downy nestling is fed on the ledge by the parents; then, when it is only half grown, but already covered with feathers, it flutters down to the sea and swims off with the old birds. Away from their nesting grounds the razor-bills live offshore, sometimes miles from land, feeding by diving for fish, crustaceans and other marine animals, and sleeping on the water. During the winter they move southward along our Atlantic coast to New York and occasionally as far as North Carolina.

Murres

The murres line the sea cliffs at nesting time even more thickly than the razor-billed auks, gathering in great, densely packed throngs and standing upright in penguin-like attitudes. They are distinguishable from the razor-bills by their slender, pointed bills, but the two species of murres, the common (Plates 151, 157) and the Brunnich's (Plate 154), are not easily told apart, the whitish line along the gape of the slightly thicker bill of the Brunnich's murre being the most obvious field distinction. Some birds, called "bridled common murres," have a color phase distinguished by a white line back of the eye. The Brunnich's murre is the more northerly, in the western hemisphere nesting only as far south as the Gulf of St. Lawrence and the Bering Sea area, wintering as far south as New York and occasionally South Carolina. In the Pacific it winters on the Asiatic side, as far south as Japan. The common murre nests on the coast of eastern Canada, rarely coming southward off the New England coast, and also nests all along our Pacific coast from the Bering Sea to California, where it is known as the California murre.

The habits of the two birds are similar; they spend the winter in flocks, swimming in the open ocean well offshore and feeding on fish, shrimp and other small sea animals. In the spring they return to their nesting sites, usually the ledges and rocks of steep-sided, offshore islands or isolated cliffs, gathering in colonies that may contain thousands of birds. Here the single egg is laid on the bare ledge with no nest construction at all. The shape of the egg, nearly conical, is such that it is said to roll in a circle rather than off the edge of the ledge, though when murres are alarmed and fly from their nest ledges, many eggs do fall over the edge. Like the razor-bills, the downy young of the murres are fed on the ledges by both parents and soon acquire a coat of feathers. By the time they are half grown they flutter down to the sea. Bouncing off rocks on the way down doesn't seem to injure them. Once in the water they swim away with their parents, who themselves leave the land until the next nesting season.

Dovekie

Only about eight inches long, the dovekie is the smallest auk of the North Atlantic. On the American side of the Atlantic it nests only in Greenland but it is enormously abundant there. Five million birds have been estimated to inhabit the Scoresby Sound district alone, and Dr. Finn Salomonsen of Denmark writes that where they nest in holes and crannies in the shattered rock of the talus slopes, their black-and-white plumage dots the talus for several miles, while the flocks that fly about look from a distance like dense swarms of gnats.

In the north the dovekies are birds of the pack ice; they rest on the floes and swim and dive in the cracks and open leads, feeding on the crustaceans that abound in Arctic waters. With winter, when the seas freeze completely over, they move southward to Newfoundland waters and along our coasts usually as far as the Carolinas. There most of the birds keep well offshore, feeding, resting or making short flights in little flocks. Each winter a small number are stranded, dying in the New England coastal area, and occasionally a few have straggled to the Great Lakes. At long intervals, however, there are widespread invasions or influxes that take an amazing number of these birds far out of their normal range. In late 1932, such an influx occurred from eastern Canada to Florida and Cuba. On a 400-mile stretch of Florida coast an estimated twenty thousand dovekies were washed up on the beach. Others were carried inland and individuals were found scores of miles from salt water. Just what brings about such mass movements is not known, but they recall the periodic migrations of the lemmings in the Arctic and the occasional southward movement of snowy owls.

Guillemots

Guillemots are very different from the rest of the auk family; their summer plumage is uniformly black except for large white wing patches, and they have bright red feet. There are two species, very much alike, but with quite different ranges: the pigeon guillemot lives in the Pacific and nests from Alaska to California, whereas the black guillemot (Plate 160) lives in the Arctic and in the North Atlantic, nesting as far south on the American coast as Maine and wintering south of Cape Cod.

On the Maine coast the black guillemot nests under boulders or well back in crevices of rocks not far above the sea. In these little caves the birds lay two eggs, a larger number than most auks, and the fuzzy young are fed until they are full grown, whereupon they accompany their parents into the sea. These birds are social, but their colonies are usually small—in marked contrast to the immense size of those of some of their relatives. Once nesting is over, the birds scatter along the coast, small parties swimming about near the rocky shores and diving for their food of fish, shrimps and crabs. When swimming they tend to float high, but when alarmed they may gradually sink down until their backs are awash, and then dive or, with a pattering of their feet to get them off the water, fly away.

The pigeon guillemot of the Pacific is similar in habits to the Atlantic bird. It is common in summer about rocky shores and cliffs, where it nests among the rocks, though at times it is said to dig its own burrow in the ground. Unlike some auks, this species can stand up on its toes and walk about freely. Though the guillemots often swim about closer to shore than most of their relatives, and frequently gather in parties on outlying rocks to rest, it is probable that part of their autumn migration takes them well out to sea, where they spend the winter.

Murrelets

The murrelets are small auks that live on the Pacific Ocean. Only about ten inches long, they are chunky in appearance and when they are on the water their heads are drawn in so close to their bodies that they appear neckless. Compared with auklets of similar size, their bills are more slender and pointed. Five species of murrelets have been recorded in our waters, but there are only three that are common on the coast of the United States. Xantus's murrelet has uniform blackish upperparts and white underparts. The ancient murrelet has a black crown and a grayish back and in summer has a black throat and a white line over the eye. The marbled murrelet in summer is barred brown and black above, and grayish brown mottled with white below, and in winter is white below and blackish above, with a white line between the back and the wing. The two other species are Craveri's murrelet, which is so much like Xantus's murrelet that they cannot be told apart in the field; and Kittlitz's murrelet, a bird of the Bering Sea which is a paler, grayer edition of the marbled murrelet.

Marbled Murrelet

The marbled murrelets are the commonest of the auk family along the inside passages formed by the many islands on the Pacific coast from Washington to Alaska, and they also frequent the open ocean to the south as far as California. Singly, in pairs, or in small parties, these murrelets swim and dive for their staple food of fishes. They rise easily from the water and like to skim over the surface; they also tend to fly at quite a height above the ocean.

Despite their abundance and the fact that their eggs have been described, the nesting of this species is still something of a mystery. From what has been discovered, and especially because the birds have been found some miles inland and have been seen flying over forests, it seems probable that they nest under logs or in burrows in the spongy ground of the humid forests of the mountains facing the Pacific Ocean from Alaska to California.

Xantus's and Craveri's Murrelet

Xantus's murrelet inhabits Lower Californian and southern Californian waters, swimming and feeding on the open ocean and nesting on islands among the rocks of broken cliffs or talus slopes near the surf. There it lays one or two eggs directly on the rocks and is said to nest twice in the season between March and June. The downy young birds are even more precocious than those of the razor-bills and the murres, for it is said that when only a few days old they go to sea with their parents. This murrelet is so similar to Craveri's murrelet, which breeds on islands in the Gulf of California and comes north to the California coast in winter, that the two may well be subspecies. They seem indistinguishable in the field, the upperparts of both being plain grayish black and the underparts a uniform white at all seasons.

Ancient Murrelet

In summer the ancient murrelet likes the quiet waters of the sheltered bays and passages among the Queen Charlotte Islands of British Columbia, the Aleutian Islands, and islands off Japan. There is also one record of their breeding in the State of Washington. The eggs are laid in crevices in rocks, under boulders and under tussocks of grass, and apparently the birds are, like petrels, more active about the nesting sites during the hours of darkness than those of daylight. The fledglings also are precocious, going to sea with their parents at an early age.

With the coming of cold weather the ancient murrelets move southward and seaward, some of them spending the winter on the ocean as far south as the inshore waters of California. Though they rise easily from the surface, they usually continue their swift flight only a short distance before dropping back onto the water, and they prefer to escape by diving. The ancient murrelet differs from the other murrelets in having a gray back and a contrasting black crown, while in summer the throat is black and there is a white line over the eye.

Kittlitz's Murrelet

Kittlitz's murrelet is a northern edition of the marbled murrelet, nesting in the Bering Sea region and the adjacent Arctic Ocean area. It is a bird of the ice-filled northern waters and the channels among the numerous islands. The flocks feed by diving for their food, which seems to be mostly marine invertebrates. They rise from the water more easily than the marbled murrelets; in fact, they seem to come up from their dives flying. At nesting time they go inland and each female lays her single egg on an open spot on the tundra in the mountains near the sea. In winter their migration takes them to the Asiatic coast of the North Pacific.

Auklets

The six species of auks that we call auklets include some medium-sized birds, which are as large as small ducks, as well as the smallest member of the auk family, the least auklet. These are all birds of the North Pacific, and in the Bering Sea area their great numbers make the rocky islands of those fog-shrouded, icy waters among the most populous bird "cities" of the world. Only two species, the rhinoceros and Cassin's auklets, nest regularly on the Pacific coast south of Alaska. All of the auklets gather in great colonies to nest, each female laying her single white egg in a crevice of the rocks or in a burrow. In winter the auklets move out to sea, where they rest and sleep on the open ocean and dive for their food of floating marine animals. Only one species of the Bering Sea, the paroquet auklet, occasionally comes southward as far as the California coast.

The bill of the auklet is heavier than that of the murrelet; it may be bright red or orange and in some species has ornamental knobs and plates during the breeding season. The plumage is generally all blackish but may be paler—and sometimes even whitish —on the underparts. It usually includes special plumes on the head.

Cassin's auklet, distinctive because of its small size and dull plumage, its black upperparts and dark gray breasts and flanks, is the only species without bizarre head decorations when in breeding plumage. The rhinoceros auklet, another dark but much larger species, has a hornlike projection on the base of the bill and two long white tufts of feathers on each side of the head. The small, black, whiskered auklet has a curly crest on its forehead and three sets of white ornamental plumes on each side of its head. The crested auklet also has a curly crest on its forehead but only one tuft of elongated white plumes back of each eye, whereas the tiny least auklet, without a crest, has two sets of elongated plumes on each side of its head. The large paroquet auklet has a curious, thick, red bill and a single tuft of white feathers back of each eye.

Cassin's Auklet

The nesting population of Cassin's auklet on the rocky Farallon Islands off the California coast has been estimated at from 100,000 to 200,000 birds. During the day none of the birds may be in sight, for they have the petrel habit of visiting their nests only at night, and they hide the nests in burrows in the soil or place their eggs in crevices, nooks and crannies among the rocks. The scene is very different at night; then the hurrying birds are everywhere, flying in from the sea, where they have spent the day, and calling to their mates, who answer and come to the mouths of the burrows. There the pairs generally bow and call for some time before one bird goes back to sitting on its eggs and the other flies away to sea. Similar scenes take place wherever the birds gather to breed on offshore islands along the Pacific coast from the Aleutians and Queen Charlotte Islands to Lower California. Because of the safety of the burrows in which the single white egg is laid, the young remain there until they are fully grown and able to fly.

Outside the breeding season this tiny auklet, only about nine inches long, lives on the open sea, where the flocks swim and dive for the small floating animals that make up their food. Cassin's auklet has a white belly, but this is hidden in the water when the bird is swimming, and its blackish back and dark gray throat and flanks make it appear very dull. It also lacks the bizarre head decorations that mark other auklets.

Paroquet Auklet

The paroquet auklet (Plate 161) is a nesting bird of the Bering Sea area, laying its single whitish egg well concealed among the boulders or crevices in the rocks on the islands. The bird is not so common or gregarious as some of its neighbors, but it is conspicuous as it sits in little groups on the rocks during the day while others fly to the feeding grounds offshore. The thick fogs that so often occur in these waters do not keep these birds from finding their way home, and the well-known ornithologist A. C. Bent writes of being guided through the fog to St. Paul's Island in the Bering Sea by following a line of birds flying there.

This is one of the larger auklets, often measuring as much as ten inches long. It has a thick, upturned bill, and over the eye a white line ending in an elongated, pointed tuft of feathers. This tuft adds a distinctive touch to a bird that is otherwise dressed in typical auk livery—black above and mostly gray below. The curiously shaped, upturned bill seems to have a very practical use, that of capturing the crustaceans for which the bird dives.

Once the breeding season is over the birds leave their nesting islands and move southward. A few have been recorded wintering off our Pacific coast as far south as California, but probably most of them spend the winter well out to sea.

Crested Auklet

One of the most abundant sea birds of the islands of the Bering Sea is the crested auklet (Plates 155, 162), blackish above and grayish brown below, with a long, curly crest on its forehead, elongated white plumes back of its eye, and a thick orange bill. Observers write of seeing the surface of the water covered with them, while flocks fly from the cliffs of their island homes. They nest in deep crevices in the cliffs and among the boulders on the beaches above the reach of the tide, sharing these locations with the paroquet auklet. Loud, weird cries sound from their hidden nests.

Cold holds no terror for these birds, for they are accustomed to swimming among the floating ice and diving for their food of shrimps and other small sea animals. In winter they move southward past the Aleutians and some of them go as far as Japan, but they are absent from the American coast south of Alaska.

Least Auklet

Of all the auks this is the smallest, measuring

only about six and a half inches long. It is also probably the most abundant in its comparatively limited range: the Bering Sea and its adjacent waters. Travelers generally speak of its vast numbers and have written of countless thousands sitting in dense masses on the water, diving or swirling up in great swarms. Least auklets gather in millions about the rocky beaches of the Pribilof Islands; myriads of them can be seen flying around the cliffs of Big Diomede, recalling a vast beehive; and they leave their nests on the rocky beaches of St. Paul Island like mosquitoes rising from a marsh. The least auklets nest in crevices in cliffs or among boulders, laying their single white egg on the rock or among the pebbles with no attempt at nest building. When the young are awing the birds evidently move southward with the ice, and presumably they spend the winter on the open ocean in the North Pacific and the Bering Sea, some of them going as far south as Japan. Like many of the auks they are blackish above and whitish below, but their wings have some white in them and their underparts have blackish blotches, which are especially plentiful on the throat. Like most auklets they have special head decorations: white, pointed feathers on the forehead, a row of elongated white plumes behind the eyes extending across the cheeks, and another from the corner of the mouth.

Whiskered Auklet

The whiskered auklet has been called the prettiest of the whole family. Certainly it is as oddly decorated as any of the small auks. Nearly as small a bird as the least auklet, its general color is a dull, dusky gray above, with the chest and flanks gray and the belly white, but its bill is bright red, with a knob at its base in the summer, and it has a long blackish crest on the forehead curling forward and three tufts of white plumes on each side of the head.

The whiskered auklet is chiefly a bird of the western side of the Bering Sea, though it does occur in the Aleutians. It appears to nest in deep, rocky crevices, feed on crustaceans that it gets by diving, and spend the winter on the open sea like some of the other auklets, but this we must surmise because the whiskered auklet is one of the rarest and least known of the group.

Rhinoceros Auklet

From southern Alaska to Washington the rhinoceros auklet comes ashore on small islands to nest during the summer. Largest of the auklets, it is about fourteen inches long; it gets its name from the hornlike projection it wears at the base of its bill in summer. Though it is a dull-plumaged bird like Cassin's auklet, with blackish upperparts and dark gray breast and flanks, it is much larger and the long, white mustache and eye-plumes of its breeding dress are distinctive.

The bird lays its single white egg in a burrow that it excavates several feet deep in the soil. Both sexes share in the incubation of the eggs and in bringing fish to the young. The birds are active around the nesting island only at night, when they fly in from their fishing grounds. During the day they are either safely underground in their burrows, or on the fishing ground, which may be miles offshore. When the young leave the the nest, the rhinoceros auklets desert the nesting island. Some of them go southward as far as the California coast and may be seen there near the shore, but many of them apparently go farther out to sea and winter on the open ocean.

Puffins

The three species of puffins are medium-sized auks with bills that are very thin and nearly as high as long. One would expect some special use for these bills in feeding, but the birds dive and catch fish in much the same manner as the slender-billed murres. It is certainly true that they have great strength in their jaws and many a human hand thrust into an occupied burrow has been powerfully nipped. The puffin's bill is largest and most massive in the breeding season, after which certain parts of it are shed, so that it is smaller in winter, when presumably the food-getting problem is most acute. We are thus forced to conclude that if the enormous size and bright color of the bills of both male and female puffins in breeding season have any function, it is one related to mutual display and not to food-getting. Perhaps these ornamentations of the bill are analogous to the weird plumage decorations on the heads of the auklets.

The nesting habits of the puffins are in general like those of other auks. They nest in burrows, but the puffins seem to be the only auks that commonly carry in nest material on which to lay their eggs.

There is an interesting parallel between the habits of at least one puffin and certain petrels as regards the development of the young and the parental care given them by the adult birds. The Atlantic puffin raises its young in its burrow, feeds it until it is full grown, and then simply deserts it, whereupon the young bird, after doing without food for a few days, leaves the burrow and goes to sea by itself—a pattern also followed by some petrels. Possibly when others of the hole-nesting tribe of auks are carefully studied a similar sequence of events will be observed.

The agility of puffins and their ability to stand on their toes and walk nimbly is unusual among auks.

Atlantic and Horned Puffins

These two recognized species of puffins are so similar that they could be called local varieties of one species. The Atlantic puffin (Plate 164), a bird of the North Atlantic, nests as far south as the coast of northern Maine and winters off the New England coast, while the horned puffin (Plates 165, 166) nests in the Bering Sea area and winters farther south, occasionally reaching California. The Atlantic puffin is black above and on the throat, with the rest of the underparts white; it has a gray face, a big, red-tipped bill, and bright orange feet. The horned puffin differs from it chiefly in having a whiter face and a longer, hornlike wattle on the upper eyelid which gives the bird its name.

Sometimes the puffin nests in crevices in the rocks, but where there is turf on the little islands in the sea it digs a burrow and often brings in grass or other material to make a nest for its single white egg. The blackish, downy chick that hatches in the security of this underground nest is fed assiduously on fishes by both parents. A puffin colony is a busy place at this time. Some birds will be standing on their toes or running nimbly about, rather than resting on their tarsi like some of the auks; others will be coming in to their nests with fishes dangling from their bills; while still others will be leaving the colony, dropping into the nearby waters to catch more fish for their young.

The puffin has a reputation for being a droll, blundering fellow, a solemn-looking bird got up in fancy dress. He may be trusting and allow a close approach as he stands on a rock, or he may crouch as if to launch himself into the air, and then change his mind several times before he pitches off into whirring flight. On the water he swims and dives like an expert, but when he decides to take off he may blunder and bumble, pattering along the surface and then deciding against flying, perhaps diving through a wave and then emerging and floating again.

Tufted Puffin

Among the mixed flocks of sea fowl that follow the schools of small fish off the Pacific coast from California to Alaska in summer, the tufted puffin (Plate 163) is most distinctive, being generally blackish and having a huge, triangular, partly red bill, red feet, and a white face with long, dense tufts of yellow plumes cascading backward and downward from a spot over each eye. These birds gather by the thousands in their colonies on offshore islands or isolated cliffs facing the sea. There they dig their burrows in the turf, or, if turf is lacking, utilize a crevice or cranny among the rocks and build a crude nest of grass, feathers or whatever else is available. After the single whitish egg is laid, the birds often sit about at the mouths of their burrows, and most students have commented on the ludicrous contrast between the solemnity of their expressions and their fantastic headgear.

While some birds are thus resting, others may be at their fishing grounds as much as twenty miles away. Apparently flocks will fly about until they locate a school of fish, then land on the water and fish by diving. When bringing food to the young, they carry half a dozen or more small fish in their bills at once. These fish are held near the head and dangle along each side of the puffin's bill and it is still a puzzle how the bird, fishing in the open sea, can catch fish after fish and line them up in its bill in this way. The tufted puffin is an expert diver and may go underwater directly from the air, continuing its flight underwater, as it were, but it has difficulty in taking off again and unless it can rise into the wind, needs a run along the surface before it is airborne.

Once the nesting season is past the puffins scatter from the colonies. Apparently most of them go to offshore waters where they spend the winter in flocks, but a few are found along the coast.

CHAPTER 35

Pigeons and Doves

THE pigeon family is nearly world-wide in its distribution. The greatest number of the nearly three hundred species of pigeons, however, live in the Indo-Australian region. Here such species as the crowned goura pigeon, nearly as large as a small turkey, and the small but brilliant green, red and orange fruit pigeons are among the most notable varieties.

This family is often placed near the parrots in classification, but it belongs to a very distinct group and has no very near relatives except the partridge-like sand grouse of Africa and Asia, and the giant, flightless dodo, which is now extinct, of the Mascarene Islands in the Indian Ocean. The appearance

of pigeons, or doves, is as distinctive as their walk, in which their nodding heads keep time with their short steps. Some are forest birds which alight mainly in the trees, on the fruit of which they feed; others walk about on the ground in the forest; still others feed on seeds in open fields. When thirsty they put their bills into the water and drink heartily rather than sipping like a chicken. Many species of pigeons go in flocks which may be of enormous size, and some are colonial nesters.

At nesting time the pigeons pair with much cooing and with a display that often includes a special courtship flight. The nest is usually small, flat and frail, so thin that often the one or two white eggs may be seen from below through the nest walls. When hatched, the nestlings are covered with a scanty, hairlike down, and are helpless. Both parents usually share in the nest duties and for the first days after hatching the young are fed pigeon's milk, a substance secreted by the walls of the crops of both male and female parents.

As game birds the mourning dove and the white-winged dove are important in the South of the United States, and the band-tailed pigeon in the West. In recent years many government agencies have been making surveys of the status of the birds and the future prospects for dove-shooting. One of the biological characteristics that makes it impractical to treat pigeons as game birds is that they lay few eggs and thus have a low reproductive potential, a factor that is only partly offset by their repeated attempts at nesting in a long season of reproduction. A number of species have been domesticated, notably the ringed turtledove, which is often used in laboratory experiments, and the rock dove which, as the domesticated pigeon, is of some importance in the poultry business. Strains of the domestic pigeon have been used for carrying messages, and others, called homing pigeons, are kept by fanciers and used in racing, the birds being released at a distance from their dovecotes and timed as they streak for home.

Key West and the other keys of southern Florida lay claim to seven species of pigeons, more than have been recorded in any other part of the United States. They are the scaled and white-crowned pigeons, the Zenaida dove, and two quail doves—some of them only accidental visitors recorded at long intervals—as well as the widespread mourning dove and the ground dove. Two other species have been recorded in the United States only from the lower Rio Grande Valley; these are the white-fronted dove and the red-billed pigeon. When we subtract the seven birds of extremely limited occurrence in the United States, the extinct passenger pigeon, and the three naturalized introductions—the rock, Chinese spotted and ringed turtledoves—from the list of sixteen species known in America, we have only five species left that are presently important in our bird life. These are the mourning dove of general distribution, the band-tailed pigeon of the West, and the Inca, ground, and white-winged doves of our southern states.

White-crowned Pigeon

In various parts of the world there are pigeons that are widely distributed on many scattered is-lands but rarely live on the mainland. Such a bird is the white-crowned pigeon that lives on islands of the Caribbean from near Panama through the Antilles, the Bahamas and the Florida keys, but only occasionally visits the Florida mainland. This large, stout pigeon is about fourteen inches long, with a medium-length, rounded tail, and a plumage that is slate-colored except for a white crown in the male. It comes to the Florida keys for the summer, arriving in March. The nest is the usual frail platform built by pigeons, though perhaps more substantial than some, and is placed in a tree or shrub or even in a cactus plant. Numbers of the birds will nest on a single small key, congregating to feed in favorite fruit-bearing trees. Where these trees are on large islands and the nests are on nearby smaller keys, the birds fly back and forth daily along a regular course.

Scaled Pigeon

The scaled pigeon is a large, slate-colored pigeon with purple neck feathers whose dark margins give a scaled effect—hence the bird's name. It is a West Indian species, living particularly in the hills and mountains of those islands, but it has been recorded on Key West.

Band-tailed Pigeon

The mountains of the western part of the United States and Canada from British Columbia and Montana to California, and southward to Central America, are the summer home of the band-tailed pigeon (Plate 168). There it lives in the forests of oak or of mixed oak and conifers. In winter the northern birds move southward as far as California, where there are band-tails all the year and where the birds from the mountains move down in large flocks into the oaks at lower altitudes to spend the winter.

Acorns are one of the staple foods of the band-tail, and when the crop fails locally or their supply of nuts or fruits is exhausted, the birds scout for new feeding areas. Then the big flocks wander about and turn up in unexpected places, sometimes visiting and feeding in cultivated fruit trees or foraging on cultivated fields for grain on the ground. When they are disturbed while feeding in bushes, they fly up with a great clatter of wings and may go to perch in the very tops of some of the tallest trees nearby.

When nesting time approaches the flocks disband and the pairs scatter. Then from the trees the male gives his deep "coo, coo" and indulges in a display flight that takes him out in a circle from his perch and back to it again. The nest is the customary flimsy platform in a tree, usually about twenty feet up, and usually only one egg is laid in it. The breeding season is prolonged, and in Washington, where the breeding is at its height in June, young birds have been recorded in the nest as late as mid-October.

The band-tail is a stockily-built pigeon, slightly larger than the domestic pigeon. It is a dark-hued purplish and bluish bird with a broad gray band across the end of its tail and a white crescent on the back of its neck.

Red-billed Pigeon

This bird is an intruder from the south, a Central American species that ranges northward only into the lower Rio Grande Valley. There in the forests and brushlands it spends the summer, making its scant nest on a branch in a tree or in a tangle of vines, and laying a single egg. After the nesting season it gathers into flocks and migrates southward for the winter. I became familiar with the bird in El Salvador, where it is a common species, feeding in flocks on the fruits of trees in the forest. It even came into city gardens, and its voice, a series of "coo's," was commonly heard. It is a large, short-tailed pigeon with reddish-purple and slaty-gray plumage and an orange-red bill.

Rock Dove

The common domestic pigeon has been so widely introduced in North America and so carelessly kept that many individual birds have escaped domestication and now lead a wild existence. Bird authorities have come to recognize this species as a part of our bird life and now list it under the name by which the ancestral wild bird is known in the Old World, the rock dove (Plate 167). The original rock dove still has a wide range in a natural state from western Europe to India and North Africa. In Britain it nests chiefly about sea cliffs, whence comes its name. In North America the birds usually depend on towns and villages for nesting and feeding places, but at least on the coast of Oregon some of them have reverted to the ancestral type of habitat and live on cliffs. The plumage of the wild rock dove is that of the common blue-gray birds of our city parks, with whitish rump, dark bands across the wings and iridescent neck feathers. Many fancy varieties have been developed in domestication, and along with the birds having the wild type of plumage, flocks in city parks or about inhabited localities often contain white, cream-colored or mottled individuals.

The call of the rock dove is a deep-voiced cooing. The nests of the birds in a wild state are built on rocky ledges, but most of our rock doves nest on ledges on buildings, making a careless arrangement of bits of grass or plant stems and laying two white eggs. The breeding season may be prolonged and several broods may be raised annually. The incubation period lasts about eighteen days, and it ordinarily takes the young bird, or squab, four or five weeks to become full grown.

Zenaida Dove

Audubon found this species a common summer visitor to the Florida keys, where he reported it nesting on the ground, but since his time there have been only a few recorded sightings of the bird on the keys. It is a West Indian species, a bird of the islands that has also colonized the arid coast of Yucatán. It is about the size of the mourning dove, which it resembles as it walks about on the ground picking up its food of seeds, but the tail is square and made up of broad feathers rather than long and pointed ones, and the inner flight feathers are tipped with white.

Mourning Dove

The mourning dove is the only native dove or pigeon that is widespread in the United States; indeed it overlaps our borders and breeds from southern Canada to Mexico, and the birds from the northern part of the range retire southward in winter to our southern states and to Mexico. The bird feeds on seeds and grain on the ground, and as it perches and nests in trees, a countryside of mixed vegetation is its favorite habitat. This is one of the birds that has profited by settlement of the country, since man-made fields provided new feeding places for it and trees planted by settlers on the plains provided new nesting places.

In appearance the mourning dove is a slender bird about twelve inches long, with brownish upperparts, pinkish-gray underparts, and a long, pointed tail with the outer tail feathers tipped with white. When feeding on the ground it walks about with short steps and bobbing head, and when alarmed it makes no effort to hide, despite its protective coloration, but flies up with whistling wings to perch in a tree or seek safety in swift flight. In the autumn considerable numbers of this species gather to feed on waste grain in stubble fields, coming and going in small, loose flocks, and in the evening these flocks often gather in communal roosts in favorite trees containing hundreds of birds. The mourning dove is hunted as a game bird, especially in our southern states, and its swift flight, as it speeds to watering places, feeding fields, or roosts, offers very sporting shots.

Although this dove is classed as a game bird in some states, it is considered a song bird in others. In the spring the loose flocks break up and the birds pair. All summer its mournful notes, usually consisting of a series of four "coo's," are a feature of the chorus of bird song around us, and the display of the male as it starts up from its perch on a telephone wire or a tree, flaps a hundred feet or so on broadly spread wings, and then glides on set wings back to its perch, is a common sight.

Each year a pair of doves takes up residence in my yard and I can therefore testify to the inefficiency of their nesting. Their flat nest is placed on a branch of a tree and is so flimsy and insecure that the birds always lose one or more of their sets of two white eggs. Sometimes wind and rain beat the nests down and I even suspect that occasionally the eggs are knocked out by a startled bird leaving the nest. However, they keep trying and in some years bring off a pair of young in the autumn. All of this helps to account for their long period of calling and displaying.

Passenger Pigeon

The story of the passenger pigeon is now only a historical record, for the bird has been extinct since the early 1900's. In 1900 the last definite record of a bird in the wild came from Ohio. There were then still a few in captivity, but the last of the species died in the zoo at Cincinnati on September 1, 1914.

Many species have been exterminated over the centuries, but no other extermination on such a scale as this has taken place before our eyes. The abundance of the birds in the old days staggers the imagination. The records tell of crowded flocks passing overhead for hours and extending as far as the eye could see in every direction, their passing shadowing the earth and their droppings falling like hail on the dead leaves. Their roosts covered acres of woodland, the resting birds crowded together so closely that here and there the branches broke under their weight. In the nesting colonies as many as ninety nests might be found in a single tree, and the colonies covered thousands of acres of forests. Dr. A. W. Schorger of Madison, Wisconsin, who has carefully sifted the records, estimates that there may have been more than three billion of these birds at one time. It was probably the most abundant species in America.

Wholesale slaughter of passenger pigeons for the market began when rapid transportation to city markets by railroads became available. But already toward the middle of the last century warnings were sounded that unless the killing ceased, the species would disappear. Between 1870 and 1880 the decrease became precipitous. Many people, including some ornithologists, refuse to believe that killing by man was the main factor, but the evidence seems clear. With gun and net and baited trap, and with raids on the nesting colonies for squabs, tremendous numbers of passenger pigeons were killed for the market. Extermination would not have been possible with many species, but two characteristics made this one especially vulnerable to this predation. One was that although the birds ranged from Canada to the Gulf of Mexico, their main breeding range was only from New England to the edge of the prairies in the Midwest, an area so completely taken over by human settlement that there remained no hinterland to hold a reserve breeding stock of the birds. The second of these characteristics was the extreme gregariousness of the pigeons. The crowded flocks and nesting colonies made wholesale killing possible. And, because the bird was so gregarious, when the big flocks were destroyed, the scattered remainder withered away and the isolated survivors seem not to have been able to perpetuate the species.

Besides nesting in great colonies and laying but a single egg, the species had such other characteristics as a voice described as a "shriek," a "chatter" and a "cluck," and a fondness for acorns or beechnuts in the fall and winter and for soft fruits in the summer. The largest and handsomest of our pigeons, it was about eighteen inches long, with a long, pointed tail. It somewhat resembled the mourning dove in general appearance, but was brighter and more vividly colored.

Chinese Spotted Dove

Among the comparatively few birds that have been introduced into the United States and have been able to establish themselves is the Chinese spotted dove (Plate 156), whose native home is in eastern Asia. So far its success as an immigrant has been limited to the Los Angeles area. It is a medium-sized bird, about as big as the mourning dove, but with a square tail. The outer tail feathers are broadly tipped with white, and it is our only dove with a broad collar of black-and-white spots on the back of its neck. This is a bird of suburban yards and parks, most plentiful around evergreen and palm trees, where it walks about on the open ground feeding on small seeds, fruits, and whatever scraps of food it can scavenge.

Ringed Turtledove

The ringed turtledove is a domesticated variety, slightly larger than the mourning dove, with a rounded tail, creamy buff plumage, and a black ring on the back of the neck. It has escaped from captivity and breeds in the wild locally about towns and villages in California, Florida and the West Indies. Sometimes it is called a separate species, but it seems probable that it is a variety of the wild collared turtledove of Europe and Asia, which has a brownish and pinkish-gray plumage. The ringed turtledove feeds largely on seeds on the ground but also takes fruit from the trees. It nests on buildings and gives its cooing notes in a series of three.

White-winged Dove

The white-winged dove is somewhat like the mourning dove but has a rounded tail and conspicuous white patches on the wings and on the tips of the outer tail feathers. It is a bird of the brushlands and forests and of groves of trees interspersed with weedy fields or open desert. In the United States it is found only in our southern states, from Texas to southeastern California, and from there its range extends southward to Panama. Locally it is a common bird, feeding on fruits of trees and those of some cactus, and flocks also gather in the grainfields to glean the stubble. When the birds are replete they fly up to perch in nearby trees, usually concealed among the leaves. Like many of their kind, they make long flights to water. Their swiftness of wing and their habit of following regular lines of flight have made them prized game birds.

At nesting time scattered pairs may nest by themselves, but they tend to be gregarious and some gather into large colonies. Mesquite flats are their favorite places. The nests are somewhat more substantial than those of most of our doves, and though the colonies may be large, the nests are spread out, often with only one to a tree. Two eggs to a nest is the usual complement. One of their nesting colonies can be a noisy place, with hundreds of birds giving their loud, cooing notes from the tops of mesquite and cottonwood trees and the males on display flights in which they flap up and then sail back on set wings to their perches in the trees. During the nesting season the birds fly out to feed in flocks, so that they are conspicuous features of the landscape.

Ground Dove

The tiny, short-tailed ground dove is particularly attractive because it is so small, measuring only about seven inches long. Otherwise it is an undistinguished bird, brown above and pinkish-gray below, with a flash of bright, rufous coloring in its wings as it flies. It ranges across our southern states, from southern California to South Carolina and southward to South America. I have known it best in Florida and in Central America, where it is a tame little bird, walking with quick, short steps and nodding head along quiet, dusty roads, over open, sandy places, even along sea beaches, in cultivated and weedy fields, and about dooryards. Often it goes in pairs in search of small seeds. When it is alarmed it flies low and directly, but only a short distance, sometimes to find cover and sometimes to light on a low perch. Its "cooing" is usually done from a high place, a telephone wire or a branch of a tree, and may be continued intermittently for a long time.

Unlike the many tropical birds that barely cross our southern borders, the ground dove is resident here. In Florida its nesting season extends from February to October and four broods in succession are occasionally raised in the same nest. The usual flat, thin pigeon nest is sometimes placed on the ground but more often in a bush or a tree, rarely more than twelve feet up. In it two eggs are laid. Though the setting birds are sometimes so tame or so bold as to allow themselves to be touched when sitting on the eggs, at other times they leave the nest at the approach of an intruder and flutter along the ground, feigning injury in an attempt to draw attention away from the nest.

Inca Dove

This dove is only about eight inches long, and half of this length is in the long tail. It has much white on the outer tail feathers, but the body is a pale grayish-brown plentifully marked with blackish crescents above and below, giving the bird a scaled appearance. It is a common bird of fields, roadsides, and pastures, and seems to delight in the proximity of human dwellings. The birds walk about on the ground looking for the small seeds which make up the bulk of their diet. When I first came upon these birds in Central America, I was confused by the different ways in which the tail was spread in flying. Sometimes as the bird flushed, the tail was suddenly spread, displaying a great deal of white; at other times it was spread little or not at all, so that no white showed, and for a time I thought I was seeing two different species.

The song of the Inca dove is a two-note "coo" with an accent on the second note. It may be heard throughout the year, but calling becomes more common in March and April as the nesting season approaches. The nest is placed usually on a branch of a tree, but in a settled area the scant platform may be placed on a house or the beam of a shed.

The birds are usually seen in pairs, but in winter small, loose flocks feed together, and I have seen dozens of them perched in trees around a water hole where they came to drink. The headquarters of the Inca dove is in Central America, whence the bird spreads northward into the arid southern part of the United States from Arizona to Texas.

White-fronted Dove

This is another of the doves that has its headquarters south of us in Central America, and comes within the borders of the United States only in the Rio Grande Valley. It is a solitary, retiring bird of the forest and shrubbery, where it walks about on the ground in search of seeds and berries. When startled it retreats by dodging among bushes at an astonishingly rapid run, or by flying low. When the nesting season approaches, however, it perches high in the trees to give its "cooing" calls. The nest, a scant platform in which two eggs are laid, is placed on a low branch or in a tangle of vines. The bird is about eleven inches long, with a rounded tail, and is mainly grayish or olive brown above and pinkish gray and white below, with a grayish forehead, a bronzy gloss on the back of the neck and white tips

on the black outer tail feathers. Though the bird blends well with its background, the white tips of its lateral tail feathers are surprisingly conspicuous in flight.

Quail-Doves of Key West

Two doves, wanderers from their home in the West Indies, are known to occur in the United States only on Key West. These are birds of the forest, where they walk around on the ground, though a close approach may send them off in low flight or to perch on a low branch. They are stoutly-built little doves with short, rounded tails, and they get their name of "quail-dove" from habits and appearance, which somewhat suggest the quail.

The ruddy quail-dove, found in Central and South America as well as the West Indies, owes its place on the list of United States species to two specimens collected on Key West, one in 1888, another in 1925, together with a recent record of one seen on Key Largo. The male, about nine inches long, has bright, reddish-brown upperparts and pinkish-buff underparts; the forehead is slightly glossed with iridescent purple and a buff bar crosses the face below the eye.

The second of these doves, the Key West quail-dove, was fairly common in Key West in 1832, according to Audubon, but since that time there have been only three records of single birds. The Key West quail-dove is about eleven inches long, with the crown and back of the neck an iridescent greenish hue, foreback iridescent purple, wings and tail brownish, underparts grayish, and a conspicuous white bar across the face below the eye.

INDEX OF BIRDS

NOTE: Numbers in boldface refer to the plate numbers of illustrations. The scientific names given here are those approved by the American Ornithologists' Union.

THIS BOOK has been printed and bound by Kingsport Press, Inc., Kingsport, Tennessee.
Color engraving by Chanticleer Company, New York. Designed by James Hendrickson.